## Masterglass

Jancis Robinson has been writing about wine since her days as restaurant critic for *Isis*. In 1975 she joined the wine trade magazine *Wine & Spirit* and then edited it for four years. She started a wine newsletter which subsequently became *Which? Wine Monthly* which she edited for two years. She was also founder-editor of the annual *Which? Wine Guide*.

She is the author of *The Wine Book* which was published in 1979, and *The Great Wine Book*, a study of the world's top wines, which won the Glenfiddich award for the best book on wine published in 1982. Her magnum opus *Vines, Grapes and Wines* was published in 1986.

The only journalist to have qualified as a Master of Wine, she was wine correspondent of *The Sunday Times* before joining the *Standard* in 1987. She has contributed to a wide range of British and foreign publications on food and other subjects, as well as wine.

Jancis Robinson is writer and presenter of the award-winning 'Wine Programme' television series, first shown in 1983. She has become a regular broadcaster, wine judge and has lectured frequently on the art of wine tasting.

# Jancis Robinson

## Illustrated by Ian Dicks

# Masterglass

**A PRACTICAL COURSE IN TASTING WINE**

**Pan Original**
Pan Books London and Sydney

First published 1983 by Pan Books Ltd,
Cavaye Place, London SW10 9PG

Second edition 1987
9 8 7 6 5 4 3 2 1
© Jancis Robinson 1983, 1987

ISBN 0 330 28097 X

Designed by Peter Ward
Photoset by Parker Typesetting Service, Leicester
Printed and bound in Great Britain by
Cox & Wyman Ltd, Reading

For Julia

*and the two people who did most to keep her so happy while I wrote this.*

# Contents

**There's no such thing as a born
taster**

# Foretaste

## A book for the thirsty

THIS IS a book for people who want to know more about wine, but have had the crucial realization that drinking wine is a lot more fun than reading about it. Happily, the practical side of wine appreciation not only has more immediate appeal than arid theory, it is also considerably more important.

It's horribly easy for those of us who earn our living writing and talking about wine to lose sight of the fact that what actually counts is how it *tastes*. The lovely liquid exists not to fill analysis books or justify vintage charts, but to give sensual pleasure. This 'wet' guide to wine is merely an accompaniment to your wine drinking, explaining why different wines taste the way they do, so that by being an informed wine taster (as opposed to an ignorant drinker) you can maximize your enjoyment.

*Masterglass* constitutes a complete wine course for the thirsty. It tells the story of how wine is made, explains what influence factors as diverse as climate and bottle-size have on the resultant taste, and demonstrates how to get as much pleasure from wine as possible by the practical way you serve and drink it. All this information is given not just with words but reinforced by scores of different practical exercises – most, but not all, involving that important sport, wine tasting.

(Other things you'll be asked to do range from tasting tooth-paste to drinking wine from a teacup.)

Down the right-hand page is the theory, which you can demonstrate to yourself by following the exercises outlined alongside on the left-hand page.

The exercises in this book equip the interested wine drinker with all the important explanations of why each wine tastes the way it does. Every taste-shaping factor is illustrated by specific examples, and everyone who completes the exercises should have an extremely good grasp of the fundamentals of wine in its most relevant, but often overlooked, context – in your glass. You can literally taste your way to wine expertise.

Halfway through the course, you should be able to tell a claret from a Burgundy and, by the end, a Rioja from a Rhône and a Mâcon from a Muscadet; making mistakes no more often than the wine professional – that is, no more than half the time.

The course starts with an outline of the personal tasting mechanism and highlights some surprising facts which may well help you get more out of everything you taste – food as well as wine.

This is followed by a detailed look at all sorts of practical aspects of serving and drinking wine. However, the main body of the book is the story of wine told by the painless method of tasting it. There are all sorts of different factors that influence the flavour of a wine, from what goes on fifteen feet below the vineyard to whether the cellar door was left open when the wine was bottled. But the single most impor-tant and recognizable factor is the predominant grape variety. For this reason, and because an increasing proportion of the world's wines are now labelled as *varietals* (Cabernet Sauvignon, Chardonnay, Riesling) as opposed to *generics* (Claret, Burgundy, Hock) the main part of the book is divided into sections on each of the major grape varieties.

Initially, this is simply to establish each variety's identity on the palate. A Sauvignon de Touraine and a Sancerre, for instance, are both examples of the same grape variety, and tasting each (plus a dry white Bordeaux and a Fumé Blanc from California) will help form a 'palate picture' of the Sauvignon Blanc grape. Grafted on to each section, however, is a set of increasingly complex and interrelated factors. After you've established what Sauvignon tastes like, for example, you are encouraged to taste examples made in very different climates, so that you can see how fifty per cent more sunshine in a bottle actually *tastes*.

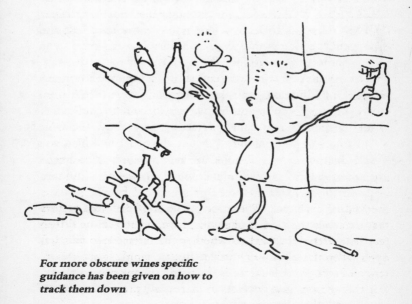

**For more obscure wines specific guidance has been given on how to track them down**

At the end of the book there are also some demonstrations of why some wine and food combinations don't work (though no dogma about which do), some suggestions for further wine-tasting exercises and a short dictionary of the jargon.

## How to use this guide

IF YOU want to learn about wine in the speediest and most systematic way that *Masterglass* can offer, you should try to follow the exercises in the order suggested by the course, as this constitutes a logical and precise way of building up your knowledge. There's no reason, however, why you should allow me to dictate your wine-drinking habits. You could perfectly easily allow the wine you happen to be drinking to dictate the order in which you tackle this book. Simply look up the wine you're tasting in the index and find out which exercise(s) it could be useful for.

Certainly, Chapters 3 and 4, on white and red wines respectively, can be tackled in tandem; though even the most free-range wine taster is advised to look first at the two chapters on 'How to taste' and 'Practical matters'.

You can learn a great deal by studying only one wine but, as shown on this course, you can learn at least five times as much by tasting two and comparing them. This means that you could accelerate your progress through this course by getting together with others also interested in finding out more about wine, or by learning how to cope with wine leftovers, or by dramatically increasing your wine consumption. You, your liver and your bank balance will determine which of the two latter possibilities are more sensible, but if you choose the first bear in mind that a normal 75 cl bottle can supply either six good glasses of wine for drinking or up to twenty samples for tasting.

In each exercise, examples of wines suitable for tasting have been described as specifically as is both necessary and possible. Many of the bottles suggested are widely available. For more obscure bottles, specific guidance on how to track them down has been given – which is why the text is littered with wine merchants' names and addresses, correct at the time of writing and supplied with apologies for the fact that the 'winescape' will change during the currency of this book. I have tried to keep the cost of this course down. Some of the bottles specified will sell for little more than £2, and I have suggested bottles costing more than £5 only if they are absolutely necessary to prove a point. It is true, however, that, to some extent, the less you're prepared to spend per bottle, the more slowly you will learn. A Vouvray costing £2.50 a bottle is unlikely to demonstrate the character of the Chenin Blanc grape nearly as effectively as one at £5.

If you really get hooked, you may also want to try some of the more advanced exercises that have been marked 'A-level' which, if done with enthusiasm and at least part of your brain as well as your mouth, will turn you into an informed wine taster.

## Why you are *Masterglass* material

NO MATTER how little you know about wine now, you can learn how to taste wine by following this course. It's designed for everyone from the complete novice (nay, teetotaller) upwards. I learnt a great deal myself while compiling it, so I hope that others, who've been exposed to wine for some years, may do so too – especially from Chapters 1 and 2. Those who are relatively new to wine should feel particularly confident, though, since it is they who invariably make the most acute tasters.

The American tasting guru Maynard Amerine points out that the average human adult can detect at least 1,000 different flavours, many of which can be found in wine, so your tasting mechanism is already well equipped to deal with the raw material. All you need is the sort of guidance this course can offer and some confidence. There is no such thing as a born taster. Only a handful of people whose physical disabilities have impaired their senses of taste will find any difficulty at all; and in *blind tasting*, tasting to identify an unnamed wine, novices often do better, because their perceptions are unclouded by previous experiences.

This course should turn you into an accomplished 'blind' taster but, perhaps more importantly, shows you how to assess the quality of every wine that comes your way and how to get the most from it.

Despite what some self-styled 'connoisseurs' may suggest, there are no absolutes in wine appreciation. There are some bottles which may, on an objective basis, be technically faulty, but which some tasters may find perfectly enjoyable. There are other famous wines which can count on enough admirers always to command a high price, that most quantifiable of wine measurements, yet they may not appeal at all to some wine drinkers. Never feel that you 'ought' to like or dislike a wine. The most important aspect of any wine is that *you* enjoy it. The aim of this book is to help you enjoy wine more.

**Explanatory note**
**On the right-hand pages is the theory, complimented where appropriate by exercises described, in italics, on the left-hand pages.**

*Blindfold yourself and get someone to offer you a food that you like, together with one that is similar but slightly different, to see whether or not you can distinguish between them. For example: chocolate cake and plain sponge cake; smoked salmon and smoked mackerel. (Of course they will have to be presented in the same way. If the chocolate has butter icing, then so should the plain sponge cake; and the smoked mackerel should be sliced in the same way as the smoked salmon.)*

# 1 How to taste

## How little we know

IT'S EXTRAORDINARY how little we know about something we do as often as eating and drinking. Once food and drink enters our digestive systems there are so many things that can go wrong that the medical profession is well clued up on what goes on there. But surprisingly little is known about the process of tasting that precedes all that, even though we should, in theory, be much more consciously involved in it than in digesting. Presumably, because a malfunctioning gustatory system is not seen as a particularly serious affliction (though it would drive me crazy), medical researchers have not thought it necessary to look very carefully at how we taste. Indeed, Britain's current specialist in the field is attached not to a school of medicine, or even a department of physiology, but to the food science division at Strathclyde University.

If the professionals know remarkably little about how the gustatory system operates in its complex role between mind and body, we ordinary eaters and drinkers understand even less about how to get the most out of the tasting experience. Even those who would claim to appreciate the pleasures of the table (a brave stance in a society where calories are counted and gastronomic pleasures rated so low) have no clear idea how and why they do so. Whether you like chocolate cake, smoked salmon or Beaujolais, your general approach will be to ram as much of it as possible into your

*You will need a very cooperative accomplice at this point: either someone who also wants to follow the course, on whom the tables can be turned after you have performed, or someone who loves you a lot and is prepared to indulge this latest idiosyncrasy.*

*Now if you thought that would be easy, you'll think this next is a cinch. But you'll probably be surprised at how difficult it is to distinguish between a red and a white wine, with you still blindfold and them served at the same temperature, of course. (A blue Bristol glass does the job of the blindfold less conspicuously.)*

*The odds can be weighted. Whites that taste very 'red' are full bodied and dry. White Burgundy, California Chardonnays, white Rhône wines such as Hermitage Blanc and some of the more traditional white Riojas are obvious examples. Reds that taste 'white' have lots of acidity and not too much weight in the mouth. Friend Beaujolais is a good candidate, as are the north Italian reds Valpolicella and Bardolino and the more elusive reds of the Loire, Chinon and Bourgueil. (Yapp Bros of Mere, Wiltshire, are good on unusual wines from the Loire and Rhône.)*

*If you want to make things easy for yourself, try to tell the difference betweeen a light, sweetish white such as a Mosel (the correct German name; for some reason many call it 'Moselle') and a full-bodied, none-too-acid red such as Châteauneuf-du-Pape. Even then, you will probably be surprised to find you have to think twice before pronouncing; and if you try the experiment simply on a red and white French 'vin de table', your local's house wines for example, you'll probably have to think very hard indeed.*

digestive system (and therefore *past* your gustatory system) as fast as you can. You vaguely know that by chewing the food you can prolong the pleasure it gives you, and that with wine there's some rather unsavoury gargling business indulged in by professionals. But that, for most of us, constitutes our knowledge of this daily activity.

We may not know much about it, but, as so many of us proudly proclaim, we sure do know what we like. Or do we? We reckon it is the taste of food and drink that we recognize and base our judgements on, but experience shows that when we are left without any clues other than our own sense of taste we can be pretty helpless. By examining carefully how it is that we taste, this wine course should leave the reader considerably better equipped to appreciate wine – and food, for we taste solids and liquids in almost the same way; in fact, physiologically, we can't taste solids until we've transformed them into liquids by chewing them. Experiments show that we can't taste totally dry foods at all, so that a well-blotted tongue would have no chance of telling even that sugar was sweet.

N*EXT TIME you are eating, try tasting a mouthful with your nose pinched tight shut. Notice how much the flavour of the food changes. If your mouth is shut too, the food is left in a chamber that's enclosed except for the passage at the back of the mouth – and it starts to taste much cruder. A bit of pineapple, for instance, tastes like something that's juicy, sweet and tart, but without the distinctive pineappleness that the nose usually picks up. A spoonful of soup tastes wet and a bit salty, but the flavour isn't nearly as intense as it is when allowed to steam up your nostrils.*

*Get someone (who will promise not to laugh) to blindfold you and put some sort of nose-clamp on you, whether it be fingers, a clothes-peg or a bulldog clip. Choose three similarly textured but differently flavoured foods, such as grated apple, potato and carrot, and see whether you can distinguish a mouthful of each. If you fail, try adding a really obvious one like grated onion. But don't despair if even the bulb eludes you; it has baffled physiologists' human guinea-pigs before.*

*NB. When not actually ingesting, do keep your mouth closed during the two experiments outlined above. If you draw in air over the food you're chewing, it will encourage the vapour given off to travel up the retro-nasal passage and give the same sort of messages as the nose would. Notice, too, that as you chew, you break the food down into a mush that you move towards the back of your mouth. It is from there, if your nostrils aren't blocked, that you 'sniff up' the vapour to the olfactory centre.*

## The importance of the nose

WE TEND to think that just as food and drink have a 'look' that is registered by the eyes, they have a 'smell' that is detected by the nose and a 'taste' that is sensed by the mouth. In fact, the line of distinction between the second two is very blurred. If you have a cold and your nose is blocked up, just think how little taste everything seems to have. When you smell something cooking in the oven, don't you feel as though you already know how it's going to taste? If you want to judge whether you'd enjoy the taste of a soup someone is offering you, you smell it.

What we call the 'taste' of something is the composite impression it makes on our minds by what we sense through our noses and our mouths. But, as suggested above, our noses are in fact more sensitive than our mouths. Without our sense of smell we find we are unable to appreciate foods or distinguish between them easily. 'Flavour' is a less misleading term than 'taste', which we tend to think of as necessarily connected with our mouths.

There are two aspects of a substance that can carry a message to our brains: what is tangible, the liquid or solid that comes into contact with our tongue and the inside of our mouth, and what is vaporized, the usually invisible gas that is given off by the substance. When we're consciously smelling something, it's this vapour that travels up our nose to the olfactory receptors at the top. When we're chewing the same thing, the vapour travels from the back of our mouths, up what's called the retro-nasal passage, to the same sensory organ. So what we think of as 'tasting' actually includes quite a bit of unconscious 'smelling', and what we call the 'taste' of something necessarily includes a bit of the 'smell'.

Although it's difficult for us to do controlled experiments,

Basic granulated sugar is not very volatile. Take a sniff of the sugar bowl. You get a sort of 'flat' smell at best, but even that is straining the imagination. Basically, sugar doesn't smell. It has no easily discernible effect on your nostrils, but it will have a major impact on your (unblotted!) tongue and the inside of your mouth once you have a spoonful of it in there. This is nothing subtle. No great nuances of flavour here, but a coating of the tongue with a great wham of what you know as 'sweetness' and a sort of grating brought about by its coarse, grainy texture. These sensations are a good example of the two possible ways a food or drink can have an impact on us when inside the mouth: respectively by taste or by texture. We look at texture later.

because we can't shut off the retro-nasal passage, it seems fairly certain that the messages which solids and liquids are able to convey are much less subtle than those wafted up in vapour. This is because our sensing equipment for vapour is capable of much finer distinctions than that for solids and liquids, the tongue and inside of the mouth. By cutting off our sense of smell as much as possible, and simply chewing, we're left with a much less complex impression of the flavour of something than if we don't have it in our mouths at all, but simply smell it – provided, of course, that it's the sort of substance that does give off some sort of vapour.

Different substances vary tremendously in the amount of vapour they have to give. If they are very volatile, and have lots of little flavour elements shooting off into the atmosphere all the time, then smelling them will be an interesting and rewarding experience. Wine is very volatile compared, say, to its biblical partner, bread. You don't get nearly as much vapour from a slice of bread as from a glass of wine – though there's a lot of vapour from freshly baked bread straight out of the oven, because the heat has encouraged all the flavour elements to vaporize. Think how much more flavour soup seems to have hot than when it has been allowed to cool. A bowl of cooled soup is not very volatile and therefore not very appetizing, whereas a bowl of hot, volatile soup can be wonderfully enticing, because of its intriguing mesh of messages carried to your olfactory receptors by the vapour. The messages conveyed to the brain by the nose are not necessarily stronger than those conveyed by the mouth, but they are more subtle. Wine is one of the most subtle substances we will ever taste, and one that is naturally volatile and doesn't need to be heated up to give off a vapour full of flavour.

It makes sense therefore to smell a wine every time you drink it.

*E*XPERIMENT *with sugar granules to see where on your tongue you experience sweetness best. Then try with whatever liquids you drink to see if you can assess their sweetness by their impact on your tongue. Now try the same procedure with every wine that comes your way.*

*Take conscious note of the amount of sweetness you detect in every wine you drink. The following are good examples for each category.*

★ Bone dry: *Muscadet; Loire wines based on the Sauvignon grape such as Sancerre, Pouilly-Fumé and Sauvignon de Touraine; most Champagne and other sparkling wines labelled 'brut'*

More detail is given on page 65 about the vital business of wine smelling (so important it has been graced with the dignified title *nosing*), but it is useful first to see how much information about a wine you can get from your mouth.

As demonstrated by the sugar exercise above, we can get very strong sensations from our tongue. Almost all of what we call our taste buds (of which we have about 5,000) are located on the tongue, each of them particularly well tuned to one of the basic elements of taste. Physiologists have identified at least four – sweetness, sourness, saltiness and bitterness – and continue to argue about others, which might include oiliness, alkalinity, fattiness and 'metallic-ness'. The first four comprise a very useful model, and different areas of the tongue are supposed to be particularly sensitive to each of them. Of course, individuals vary in their own sensitivities, and you will be able to identify exactly where on your tongue you are most sensitive to each. It is also, therefore, important to try to 'rinse' as much of your tongue as possible with everything you taste. To paraphrase: take a good mouthful.

## Sweetness in wine

IN VERY general terms, the highest concentration of those taste buds particularly aware of sweetness is around the tip of the tongue. Perhaps this is why we need only a tiny lick of ice cream to know how sweet it is.

Grape juice becomes wine when yeasts act on the sugar in ripe grapes to convert some, or nearly all, of it (in a way too complicated for most of us to even contemplate) into alcohol. The resulting liquid is therefore drier and stronger than grape juice, but the amount of sweetness left in the finished wine – the residual sugar – varies enormously. Wine can be extra

*(though it's a fallacy that these are 'slimming'); Chablis,*
*although some very ripe years such as 1978 and 1976 will*
*produce wines that are just 'dry'; Germany's 'Trocken' wines.*

★ Dry *(the biggest category by far, though even within it there are*
*variations – all white Burgundy can be described as 'dry',*
*though wines such as Montagny and Rully tend to be drier*
*than a great Montrachet or Meursault): Loire wines labelled*
*'sec' and based on the Chenin Blanc grape, such as Vouvray*
*and Saumur; most Alsace wines; white Rhône and Provence*
*wines such as Hermitage Blanc or Coteaux d'Aix-en-*
*Provence Blanc; most white Bordeaux labelled 'sec' or in a*
*green glass bottle; most white 'vin de table' labelled 'sec' or*
*'dry'; Soave, Verdicchio, Pinot Grigio, Pinot Bianco and*
*most white 'vino da tavola'; white Rioja; most whites from*
*around the Mediterranean such as those from Greece and*
*Cyprus; California's Fumé Blanc and (just) Chardonnay;*
*Germany's 'Halbtrocken' wines and some of her lightest*
*'Kabinett' wines.*

★ Medium dry: *most French wines labelled 'demi sec', especially*
*Vouvrays, and Coteaux du Layon; Gewürztraminer from*
*Alsace; richer Graves; Frascati; most basic white wine made*
*in California, Australia, South Africa and New Zealand,*
*plus Chenin Blanc, Steen, Semillon and Müller-Thurgau*
*('Riesling-Sylvaner') made there; the great majority of*
*German wine sold in Britain, including most 'Tafelwein' and*
*'Qualitätswein' (which includes Liebfraumilch).*

★ Medium sweet: *most French wines labelled 'moelleux';*
*'vendange tardive' wines from Alsace; Asti Spumante and*
*Moscato Spumante; Moscatel de Setubal; commercial Tokay*
*from Hungary; Rhine Auslese and Mosel Beerenauslese.*

★ Sweet: *Sauternes and Barsac; most Muscats such as the popular*
*one from Beaumes de Venise; Rhine Beerenauslesen and*
*Mosel Trockenbeerenauslesen.*

★ Very sweet: *Spanish Moscatel; Australian Liqueur Muscat;*
*Port; Cream Sherry; Sauternes in a year like 1976; Rhine*
*'TBA'; a host of fortified wines.*

dry, dry, medium dry, medium sweet, sweet and very sweet; though even wines we normally label 'bone dry', because they seem to have no sweetness at all, contain a tiny amount of residual sugar. Sugar content ranges from about 1 to 200+ grams per litre, with dry wines usually having less than 10 grams.

Many British wine retailers nowadays are using a numerical coding system on shelves or even labels to denote sweetness. 1 means bone dry, while most Sauternes would rate 9.

In recent years the mass market has been schooled to feel proud of liking something dry, though now there are instances of inverse snobbery in people such as myself, who perhaps make a bit more noise about liking Asti Spumante and Sauternes than we would if they were more generally liked.

**Bordeaux shape**

**Burgundy shape**

*Vinho Verde varies tremendously in sweetness because some brands
are specially sweetened (to differing degrees) for export. Compare
different specimens of these inexpensive Portuguese whites, noting
for instance that the best-known Aveleda is medium dry, whereas
Casal Mendes, Verdegar and Magrico are tooth-tinglingly dry.*

*Try some of these to see how sweetness can vary in red wines, though
admittedly about 85 per cent of all reds can be described as 'dry'.*

★ Bone dry: *red Loires such as Bourgueil, Chinon and Saumur
        Rouge; Italy's 'high altitude' wines such as Barolo,
        Barbaresco and Brunello di Montalcino.*
★ Medium dry: *California's Cabernet Sauvignon, much
        Zinfandel; Châteauneuf-du-Pape; Lambrusco; many
        Tyrolean reds; Australian Shiraz; Piat d'Or red; Hirondelle
        red table wine; Paul Masson California Carafe Red.*
★ Medium Sweet: *California's late harvest Zinfandels; some of
        South Africa's beefier reds.*

**Take a note of the amount of
sweetness you detect in every wine
you drink**

*T*AKE *A smell of something high in acidity. Vinegar of any
        sort is fine (lemon juice is not as volatile). Notice how the
        edges of your tongue curl up in anticipation of the experi-
ence of how it would taste in your mouth. Acidity has such a strong
effect on the tongue, it is the easiest of the four basic tastes to imagine,*

We tend to think that it's only white wines that vary in sweetness. Rosés do as well, of course, with Provence being responsible for good examples of bone-dry pink wines and most Rosé d'Anjou being medium dry to medium sweet. But it is perhaps more of a revelation to examine the varying degrees of sweetness in red wines. Port is the supreme example of a very sweet red, but it is a wine that has been *fortified* by the addition of extra alcohol – other popular examples of fortified wines being Sherry, Vermouth and to a lesser extent Madeira and Marsala.

Ordinary unfortified wines are known in EEC parlance as 'light wines' (we can no longer use the term 'table wines' because they have nabbed this for everyday, basic-level-of-quality wine) and even light red wines can be anything from bone dry to medium sweet.

Most very cheap wines and many very popular ones have quite a lot of residual sugar because, respectively, sweetness can mask many a rough edge and it is a very easy taste to appreciate.

## Acidity – the vital spark

SWEETNESS (or lack of it, i.e. dryness) may be the most obvious of the four basic tastes to students of wine, but what physiologists call sourness is the most vital to the wine itself. Sourness is a measure of acidity, of which there's a lot in lemon juice and vinegar and little or

*without any liquid or solid stimulus at all. But if you really want to prove the point to yourself, sip some lemon juice or vinegar. Whether imagining, smelling or sipping, notice which part of your tongue reacts most strongly to acidity.*

*Now start smelling every drink you take, whether it's alcoholic or not. Notice that most drinks do actually have some sort of refreshing acidity in them. Still water won't make your tongue crinkle – it marks the frontier between acid and alkaline – but all fruit juices, carbonated drinks, milk, and even tea and coffee have some sort of tingling effect on the tongue. Notice too how important a component acidity is in fruit; lemons, grapefruit, gooseberries and blackcurrants are all common examples of fruits with so much natural acid that most of us have to add sweetness before we can eat them. Monitor the different tastes in a batch of fast-evolving fruits, such as pears or tomatoes, as they lose acidity and start to taste dull.*

**Start registering acid levels as you taste wine**

*If you have some cream of tartar in the house, make up a solution of it and add it in varying amounts to an ordinary table wine. (Heaven forbid such desecration of anything smart.) If you choose a fairly sweet wine, a cheap old-fashioned Spanish white for example, you might even be able to 'correct' it to a more acceptable level of acidity.*

*To get a very, very crude idea of the flavours of different sorts of acidity found in wine, familiarize yourself with these:*

*tartaric acid – cream of tartar in solution*

none in flour and water. The upper edges of the tongue
(towards the back of the mouth for me) are most sensitive to
acidity.

Too much acidity makes something sour; just enough
enlivens it, giving it appealing 'zip' or a crisp tartness. Sweetness and acidity are closely interrelated. As a fruit ripens, it
gets sweeter and sweeter while losing acidity. An over-ripe
pear, for instance, is bland and unappetizing because it has so
much less acidity than one picked at just the right moment.

Getting the balance between sweetness and acidity right in
wine grapes is crucial. The winemaker wants his grapes to be
as ripe as possible for two reasons. Firstly, the longer they're
on the vine the more interesting flavours they will have had
time to develop; and, secondly, the sweeter the grape juice the
sweeter and/or stronger the resultant wine will be, strength
being seen as a tantalizing commodity in wine regions far
from the equator. He mustn't, on the other hand, leave the
grapes on the vine so long that the acidity falls to a level that
will make the wine bland (and so long that they will be ruined
by hail, rain or frost). And, for white wines designed to live
long, acidity acts as a sort of embalming fluid.

There are many different acids in wine, the most common
being tartaric; indeed, scrapings from wine vats are the chief
ingredient in commercially available 'cream of tartar' preparations. The embryonic wine taster need not worry if he is
unable to distinguish between, say, gluconic and glyconic
acids; all you need be concerned about is the general level of
acidity as it appears to your senses. The acidity level may be
high for several reasons: the wine was made from grapes
grown where ripening sunshine has been at a premium (either
because of distance from the equator or altitude of the vineyard); the grapes were picked before they were fully ripe;

*malic acid – apple juice*
*critic acid – lemons, grapefruit or orange juice*
*lactic acid – milk or yogurt*
*acetic acid – vinegar*
*carbonic acid – fizzy drinks*

*Next time you decide to treat yourself to the taste of a good Sauternes, which in general means a classed growth with the words 'cru classé' on the label, and costing upwards of £7 a bottle, spend another £3 on a bottle labelled simply 'Sauternes' or 'Barsac'. (All Barsac is Sauternes, but not all Sauternes is Barsac; such is the law governing the use of the names of these two villages near Bordeaux.) You can use the remains of the cheaper wine for cooking a poulet sauterneais perhaps, or, better still, use the Grants of St James's generic Sauternes as your example of uninspiring sweet wine – available in half-bottles for about £3 from Victoria Wine.*

*Start registering acidity levels as you taste wine. The following are some possible examples of wines at each extreme:*

★ Green or tart: *Gros Plant Nantais from the Loire; Coteaux Champenois (the still wines of Champagne; I always think they demonstrate perfectly why Champagne should have bubbles in it); many English wines; Luxembourg's wines; 1977 Claret; 1977, 1975 and some 1981 red Burgundy; Vinho Verde from Portugal; Valdeorras from Spain (just across the border from Vinho Verde country).*

★ Crisp: *almost all Loire wines, no matter how sweet they are; Mosel wines; Chablis and lots of other white Burgundy; lots of other well-made whites from slightly warmer regions.*

★ Flabby or flat: *much more difficult to generalize here as it depends on individual winemakers' skills, but many North African and other wines, red and white, made close to*

there was not enough sunshine in that particular year to ripen the grapes fully; or acidity has been added chemically to the wine or must (the fermenting grape juice). This practice is allowed in a surprising range of countries and, when done carefully and undetectably to the taster, can often make for a better end-result.

The delicate balance between sweetness and acidity in ripe grapes is reflected in the resulting wines. The sweeter the wine, the more acidity is needed to stop it being cloying. The most obvious difference between a poor and a great Sauternes is the amount of acidity there is to counterbalance all that sugar.

At the other end of the spectrum, a very dry wine doesn't need all that much acidity to make it appetizing and crisp. A bone-dry wine that had as much acidity as a Sauternes would be mouth-puckeringly tart. The acidity of wine tends to be between 3 and 9 grams per litre.

Getting the balance between sugar and acidity right is an important part of winemaking. Wines that are too high in acidity right from the start are called *green*. (Other sorts of acids may develop and become apparent to the taster at specific points in the wine's life, but this is A-level stuff and discussed on page 51.) There is nothing sacred or technical about the term 'green', of course; it just happens to be an adjective commonly used for over-acid wines. *Tart* is another word used for the phenomenon, though more often for whites than reds. Noticeable but not overwhelming acidity is a very desirable quality in white wines, for we expect them to refresh us, whereas most red wines are expected to provide more nourishment and a bit of intrigue. Whites with marked but not unpleasant, acidity are often called *crisp*. 'Hmm, nice and crisp,' a taster might mutter appreciatively over a white wine feared to be a little low on acidity because it was grown

*Mediterranean shores tend to flab. You will sense a sort of drabness in the overall impact of the wine and find yourself still looking for the 'lift' of a bit of acidity as the wine goes through the mouth.*

★ Cloying or too sweet: *cheap very sweet wines of all sorts, either sweet white Bordeaux such as poor quality Sauternes or Barsac or the sweetest representatives in a range of branded wines such as Rocamar (Arthur Cooper).*

*Now try the 'dry white' in such a range – perhaps a glass of dry white at your local pub – and see if, by carefully registering how your tongue reacts, you can sort out the sweetness from the acidity.*

---

*M*AKE UP *a saline solution by dissolving some salt in water and swill it about your mouth, noticing which bits of the tongue react most strongly. I find it is the part just in from the ultra-acid-conscious edges at the back, and bits of the front edges too. Next time you want to check the seasoning in some savoury dish, make sure this part of your tongue is exposed to your sample of it. Next time you smell or taste a Fino or Manzanilla Sherry – the very dry light ones, Tio Pepe and La Ina, are good examples – notice how the salt-sensitive parts of your tongue react.*

**Make up saline solution**

somewhere quite hot. Wines, both red and white, that have rather too little acidity are often called *flabby*, one of those words that gets wine tasting a bad name. Yes, it does sound a bit ridiculous. If you can't bear to use it, you could use 'flat' instead. A flat or flabby wine is merely dull because it lacks sufficient acidity to enliven it. A *cloying* wine is one that is really sweet and doesn't contain enough acidity to balance the sweetness.

It can be devilishly easy to confuse acidity and dryness. A lot of us think we're drinking a very dry wine because it seems like hard work, when in fact it may simply be too high in acidity. Because a little sweetness is useful to mask none-too-brilliant winemaking, it's a favourite trick of the blenders of cheap 'dry' whites to market a medium dry wine with a massive dollop of acid in it to keep the fans happy.

## The other basic tastes

SALTINESS is a basic taste that is vitally important in food but rarely found in wine. One of the wonderful old chestnuts of wine lore is that the difference between a Fino and a Manzanilla Sherry is that Manzanilla acquires a salty tang because it's matured on the coast of Sanlucar de Barrameda instead of inland at Jerez. One has only to consider for a moment that the town also produces a Fino, and that the other 'Sherry port' Puerto de Santa Maria does not produce a Manzanilla, to smell something fishy rather than salty. In fact both Fino and Manzanilla can be slightly salty, and I have even tasted a trace of saltiness in some white wines from New Zealand, but such perceptible saline intrusions into the world of wine are exceptional. The description of the saltiness–tasting mechanism is included here more for comprehensiveness than for usefulness in wine tasting.

*To isolate bitterness, you could try putting a few drops of bitters such as Fernet Branca, Underberg, Angostura or Suze in some water and rinsing that round your mouth, noticing a flat, rasping sensation on the back part of your tongue. Campari is another very bitter liquid, but it is also very sweet – an interesting tasting exercise in itself. See how it needs the acidity of soda water (carbonic acid) and/or a slice of lemon or orange (citic acid) to make it a refreshing drink. The Italians obviously have a certain monopoly on bitterness. Assess each Italian red you taste for it. Some of the most renowned Brunello, Vino Nobile di Montalcino and lots of Piedmont reds, such as Barolo – have some degree of bitterness, but then so do many examples of the much lighter and more humble Valpolicella and Bardolino.*

**Allow tea to stew in a pot and take a mouthful**

*Allow some tea to stew in the pot and then take a mouthful, without any milk to soften the impact of this ungenerous liquid. Notice how you react. There's a bit of acidity there, perhaps a trace of bitterness*

The fourth and final basic taste that the tongue is capable of registering is bitterness, to which the flat back part of the tongue is particularly sensitive. Like saltiness, bitterness is much less important to wine tasters than sweetness and acidity, but quite a number of Italian reds leave a bitter taste at the back of the tongue.

So now your tongue should be fully trained to do its damnedest with any wine (and, more importantly, food) that comes its way. You should be able to assess the sweetness and acidity of any substance – as well as its saltiness and bitterness if necessary. You may be glad to hear that you now have a scientific excuse to take your wine in fairly large mouthfuls, for you should expose all of your tongue to the liquid.

Of course, you won't always carefully identify each basic taste separately. The wine makes a composite impression on your senses as you swill it about your mouth, but sweetness and acidity are crucial to that overall impression.

## More crude feelings

YOU CAN learn a bit more than the simple sensations of sweetness, acidity, saltiness and bitterness by the tangible effect of a wine on your tongue and insides of the mouth. One of the most obvious, and sometimes even pain-producing ingredients in many red wines is *tannin*. This is a convenient shorthand term for all sorts of tannins or polyphenols that either find their way into a wine from the pips, grape skins and stems, or develop as a result of the wood in which the wine has been stored – or sometimes both.

In ordinary eating and drinking, tannin is most noticeable in tea, particularly when it has been allowed to stand and lots of tannin has been extracted from the leaves. (That thin skin on

*too, but there's also something quite different from either of these components that is so distasteful it almost makes you want to screw up your eyes. This is tannin, and I feel the puckering sensation strongest between my gums and the insides of my cheeks. Notice where it affects you most, as it will depend on how you drink. Some people notice it particularly on the roof of the mouth.*

*Now try to assess every red wine you drink for its tannic impact on your mouth. Somewhat ironically, most examples of over-tannic wines cost rather a lot because, although they're youthful, they are rather smart. For a textbook example of good wine at this early, unfriendly stage, you will have to spend at least £6 on a bottle of good 1983 Claret from a Médoc village such as St Estèphe, Pauillac or St Julien. Compare this with a similar wine (ideally one from the same property) from the 1982 vintage in which the tannins seem much less obvious. The 1982 vintage demonstrates well the modern trend in Bordeaux to pick grapes significantly later than of yore so that the tannins themselves have softened or 'ripened'. Thus, even though the average tannin level of the 1982s is higher than that of the 1983s, it seems lower. And a bottle from a much older, good vintage – 1971 or 1970 perhaps – would show how lovely a wine can be once the tannin has retreated into the background and allowed the fruit and oak flavours to marry and produce many different nuances. Some mature Portuguese reds are hard because they have been left in wood too long, and can provide the tannic experience cheaply. Most other inexpensive wines won't have much tannin. This is due in part to their not being made from the aristocratic grape varieties that tend to give tannic wines, but also because no one would dream of treating them to the new, small oak casks in which great Clarets are aged. There are, however, many moderately priced examples of 'soft' young wines.*

*Tannin is not an important constituent of Beaujolais, for example, and nor is it in most Riojas. The wines of north-eastern Italy, as well as Merlot and Cabernet, are also soft, and even Bordeaux is*

walnuts is a good example of tannin too.) The sensation that tannin produces in the mouth is perhaps even more crude than any we have studied so far. The insides of the mouth and the gums seem to pucker up in a pretty nasty way when confronted by noticeable tannin: one reason why tasting young red wines that are destined for great things can be hard work.

Wines don't contain tannin to taste good now, but in the hope that they'll taste good in the future. Just as white wines to be kept need acidity in their youth, tannin acts as a sort of preservative to prolong the active life of a great red wine. Wine is capable of absorbing all sorts of tiny flavour elements when it is young, but needs time for these to knit together to produce a complex, mature wine. The tannins themselves break down and combine with other elements to contribute towards this ideal. One of the skills of the winemaker is to judge just how much tannin is needed at the beginning to balance the other flavour elements, most of them from the grape, as they evolve. Red Bordeaux or Claret provide the best examples of this. These are wines many vintages of which are capable of achieving venerable and gracious old age, which will be all the more gracious if they contain a fair amount of tannin at the outset. A tasting of young, good-quality Clarets, under three years old, say, can be a great strain. The tannin content is so high that it puckers the mouth immediately, leaving the senses straining to detect some indication of fruit. Very few people are sufficiently experienced and masochistic to judge wines of this sort. *Hard* is the word used to describe a wine that has too much tannin.

As the wines mature, the tannins become less evident and the taste seems much *softer*. The fruit-based flavours at last start to emerge in subtle and complex formations. Ideally, the tannin

*producing some low-tannin wines based on the usually tannic Caber-net Sauvignon grape. Belair Claret from Sichel and some Pierre Coste wines, available from Adnams of Southwold, are good examples of wines made with such new techniques.*

*The 1957 vintage in Bordeaux was one of those that simply had too much tannin to give any other flavours a chance. You'll be hard put to find a representative (and why should you, after all?), but try as many 1975s as you can find. There is current debate at the spittoon about whether that vintage won't also turn out to have too much tannin for its own good, like the 1983s in Burgundy.*

*White wines have an astringency of their own. We tend to call whites 'astringent' instead of tannic, but the feeling in the mouth is the same. Next time you taste a cheap Italian white, notice what happens to the most puckerable bit of your mouth. For me, many cheap Soaves produce the same sensation as youthful Clarets.*

**The addition of tannins is more widespread than people realize**

will finally fade to insignificance as the wine's flavour reaches its peak of maturity (though of course no one knows when this peak has been reached until it's been passed). Part of wine's great interest is that it is so unpredictable. A vintage that can look good at the outset, so good that winemakers are happy that the wines contain lots of tannin to preserve them for a glorious future, can fail to come up with the luscious goods, and the fruit fades long before the tannin dissipates.

Wines can also have too little tannin, though this doesn't make for unpleasant drinking in the way that over-tannic wines do – it's merely a waste of potential. A wine may have lots of lovely gutsy fruitiness when young, offering immediate attractive soft drinking; but all these flavours would have been capable of maturing into something more magnificent had there been more tannin to preserve them into middle or old age.

Tannin is chiefly an important component of red wines, partly because grape skins, stems and pips don't play an important part in white winemaking (see page 119) and partly because the pigments derived from the skins are needed to interact with the tannins to soften them. Some white wines taste astringent, in the same way as tannic reds, because they have been made from grape juice that has been pressed very hard and roughly out of the grapes, so that they contain a certain amount of tannin from the skins and pips.

Different red grape varieties tend to produce wines with different levels of tannin. The 'pippier' the grapes and the thicker the skins, the higher the tannin content in the must. Cabernet Sauvignon, Syrah and Nebbiolo grapes are particularly tannic. Vintages when there has been a shortage of rain to swell the flesh of the grapes also tend to produce tannic wines because skins and pips represent a high proportion of the must.

*Whenever a bottle of Barolo from a lesser vintage (1977, 1975, 1973 or indeed any that costs less than £7) comes your way, see what you think is its predominant characteristic. So dry and so drying is such a Barolo typically, that drinking it without food is unthinkable. Drinking such a Barolo can be like sucking a matchstick.*

*Less expensively, the Portuguese reds of the early and mid-1970s, which were a speciality of Oddbins at one time, can demonstrate the same phenomenon. What original fruitiness they had has, in many cases, disappeared without trace, leaving an unpleasantly hard wine.*

*S*TART TAKING *note of the alcohol content when it's stated on a wine label and relating it to how 'heavy' the wine feels in your mouth. If a wine is very alcoholic, you may well feel like avoiding naked flames when you breathe out. Beware the candles after the Châteauneuf. Notice particularly the hot, alcoholic sensation you feel on your breath after swallowing a glass of port.*

The winemaker can try to extract as much tannin as possible from the grapes by the way he chooses to make the wine. If he encourages a long fermentation and then lets the wine rest in contact with the skins for an extended period after that, called the *cuvaison* in France, there will be ample opportunity for lots of tannin to seep out of the skins and into the wine.

When wine is left in contact with wood it tends to extract what tannins there are in that material. The less an oak cask has been used before, the more tannins there are available. So really great wines that are thought capable of ageing up to perhaps five decades are often put into new casks. Although such casks are much more expensive than used ones, they set the wine up better for a long life.

The longer a wine is left in wood, the more its natural fruitiness will dissipate. Some very traditionally made Barolos are good examples of wines that have been kept so long in wood that the tannin overwhelms every other flavour component. There has been a discernible move towards making slightly softer, more approachable wines in Piedmont, however.

## Slimline and fuller-bodied wines

JUST LIKE people, wines have a weight – though there is no vinous shame in being full bodied. A wine's weight is a measure of how much extract and alcohol it has. A full-bodied wine has an alcohol content upwards of, say, 12.5 per cent and has lots of flavour. A light wine will probably be less than 10 per cent alcohol and is a much flimsier specimen. It's difficult to describe how you assess weight, but it is actually quite easy to do. Simply by looking at the wine you can get a clue (see page 63) and, with practice, when you smell it you often get quite a strong hint.

**Take a note of how heavy wine
feels in the mouth**

*Examine a glass of everyday German wine alongside one of every-
day Spanish. Notice how much more of an imposition on your senses
the Spanish one is.*

*Now 'look at' (great wine-trade euphemism for 'taste') the everyday
German, making sure it's not a 'Trocken' or 'Halbtrocken' – our old
friend Liebfraumilch would be fine. By shutting your eyes and
concentrating on a mouthful, make sure you can distinguish between
the sensations of sweetness and its lack of body.*

*Try to taste a Barolo and notice how dry yet full bodied it is. Next
time you can sip at some Asti Spumante (some are awful, but most
are fresh, grapey and delicious) savour its lightness at the same time
as noticing how sweet it is on the tip of your tongue.*

But it is in the mouth that wine sends its strongest 'guess-the-weight' message: it really is the physical sensation of how heavy the liquid feels in the mouth. When you have a mouthful of the wine do you feel overwhelmed by the intensity of what's in there, or is it a much more watery liquid? (Water makes up well over 80 per cent of the volume of most wines.)

Fortified wines are all very full bodied because they contain added alcohol. Most of the heaviest non-fortified wines are reds such as the Amarone wines of Italy, Hermitage and Châteauneuf-du-Pape of the Rhône and typical Cabernet Sauvignons from California, Australia and South Africa. Great white Burgundy, Sauternes and, especially, California Chardonnays can, however, be very full indeed. Much alcohol actually tastes rather sweet, which is why many California Chardonnays taste as though they contain more residual sugar than they do, i.e. some.

Most German wines are very light bodied; indeed, some are only about 6 per cent alcohol. Vinho Verde, whether white or the rarely exported red, is also light. Beaujolais and a host of southern French reds such as Costières du Gard, Minervois and most *vins de pays* are very light, even though most of us think of all reds as fairly full bodied. Many New Zealand wines are very light.

A wine doesn't have to have lots of residual sugar to be full. Great Italians such as Brunello and Barolo can be full but dry, while Asti Spumante is sweet but light. If you're watching your weight, go for wines that are both light and dry. Perhaps this is what accounts for the popularity of Muscadet, Sancerre, Chablis and Beaujolais.

There is now an official code to body in red wines, from A for very light wines like Beaujolais, to E for wines like Australian Shiraz.

## Capturing the flavour

IF ALL A wine could tell us was that it was crisp, medium dry, fairly light and slightly astringent, there would be no need for this book, and little pleasure in wine drinking. Wine's great attraction is that, more than any other drink, it is capable of an amazing variety of flavour – particularly when one considers that there is only one raw ingredient. (Imagine smart societies devoted to tasting different vintages of fermented carrot juice, or specialist gourmet tours of banana warehouses.)

As we have seen, the taste buds alone are capable of receiving only the fairly crude messages that the liquid wine can transmit. The really interesting bit, the wine's identity that we call its flavour, is carried by the volatile elements – up through the nose when we sniff and up from the back of the mouth when we taste – to the olfactory centre, the ultra-sensitive mechanism that deals with flavour. The *vapour* of the wine consists of the volatile esters and aldehydes that form a tiny but vital proportion of each wine's composition. It is their particular profile that makes up each wine's flavour, and to experience this flavour fully it does, of course, makes sense to get the vapour up to the olfactory centre by smelling or nosing the wine.

Now for the problem: how to describe wine flavour. 'Mmm, delicious' or even 'Uuugh' will do – if you never want to communicate with anyone else about wine; if you see no need to remember anything about specific wines; or if you choose not to enjoy the pleasures of comparison and monitoring that wine can offer. Readers of this book, however, will already have decided that they are interested in tasting wine properly, in order to assess it and to enjoy it more – possibly even with a view to blind tasting. What you will find is how frustrating it is to be confronted by a wide and thrilling range of sensations for which there is no cut-and-dried notation or vocabulary.

Music lovers know perfectly well what is meant by middle C and *fortissimo*. Connoisseurs of the visual arts agree on what's meant by square and (more or less) Cubism. For wine tasters there is no definitive term or mark for something as simple and distinctive as the flavour of the Gamay grape, say; let alone for the nuances it's given by the various other factors that paint the 'palate picture', such as the soil the grapes were grown in, the weather that led up to the harvest and the way the wine was made and stored.

An accepted vocabulary would clearly be very useful for wine tasters, and considerable efforts are being made to agree on one. The most respected attempt on this side of the Atlantic is the listing formulated by Michael Broadbent, head of Christie's wine department, in his classic *Wine Tasting*, while Maynard Amerine's much shorter and more rigorous collection in *Wines: Their Sensory Evaluation* provides a reference for American tasters.

But there are curious disparities, even between these two authorities, using the same basic language. The eminent and urbane Broadbent cites *flinty* as 'an evocative overtone. Certain white wine grapes grown on certain soils have a hint of gun-flint in the bouquet and flavour, e.g. Pouilly Blanc Fumé.' Amerine and his colleague Roessler on the other hand dismiss the tasting term with notable acidity: 'We confess that this flavor has never come our way. Perhaps *metallic* would do as well. Best to avoid it.' They describe the characteristic scent of Cabernet Sauvignon as *green olive*, while we British tasters are schooled to call it *blackcurrant*. The Australians, that other wine nation divided from us by a common language, are even blunter in their tasting vocabulary. An A-level in chemistry and maths would help you with the problem, but one in English would be a definite disadvantage. And you can doubtless imagine the variance between our tasting terms and those of the French.

Some work has been done by an enterprising Burgundian and, separately, by a hard-working Welshman to come up with definitive *essences* representing in a very concrete and indisputable way exactly what each term 'smells' like. The Burgundian has even marketed a little box of phials so that, as you taste a wine, you can smartly refer to the essence bank to see whether you're right to describe it as 'woody' or as 'violets'.

As these two last examples suggest, choosing words to describe wine is largely a matter of making comparisons with things that are not wine. Earlier parts of this course suggested terms such as 'medium dry,' 'green' and 'soft' which are fairly widely accepted conventions for describing some of wine's more obvious dimensions. When it comes to something as subtle as the wine's flavour, however, things are more difficult. It's a bit like the difference between describing someone's physical attributes (height, complexion and so on) and their character. Tasters tend to look for similarities to other flavours they've experienced or can imagine. Michael Broadbent notes *goaty*, for instance, as 'a rich ripe animal-like flavour. For example, ripe fat Pfalz wines made from the Traminer grape.' I find it hard to imagine him earnestly sniffing a goat preparatory to making this observation; this is merely an accepted term that has evolved.

You can evolve your own wine-tasting vocabulary. If a wine smells like clean sheets to you, then register it. All you need is a term that leads you from a sniff of the wine to a judgement of it. If Michael Broadbent takes a whiff of a ripe fat Rheinpfalz Gewürztraminer, he will say 'Ah, goaty' to himself and come up with an identification of the wine using this trigger word. We all have our own trigger words for various flavours. Throughout the rest of the wine course I will try to suggest a wide range of possible terms for each flavour examined, in the hope that they will help you to develop your own tasting vocabulary. It will be useful, but not essential, if your vocabulary is like that of other people. Non-professionals can make up their own rules for the game of wine tasting – though people in the wine trade who attempt its stiffest test, the Master of Wine examinations, are expected to use commonly accepted terms.

On page 249 there is a glossary suggested of terms to describe the dimensions of a wine, together with words commonly used to recall wine flavours. At this stage it is useful to distinguish between the two words *bouquet* and *aroma*. The first is conventionally used to describe the smellable flavour that has developed during the wine's maturation, while a wine's aroma is directly attributable to the grapes that made it.

**Capturing the flavour**

*LEAVE SOME not very precious wine standing out in a glass for a couple of days, somewhere you visit regularly such as the* kitchen. *Every time you pass it, take a sniff and notice how it changes. It gradually loses its fresh, fruity aroma and begins to get stale. Then the flavour goes flat and the wine is distinctly unappetizing. This is oxidized wine. If you leave it out for even longer the wine will eventually turn to vinegar, and along the way it can be described as acetic. The length of time this process of deterioration takes and how great an effect it has on the senses vary tremendously from wine to wine. Fortified wines like Sherry and Madeira deteriorate very slowly indeed. In general terms, the more body a wine has the longer it will last before deteriorating. Some very strongly flavoured 'light' wines can seem more attractive after a day or two of being exposed to air. Some youthful Australian and California reds, as well as some Italians, can benefit from a bit of aeration. (See page 89 for more on air, wine and decanters.)*

**Effect of lemon juice on the tongue**

It would be a waste of your money to buy bottles that might demonstrate wine faults to you. Try befriending a local wine merchant or the manager of the local off-licence, whose eyes should light up when you say you're taking a wine course; capitalize on this and

## Three pointers to quality

SWEETNESS, acidity, tannin level and body give you the dimensions of a wine. The flavour is the vital clue to its character. But if you want to be able to pick out wines you particularly like, and avoid the mean ones, it's helpful to know about three final aspects of wine that can be judged by the nose and mouth, and which point directly to quality or lack of it.

## Cleanliness

THE FIRST of these is rather negative. A wine is described as *clean* if it has no obvious faults. Your nose is by far the best judge of this. If after the first sniff you feel you still want to go on, then the wine is clean. Here are a few of the most common nasty smells or, in rather more polite American parlance, 'off-odors'.

★ *Acetic/vinegary/'pricked'*: a wine that has already started to turn to vinegar and smells like it (Britain's vinegar merchants buy up job lots of acetic wine from the British wine trade).

★ *Cardboard*: this is a very personal one, but I find it a common smell in cheap wines. It probably arises from the wine being treated with less-than-pristine equipment. 'Dirty filter pads,' mutter some tasters darkly.

★ *Corked/corky*: a catch-all term for a wine that is undeniably off. The wine smell is a combination of musty, mould and just plain old 'orrid. In ancient cellars weevils eating their way through corks used to be a common cause. Nowadays the cause is more likely to be a substandard cork the structure of which allows in air and even nastier things. It is thought by some that the average quality of corks, which come chiefly from Portugal, has fallen.

*ask for any bottles that are returned because of a fault – well, 'suspected fault' might be a more tactful way of putting it. There is no shame in a corked bottle. It's not a sign of poor winemaking, merely of bad luck. Though if a particular bottler seems responsible for a string of corked bottles, that suggests he's trying to cut corners on his corks.*

*Wine boxes, especially those containing red wines, seem to hasten the oxidation process. Most wines start to oxidize if kept in an opened wine box for more than about a week (though – still – the manufacturers are trying to improve this).*

*To familiarize yourself with the two sulphur-inspired stinks, try to memorize the two very different smells of half a boiled egg left out for a day or two ($H_2S$) and that of a newly spent match ($SO_2$).*

*Don't go around with wine faults up your nose. It would be a great shame to spoil your drinking pleasure by anticipating any of the off-smells detailed above. If a wine has one, it will impress itself on you soon enough.*

★ *Geraniums:* this reminiscent whiff is a sign that a wine has
   been coarsely treated with sorbic acid.
★ *Oxidized:* recognizing this takes a bit of familiarization.
   Sherry and Madeira are oxidized, i.e. exposed to
   oxygen, somethng which is usually deliberately avoided
   in winemaking. Oxidation is a fault in light wines and
   makes them taste/smell flat and stale. 'Maderized' is
   almost synonymous, but used chiefly for white wines.
★ *Pear drops:* the smell of acetate is quite common in young
   Beaujolais. Not a very serious fault, unless you hate
   pear drops.
★ *Rotten eggs/mercaptan:* this is the smell associated with
   hydrogen sulphide or $H_2S$ and comes about when
   sulphur, the winemaker's invaluable antiseptic, has
   combined with other elements in the wine. Australian
   noses seem particularly susceptible to mercaptan.
★ *Sulphury:* this smell of sulphur dioxide or $SO_2$, like a
   recently struck match or a solid fuel stove, sometimes
   lingers over wines that were treated to too much
   sulphur at some point and is common in cheap sweet
   whites. It will usually disappear if you swirl the wine
   around in the glass.
★ *Volatile acidity:* the whisper 'VA' goes up occasionally in
   the tasting room when a wine is obviously unstable or
   just about to become so. All wines with a smell are
   volatile to a certain extent, otherwise they wouldn't
   produce a vapour for us to smell. But very old, and
   sometimes very full-bodied, reds can smell as though
   they're hurling so many messages at you there can't be
   anything left in the glass.

It should be stated clearly after all this alarmism, however,
that 90 per cent of all the wines I've ever tasted have been
'clean', and most of the rest showed only a hint of one of these
possible faults – though there are still some shocking basic
table wines around.

*N*OTE WHETHER *the wines you drink in future are well balanced. 'Harmonious' is another word used to describe wines whose components make up a pleasurable whole. Balance has nothing to do with price or status. Even very modest wines can be perfectly balanced, and many venerable greats which have had years for one component to fall out of line can be slightly out of balance.*

*T*AKE TIME *to monitor how you feel just after swallowing a wine. You could find that you can double the pleasure a wine gives you by positively enjoying its 'long finish'. Wines which 'finish short' won't give you this added extra, and you might find yourself gulping them instead of savouring them.*

## Balance

A WINE IS well balanced if all its components blend into the whole with none standing out of it. A wine could be out of balance because it has too much acidity, because it is too sweet, because the tannin is too evident or because the alcohol dominates the flavour. There is no single sensation that can help you make up your mind about whether or not the wine is balanced; you simply have to weigh up all the individual components. All good wines should be balanced by the time they are ready to drink, but a wine that seems to have a great future ahead of it may well be unbalanced in its youth.

## Length

A NOTHER sure sign of wine quality is what tasters call the *length* or *finish* of a wine. If, having swallowed (or even spat out) a wine, you're still aware of its flavour lingering in your mouth and nose – in a good way, of course – then the wine must have been well made. A mouthful of great wine can seem to hang about for minutes, if not hours, after the liquid has gone. This is why, in terms of total amount of pleasure given, 'expensive' wines are not always poor value compared with lesser liquids whose impact is lost once they're swallowed.

## The eyes don't have it

S TANDARD texts on wine tasting point out at an early stage that three organs are involved: eye, nose and mouth, in that order. So usually they start with a detailed exposition of what the sense of sight can reveal about a wine. Literally looking at a wine is indeed the first thing a professional taster does, and it can often give him vital clues if he's tasting blind. But this book is about tasting for enjoy-

*Among wines that are meant to be slightly sparkling are the following.*

★ Whites: *anything described on the label as 'petillant' or 'perlant' (with little pear-like bubbles), otherwise not many from France other than some from Savoie and those from new-wave outfits, such as Listel, making experimental wines in the deep south; many everyday wines from the German-speaking wine-producing countries; Vinho Verde; some adventurous dry Italian whites designed for early consumption; many youthful little numbers from Australia, New Zealand, South Africa and California – especially Rhine Riesling, Chenin Blanc and anything else with a bit of residual sugar.*

★ Reds: *much less common, but Lambrusco, red Vinho Verde (rarely exported) and some youthful Chiantis are allowed a little 'prickle'.*

*If you want to convince yourself about the harmlessness of these crystals, try chewing them next time you encounter any in a white wine. You'll find that they taste very acid – for that, in fact, is what they are – and not at all sugar-like. Note the similarity of the taste to that of your trusty carton of cream of tartar. Red-dyed crystals taste much the same, but seem even crunchier.*

ment and, beautiful though the rich red of a well-made Claret and mellow yellow of a mature white Burgundy may be, the pleasure that our eyes can give is as nought compared with what the nose and mouth can do for the voracious amateur. For that reason, this section on 'winesight' is relegated to third position *after* wine in the mouth and up the nose.

The only vital role played by the eye of someone who's tasting for pleasure is an obvious one: anticipating a fault. If a wine is hazy, it is usually suffering from some sort of malady and won't taste very good. If a wine, red or white, is much browner than you'd expect it to be, then it is probably oxidized. If it's full bodied and slightly sparkling, then it could be going through unintentional second fermentation in the bottle. This will make it taste worse than it should (though the slight 'prickle' in many lighter whites and reds is designed to refresh).

Most particles found in wine are quite harmless, merely a nuisance if not picked out (if they're lighter than wine) or allowed to settle at the bottom of the bottle before it's poured (if they're heavier). Tiny bits of cork or deposit from the lip of the bottle that fall into your glass signify nothing more sinister than that the bottle was opened and served rather carelessly. White crystals in white wine and bits of dark deposit lurking in reds are as innocuous. Although they look so different, they're actually very similar, harmless solids precipitated by the maturation or storage of the wine, usually little crystals of tartaric acid. The tartrates are dyed dark red by the pigments in red wine, but in white wines they are left

**Look at wine against as white and
plain a background as possible**

---

*T*O GET *the best look at a wine's colour, tilt the glass at an
angle of 45° away from you, against as light and plain a
background as possible. A white tablecloth would be perfect, or even
a white plate. In this respect, the average dinner table or sitting room
is not often well geared up for optimal tasting conditions. You won't
get much of an idea about delicate nuances of shading by candlelight,
or against a wooden table – but then you probably won't want to try
blind tasting in such circumstances. Bear in mind that if you're going
to make a serious attempt at guessing what a wine is, you (or the
person who's trying to test your skill) should give serious thought to
lighting. There is more about this on page 73.*

*The best clue to a wine's real hue is often to be found just inside the
watery rim. This is particularly true in very deep-coloured red wines
which may be almost black except just here at the inner edge. With
red wines, colour is a prime indicator of their state of maturity.
Anything with a blueish tinge must be fairly youthful; the merest
hint of yellow or orange suggests age.*

shining white and looking suspiciously like sugar to the wary wine-buying public. Because the wine trade is heartily sick of having bottles returned in this innocent condition, nowadays they usually do their best to avoid it by freezing out the tartrates in advance, or they remove them by fastidious filtering. However, I always rather warm to a wine that's butch enough to throw a deposit.

Now for the Sherlock Holmes part of the course. Those interested in becoming a whizz at blind tasting read on, for the sense of sight will be as useful to you with your wine glass as it was for the great detective with his magnifying glass.

## A first glance

IF THE colour's rather dull and homogeneous – doesn't seem to vary much between the centre of the glass and the rim – then it's probably a very ordinary specimen. Most good wines actually *look* interesting, with nuances of colour shading towards a lighter rim. This is especially true in mature reds. The older a wine is, the greater will be the difference between the colour at the centre and an almost watery rim. If the wine has a very slight sparkle, then it could be any of the wines listed on the previous page.

## Second sighting

IN TERMS of hue, 'red' wines tend to go from purple to crimson to brick with age, while 'whites' can start off colourless but usually go yellower and then browner as they age. Particular colours are associated with particular areas or grape varieties, as detailed below.

REDS

★ *Purple:* most youthful wines of quality, and many light reds

*Colour is rather less revealing about the identity or maturity of white wines. Most whites fall into that narrow band between watery pale and pale straw, and their colour changes much less dramatically with age.*

such as Beaujolais, Chinon, Bourgueil, Valpolicella,
Bardolino and some New Zealand reds.
★ *Mulberry:* if the colour is deep too (see below) then the wine
may well be made from the Nebbiolo or Syrah grape, or
it could be a hot-climate Cabernet Sauvignon.
★ *Mid-red:* not many helpful clues from this.
★ *Reddish brown:* this wine will probably be mature. An
orange tinge is characteristic of Brunello di Montalcino.
A blackish tinge suggests the wine might be from South
Africa or Australia and, though mature, may not be old.

## WHITES
★ *Almost colourless:* Soave, English wines, Muscadet, young
German wines. Mosel wines can have a greenish tinge,
as can Chablis.
★ *Pale, pale yellow:* standard colour for most young dry
whites.
★ *Yellow gold:* in Europe, the extra colour indicates sunshine
or age, or some residual sugar, in a dry wine. Even very
youthful Chardonnays made in California and Australia
tend to have this colour, and the grapes
Gewürztraminer, Semillon and Viognier usually
produce deep-hued wines wherever they are grown.
★ *Deep gold:* great sweet wines can even go brown with age
without deteriorating in any way.

## PINKS
★ *Pale purple:* could be a Cabernet d'Anjou or a wine from
Germany or Alsace that hardly knows whether it's a red
or a rosé.
★ *Pale orange:* many Provence and other southern French
rosés are this colour, but blind tasting pink wine is
almost a contradiction in terms. If ever a wine was made
not to be taken seriously, it is rosé.

*T*HE BEST *way to get an accurate measure of the depth of a wine's colour is to put a glass of it on a white surface and look down into it from directly above. With samples of the same depth, you will notice a surprisingly wide variation in intensity between a wine (white or, more commonly, red) made around Mediterranean shores, such as those from Greece, Lebanon or North Africa, and one from the more temperate vineyards of northern France. Most red Burgundy is surprisingly pale.*

*T*HIS SWIRLING *business is much easier to do with a glass that has a stem (one of the reasons why stemmed glasses are favoured for wine tasting). With your preferred hand, clasp the glass by the stem using your thumb and as many fingers as you like, and gently orbit the glass around a vertical axis so that wine splashes up the sides. Now put the glass down and look at the insides of the glass. Are there great sticky streamers or just slight patches of dampness?*

## A third peer

NOT ONLY hue, but intensity of hue is an important clue. Red wines get paler with age (except for some wines from the amazing Domaine de la Romanée Conti which take on a mysterious blush in their teens). A very deep colour in a red suggests that it is either very young, made from thick-skinned grapes and therefore from close to the Equator or from an exceptionally sunny vintage further away, made so as to extract maximum colour from the skins, or made from a grape variety such as the Nebbiolo, Syrah or Cabernet Sauvignon in a ripe year. A red might be pale because it is old, made far from the Equator or in a vintage which suffered from excessive rain just before harvest.

Conversely, depth of colour in a white wine indicates age. It may also suggest that the wine is relatively sweet, or has spent some time in oak.

## A fourth twirl

THE FINAL trick is simple, in fact rather a dashing thing to perform and sound off about at the dinner table. By swirling the wine around in your glass and watching the sides of the glass afterwards, you will notice a wide variation in how viscous, or *sticky*, each wine is. Very viscous wines leave streams of something that looks like gin or clear nail-varnish falling slowly down the inside of the glass. Viscosity is a good indicator of body or weight, and therefore of a high alcohol content, lots of extract or both. Light-bodied wines won't usually leave much trace on the sides of the glass, whereas full-bodied wines leave very pronounced streams, sometimes called *tears* or even *legs* (though this last term was surely thought up to ballast all that 'wine is like a woo-man' analogizing). Low-temperature fermentation tends to increase viscosity slightly, however.

*Enthusiastic wine tasters make all
sorts of unsavoury gargling noises*

## The tasting technique – a summary

FIRST, LOOK the wine squarely in the glass. If you're tasting for enjoyment, you can merely look to make sure the wine is *clear* and not *pétillant* if it's not meant to be. You can also take careful note of its colour or hue by tilting it away from you at an angle of 45° against a white background, and examine *depth* or intensity of this hue by looking at the glass from directly above, as previously outlined. If you're trying to identify the wine, or get some measure of its quality, then these last two exercises are invaluable. Although authorities could talk for hours about the different hues and shadings they associate with different wines, in practice this 'seeing' stage usually takes only a few seconds.

Now to the all-important smelling· or 'nosing'. You could simply lift the glass to your nostrils and sniff, but a much stronger vapour is given off if you swirl the wine around a bit, as described for testing viscosity, just before sniffing. The volatile elements that make up the vapour are given off at the surface of the wine, so by swirling you maximize the amount of wine in contact with air, and thus the vapour or 'smell' that is given off. You could simply jiggle the glass from side to side, but you'd be in more danger of spilling some of this highly taxed liquid than if you move it around rhythmically. It doesn't matter, by the way, whether you keep the glass in contact with the table while you swirl or do it in mid-air – though airborne swirling means you can get the glass to your nose even faster.

Now get the nostrils hovering over the surface of the wine, preferably with the glass tilted at 45° towards you to maximize the wine's surface area and therefore its impact – even now that it's subsided. If the nose hovers just over the top of the glass, it will be able to benefit from all the vapour that collects inside it. Practice will probably show you that the best way to nose is to concentrate for a moment on nothing but the wine and then to take one short sniff. Shutting your eyes at this point helps enormously to get the most out of the wine, but it does make you look a bit of a ninny.

When nosing you should first do an almost subconscious check that the wine is *clean*. The message 'I am obnoxious' will get to the brain fast enough, so you hardly need expend thought on this before going on to the whole point of smelling the wine: to experience its *flavour*. As we have seen, the olfactory centre, our personal flavour-detecting agency, is located at the top of the nostrils. Luckily for blind tasters, and for those of us who like making comparisons between different wines, its signals appear to arrive in the brain close to that bit we call memory – which is why smells can be so uncannily evocative, and why wine tasting can be so much fun. Try to develop the ability to identify smells or flavours, to assess them qualitatively and to programme them into your memory so that you can relate them to other smells in the future. Don't worry if at this point you feel confused about actually describing them. There are guidelines for individual wines throughout the second half of this course.

**How the brain receives the message**

Now at last you're allowed to get some of the wine into your mouth. It will make a composite impression on you of *sweetness, acidity, tannin level* and *body* via the tongue and insides of the mouth, and will confirm the *flavour* by way of the vapour that gets up the retro-nasal passage. To make sure all the bits of your mouth most sensitive to each of the four taste components are well exposed to the wine, you will need to take a fairly generous mouthful. For the same reason, hold the wine in your mouth for a little while before either swallowing it or spitting it out. (See page 105 for details of when this apparent sacrilege is recommended.) If, when you have some wine in your mouth, you open your lips slightly and take in some air at the same time, you will further encourage the wine's volatile elements to vaporize and pass up the retro-nasal passage to the olfactory centre – hereby maximizing the impact any wine can make on you at any one time. This is why some enthusiastic inhabitants of the professional tasting room make such unsavoury gargling noises. This practice should be avoided in the dining room.

While the wine was in your mouth, you should have had a chance to weigh up each of the taste components and work out your assessment of its *balance*; and, as you consider how

**Swirling**

**Try blending red and white wines together**

your mouth feels after you've swallowed or expectorated, you should notice its *length* of flavour.

All of that took some time to explain, but it takes only a second to do. Just that simple technique will ensure that the relevant receivers are tuned in for every message a wine has to transmit. By nosing the wine first, you can experience all the pleasure of its flavour unencumbered by the distractions of the liquid in the mouth. By the time you have a mouthful of it, you are well equipped to understand the coarser but important messages transmitted there.

However, it is important to realize that tasting is extremely subjective – not only psychologically, in that we all like different wines and would choose different words to describe their flavours, but also physiologically in that our sensitivities to different aspects vary enormously from person to person. Some people can find it very difficult to assess sweetness, for instance, whereas I happen to find it a struggle detecting even hideously high $SO_2$ levels. There are all sorts of weird explanations for this. Physiologists have worked out that the reason some people take lots of sugar in their tea and coffee is that the tips of their tongues don't actually come into contact with the liquid. By being 'taught to drink properly' they can dramatically lower their sugar intake. My explanation for my own sulphur insensitivity is being brought up in a house equipped with a coke-fired Aga. Don't laugh; it could well be right.

*Try tasting at different times of the day*

# 2 *Practical matters*

YOU NOW know how to taste wine, a more rewarding yet hardly more taxing business than merely drinking it, and can use every tasting opportunity as part of this course. The circumstances in which you taste may vary from the most clinical lab conditions (the sort of Daz-white atmosphere in which professional quality-control tasters work), through the various rooms of your house, to picnics. This chapter describes the ideal conditions for tasting, including the right equipment and practices as well as the right surroundings. Of course you won't always be able to taste under ideal conditions. Indeed, you will make yourself extremely unpopular with your friends and family if you insist on complete silence at the dinner table as the wines are tasted, or on the perfect wine glass at a picnic (though that's not so unreasonable – my ideal wine glass costs about 45p and is quite sturdy enough for the picnic basket). Adaptation and compromise are the keys here. Your wine-tasting experience will not be completely ruined if conditions are less than ideal, even though specialists can be dogmatic about this. If necessary, go ahead and make simple changes to your pre-wine-tasting lifestyle, but it would run counter to the philosophy of this book if your pursuit of the grape and its delights made anyone else feel uncomfortable.

N*EXT TIME you have a day to yourself – at the weekend perhaps or, even better, when you're on holiday – try tasting a single wine at different times of the day. Write down your impressions on each occasion (there's more on tasting-notes on page 99) without looking at what you've written previously and see if you can tell when you were at your most perceptive (actually perceptive as opposed to apparently so). You'll probably be in peak condition towards the end of the morning, just as you start feeling ready for lunch. I certainly know from experience that the first wine of the day usually tastes the best, but that rule did not hold good for the jug of rich red I was once served with breakfast on a Spanish wine estate. You do need to be fully awake before you appreciate that first glass. Conversely, I am guiltily aware of the amount of good wine I have drunk at the end of the day without fully appreciating every nuance of its flavour.*

**Tasting in the comfort of your favourite armchair**

*Different tasters feel differently about whether they taste better when seated or standing. I don't find it makes much difference myself; my*

## Timing

O UR SENSES are keenest early in the day, perhaps not from the moment we first raise an eyelid but certainly towards the middle of the morning. This is why most professional wine tastings are timed for about eleven thirty a.m. However, there are few of us whose lives can easily encompass something as relaxing as a wine tasting in the first half of the day. In practice, you will probably do most of your wine drinking during, and just before, meals and will be at your most enthusiastic about wine in the evening. If you are thinking of trying some serious wine tasting, either by yourself or with friends but without the distraction of a meal, then try a Sunday-morning tasting. During the rest of the week, when daytime tasting is difficult, early evening is better than late. Wine, as doctors well know stimulates the appetite. (Such a shame the NHS no longer allows prescriptions for wine.) Wine tasting therefore makes a good prelude to eating; if you leave it till after you've eaten a heavy meal your senses will have lost the keen edge so useful to the wine taster.

## Physical environment

I F YOU want to get a good look at a wine's clarity, colour and intensity, then you'll need a surprisingly strong light and a plain white surface against which to hold the glass. Strong daylight is best, but usually impracticable. And even if you *are* able to taste during the day, sadly you may be better off staying indoors. The great outdoors has a habit of wafting the bouquet of a great wine into the far distance, and direct sunlight overheats both wine and tasters.

When setting up a tasting indoors, try to choose somewhere with plenty of soft light (not colour-distorting strip lights)

*nose and mouth seem blissfully unaware of what's happening to my legs. But certainly, it's usually more comfortable to spit when standing than sitting – if only to put the contents of the spittoon at a greater distance from your nose and eyes.*

**Spittoons should be placed strategically**

*Look critically at the lighting over your table. Is there a way you could make it easier to get a good look at your wines without totally disrupting things – perhaps by moving a standard lamp?*

*Next time you buy place mats, plates and table linen, spare just a thought for how useful a plain white surface would be when enjoying wine.*

and work out how you are going to find that white surface. Ideally sit at, or even better, move round a table covered with a white tablecloth. Irish linen would be lovely, of course, but a strip taken from a roll of disposable paper table-covering won't make you taste any less acutely. Remember, too, that most tabletops need to be protected from the ravages of spilt wine by laying several layers of newspaper underneath the tablecloth. If you want to taste in a comfortable, informal way in your favourite armchair – treating a couple of samples of wine as a substitute, say, for the evening paper – then there's an easy solution to the white surface problem. If you have your wine glasses on a side table next to you, you can simply hold them up against a piece of white card in your lap. An envelope will do, though if you're really getting into the swing of this thing you'll probably want to write tasting notes and you can use the piece of card to write on.

Surprisingly few dining rooms make very good tasting chambers. Candlelight is seen by advertising executives as inextricably intertwined with wine drinking. This is presumably because the candle is a conveniently portable light against which wines with a strong sediment used to be decanted, and because wine is traditionally associated with romance. But you need to have a lot of candles set pretty high above the table's surface to throw enough light for easy tasting. You can make the most of the light they give by using a white tablecloth, but you may well want to show off that beautifully polished table to your dinner guests. In these circumstances, a plain light plate should provide a suitable backdrop for wine examination. If all else fails, you can always hold a glass up to the nearest available light source for examination (this is the origin of that rather pretentious-looking stance). However, this doesn't give you nearly such an accurate and detailed picture.

*Scour your house for good places for tasting. You need good light and no strong smells. If you're tasting a lot of wines at one time, a big flat surface, on which to line up the bottles and glasses, is useful.*

*Next time you're drinking wine with friends, swap glasses and notice how some people leave a hint of their own personal aura on a glass.*

*If you're a smoker, try not to smoke while someone else is concentrating hard on a wine, but don't despair in the fear that you'll never be able to taste as well as the non-smoker. If you're a long-term smoker, try the blindfold test on page 16 at the same time as a non-smoker friend. You will probably do every bit as well.*

Another good place for tasting at home is the kitchen. You may well have a useful white work-surface that can easily be wiped clean of all wine's purple circles and blobs, and may even be conveniently close to the kitchen sink (a good spittoon if you can bear it). The only problem here may be very distracting smells. Because our noses are so important in wine tasting, it makes sense to distract them from the glass in hand as little as possible. If you're seriously trying to distinguish the difference between two glasses in front of you, it's made all the more difficult by a strong whiff of cooking or cleaning smells.

This is why participants at formal tastings are adjured to 'come clean', untainted by scent or aftershave; why the organizers try to serve food only in another room; why there are no floral decorations, and why they even hand ostentatious no-smoking signs above the tasting table. You should hear the shocked whisper that goes up if a whiff of Dior or Dunhill is detected.

Mine may be a rather heretical view, but I think the need for an olfactory vacuum in which to taste has been a little overstated. We all have our own body smell; it can be so pronounced that others call it body odour, or discernible only by very close friends indeed. We don't really notice our own body's smell – not knowing what life would be like without it, after all. We get used to our own little 'aura'. This is true even of heavy smokers who reek of stale tobacco. Those same people, I have noticed, are as able as the next person to distinguish nuances of flavour in wines, because they're used to tasting through their own tobacco-scented atmosphere. If, on the other hand, the heavy smoker says, 'Here, taste this!' and hands you a wine glass he's been nursing for ten minutes, you'll first smell him and only later, through the haze of his aura, the wine he's so excited about.

*Next time you're drinking wine, or otherwise using your nose, in an atmosphere where there's a particularly strong smell, notice how the smell that at first is so noticeable seems to fade with time. I've tasted wine in all sorts of circumstances – from the standard French tasting room, where the host almost invariably lights up a Gauloise as you start to taste, to a room that was in the middle of being painted. At first I thought the wines would have no chance against the opposition for my nasal attention, but very soon I'd forgotten the distraction as my nose got used to the overall atmosphere. After all, people who live in towns where industry produces particularly noxious fumes don't even notice them.*

*When enjoying wine and food at the same time, especially hot or very aromatic food the flavour of which drifts up into the atmosphere, try to work out your own practical way of getting the most from your glass of wine. You may want to turn slightly to one side, away from the food, when 'nosing' the glass. Try to get the chance to examine a wine before food gets to the table; it will show itself best without edible distraction.*

**Tasting – possible distraction**

Similarly, a glass held by someone who purposely forswore the scent bottle before a tasting, but who always uses a fairly distinctively perfumed soap, to someone else will smell primarily of that soap and only then of the wine inside it. No matter what precautions are taken to make a tasting room as 'unsmelly' as possible, there will be as many different little personal auras as there are people. Eventually the room will take on a smell, discernible to those with a particularly keen nose, that is the mixture of all these together with the smell of all the wines that have been opened. There's no need, therefore, to get worried about the odd whiff of recently smoked cigarette or newly applied scent. It will soon dissipate and add itself as just one component to the overall atmosphere – and our sense of smell is anyway constantly adjusting itself to its environment. If we hold the heavy smoker's or the clean-handed person's glass for long enough, we'll start compensating for their respective auras and start smelling the wine.

To ban the smell of food may be sensible when tasting clinically as part of a job or test, but food plays such an important part in the enjoyment of wine, it's unnecessary to bar it from every wine tasting. After all, at the dining table a wine's bouquet has to battle against the smell of the dish with which it is served, and this can be a much bigger problem than the odd plate of edible blotting paper that can be so appreciated by amateur wine tasters. Under such circumstances, you may find dry savoury biscuits helpful tasting companions.

So, a few ground rules when tasting wine.

★ To appreciate colour, you'll need some sort of white surface.
★ At a formal tasting you will be unpopular if you smoke or are obviously anointed with something smelly.

*T*RY, ONCE ONLY, *the following tastes immediately before taking a mouthful of wine:*

*toothpaste (it makes fruit juice taste*
    *dreadful, too)*
*cough linctus, drops, pastilles*
*throat lozenges such as Victory V*
    *and Fisherman's Friends*
*Trebor extra-strong mints*
*Doublemint chewing gum*
*Mars Bars*
*vinegar*
*tea*

*They each leave the mouth feeling different, usually hyped up to receive one particular message and therefore not very good at making a sound critical assessment of a wine, let alone getting the full pleasure potential from it.*

*Work out your own 'neutralizing' technique so that you don't have to spend the rest of your life avoiding certain foods or preparations just in case someone might offer you a glass of wine.*

★ In any surroundings you will find it easier to taste without
the distraction of other smells, though you may well
decide you'd rather sacrifice the fleeting aroma of the
Viognier grape for the exotic allure of your scent or the
enveloping comfort of your favourite tobacco.

## Possible distractions – feeling right

BEFORE HOISTING the no-smoking signs to limit
other people's behaviour, make sure you are doing
everything right for wine tasting. Far more
important than what's going on ten yards from you is what's
going on inside your mouth. Before setting off to enjoy a
glass of wine, think about what you last ate and drank. Most
toothpastes make anything high in acidity tasted after them
seem pretty awful. It would certainly be a crime to taste a fine
wine less than an hour after brushing your teeth with paste.
Strong cough and throat preparations can leave their mark in
the mouth so forcefully that wine tasting is difficult, as do
strong mints and chewing gum. Also, eating or drinking
anything that is particularly high in one of the basic taste
components most commonly encountered in wine – sweetness, acidity or tannin – seems to make assessing wine soon
afterwards difficult. Chocolate, sharply dressed salads and
even an apparently innocuous cup of tea seem to leave the
mouth too highly tuned into their own particular strength.

The simplest way to 'neutralize' your mouth after one of
these problem tastes is to chew a mouthful of something
absorbent but fairly bland, such as bread, or to try to rinse out
the flavour with water (though I've found this less effective). I
was once part of a tasting group that met at eight o'clock in
the morning (it seemed the obvious solution for people who
were working all day and studying at night – at least I *think*
that was the reason). The disadvantage of toothpaste soon

*If you reckon your palate and judgement are unswayable by tiresome details such as the weather or the telephone bill, then try a few simple exercises.*

★ *If it's deep midwinter, think of a wine you remember particularly enjoying in the summer – a beautifully refreshing Mosel or Frascati, perhaps, something that brings back memories of sipping in the sunshine. Try tasting it one frosty day. Doesn't it seem a bit thin, a little lacking in flesh?*

★ *If, on the other hand, you're currently enjoying a heatwave, try a rich red that gave you pleasure last winter. That Rioja or Dāo that seemed such good value then surely seems a bit rough and overblown in warm weather.*

*Practise giving each wine that you drink just thirty seconds' attention as you approach it for the first time; that's thirty seconds during which your ears are metaphorically plugged, safe from the distraction of general conversation and, even worse, other people's comments on the wine.*

became apparent and so I took to brushing my teeth without toothpaste and experimented with various mouthwashes. For your information, I found Listerine (though not Listermint) does the freshening trick and doesn't interfere with the wines.

As well as having the inside of your mouth in order, it helps if the inside of your head is also geared up for wine tasting. It's amazing how one's ability to taste can be affected by mood. As outlined above, I think it helps to be just slightly peckish to have that edge on your appreciation and you also need to be alert and relaxed enough to concentrate, almost in your own little world, on the wine in hand.

No matter what the main purpose of your tasting – identification, assessment or straightforward enjoyment – you'll find the most serious distraction from forming your opinion will be other people. The whole business of wine tasting is so subjective, and even the most experienced tasters can feel so suggestible, that an early comment (delivered with sufficient confidence, of course) can sway a whole roomful of tasters. With any wine, your first impression – what you sense with the first concentrated sniff – is by far the most important.

Allow yourself a moment's intense concentration as you nose a wine for the first time and take note of your reaction. If you think it's a Claret and someone says, 'Positively *yells* Burgundy, wouldn't you say?', don't allow yourself to be talked into smelling Burgundy on the second sniff. However knowledgeable other tasters may be, there is no reason why their judgements will be more accurate than yours. In my experience, it is the relative novices who get things right in blind tasting. The old hands have far too many contradictory signals to confuse them.

NOTICE THE temperature in the room in which you usually drink wine. Unless you are a healthy relic of a bygone age, it is likely to be more than 65°F when you're actually drinking wine, too hot a temperature to match your wine. Kitchens, in particular, encourage mulling.

Take any red and any white wine, as basic as you like. Pour out two half-glasses of each and cover all four of them with cling-film to keep the bouquet in the glass. Put one red and one white into the fridge for half an hour and leave the other two in a normally heated living room. Now compare the two pairs, whites first and then red. When you take off the cling-film, you'll see how much more bouquet the warmer wines seem to have.

Next time you are drinking a chilled wine with food, try to work out what benefits you're getting from the coolness of the wine. Once the mixture of wine and food is in your mouth, it tends to warm up speedily towards body temperature (from 45° to 75°F in ten seconds). Do you savour the wine for its refreshing coolness, or are you simply chilling it out of habit? Remember the exercise, described on page 18, of trying to distinguish between a red and a white wine when blindfold. If you found it difficult to tell them apart, why treat them differently when deciding on serving temperatures?

Experiment by serving different wines at different temperatures to find out what suits you and the wines best. Of course, when you're drinking for refreshment you'll want the wine to be a bit cooler than when you're trying to eke the last ounce of flavour from it. Start gently edging up the temperature at which you serve full-bodied white wines. If they're good, you'll find them much more rewarding.

## The right temperature

THE CONVENTION is that white wines and rosés are served cool, and red wines at a higher temperature somewhat loosely called 'room'. It's useful to realize that this is very little more than a convention, and that by not sticking to it too rigidly you may be able to increase your enjoyment.

Generally speaking, the warmer a wine (or anything) the more volatiles it gives off and the more flavour it seems to have. There is an upper limit to this, however, as demonstrated by those restaurateurs who think that if a little warming is a good thing then lots of it will be very good. A red wine that's served too hot, say at 70°F, will start the irreversible process of turning acetic and breaking down. If you want to get maximum *flavour* from any wine – red, white or pink – you should drink it at a temperature between 60° and 65°F.

Another factor comes into play here: we cherish wine's ability to refresh us, as well as intrigue us with its flavour. Just as we like soft drinks to be chilled, we have come to expect aperitif wines drunk to refresh (which are usually white or rosé) to be chilled too. And that custom has somehow been extended to encompass the chilling of all whites that we drink – even if it's a full-bodied white Burgundy to accompany a hot fish dish.

What determines whether or not a wine's flavour can survive chilling well is, in fact, dependent not on colour but on body. The more full bodied a wine is, the warmer it will need to be before its esters and aldehydes vaporize to yield its flavour. The lighter it is, the more easily volatiles are given off even at lowish temperatures. Because white wines tend to be lighter

*If they're not so good, this will be demonstrated very obviously and you may decide not to choose that particular wine in future.*

*At the bottom end of the price range, it's much easier to find acceptable light reds (such as the army of 'vins de pays' from Southern France) than it is to find clean, dry whites. Try serving one of these light reds slightly chilled, just like smart restaurants serve Beaujolais, and see how you can turn it into an inexpensive refreshing red aperitif.*

*You will want to evolve your own regimen on serving temperatures, but these are some useful guidelines.*

★ *Keep wine in an unheated room, or outhouse, where the temperature doesn't vary too much during the day, or even from season to season. Ideal 'cellar' temperature is about 50°F, though experiments involving keeping wines for long periods at much higher temperatures suggest it is the constancy of temperature that is more important.*

★ *For tasting purposes, most wines are fine served straight from a 50°F cellar. Whites should reveal all, and reds can be swiftly warmed by being poured and cradled in the glass.*

*You may want to cool some wines, Champagne and other sparkling wines for instance, well below 50°F if you want to enjoy their refreshing aspect more than their flavour. You can put the bottle in the fridge for an hour or so, depending on how cool your fridge is. If this is an unplanned refresher you can chill the bottle by putting it into the ice box, or even the deep freeze, for about twenty minutes. This is supposed to give the wine too great a shock, but I have never known it to cause any more harm to the flavour than the standard*

than reds, the conventional wisdom of chilling them usually works – but there are exceptions. Full-bodied whites, such as great Burgundy, white Rhône, Chardonnays in general and many massive whites from warm climates, will be spoiled by chilling them too assiduously. Conversely, light-bodied reds, such as Beaujolais, red Loire wines, many early-maturing red Burgundies and north Italian reds, can be very attractive and refreshing if slightly chilled.

The convention may also have something to do with the fact that heat tends to decrease our sensitivity to tannin and to sweetness (and sulphur). That's why tannic red wines taste so tough if cool and why very sweet wines taste less so if very cool. Baron Philippe de Rothschild has the curious habit of serving his customary Château d'Yquem so cold with dessert that it has ice clinks in it. That deprives him of its wonderful bouquet, just as overzealous wine waiters who try to keep their white wines permanently under 40°F cheat their customers of much that the wine has to give.

If you have a really nasty white wine, the best way to serve it is very chilled, as this will mask its nastiness. If you want to experience as much as possible of what a wine has to give, good and bad, then it is best to taste it at that convenient midway temperature known as 'cellar', i.e. about 50° to 55°F. Reds can take rather higher temperatures than this, but the glass can always be warmed up quickly in the cup of your hand. Once served, the natural progression of the temperature of a wine is, after all, upwards, by about 1°F every three minutes. Once it's poured, it will be exposed to the hot air that inevitably surrounds all of us wine tasters, so don't worry if you fear you have served a wine too cool. Just realize how important it is to wait until it has warmed up enough to give its true flavour.

It is also worth pointing out that, once wine gets into the

*method of immersing the bottle in a mixture of water and ice cubes in an ice bucket or other roomy container. The icy water works much better than ice cubes alone, by the way, because there's something cool in contact with every bit of the bottle's surface. If aesthetics are not a factor, ice cooling packs, kept in the ice box, can be used instead of ice cubes.*

**Try chilling wine to different temperatures**

mouth, it inevitably warms up there. Experiments have shown that even heavily chilled wine rapidly thaws in the mouth, but by then it will be too late to get the full benefits of experiencing the bouquet in isolation.

## The decanter – dead as a dodo?

THERE IS still surprisingly little debate about serving temperatures for wine; most drinkers continue to follow the accepted wisdom unquestioningly. The Great Decanting Debate, however, goes on strongly and those following this wine course could well add useful observations to it.

The decanting tradition grew up from a time when wine was drawn off into a jug from a cask in the cellar, and later when winemakers left a deposit in the bottle. It then made sense to pour wine off this deposit into a decanter so that one could drink without chewing. Nowadays, it still makes sense to decant those few wines that have thrown a heavy deposit, provided they are robust enough to withstand it. Some very old wines and some very lightly perfumed wines would simply lose their bouquet if they had to suffer the fairly boisterous treatment of being poured twice. This is akin to the dangers, already described, of trying to serve a wine in the great outdoors. Wine and too much air do not make a good mixture.

The debate centres on the question of how good a mixture wine and *some* air is. For a long time it has been thought that the process of ageing in wine was simply one of slow oxidation, that small amounts of air either already present in the sealed bottle or entering through the cork gradually react with the wine to make it develop into something more complex and ramified. It was thought therefore that if you poured

A-level: *Very much an optional exercise this, but one you can save for a rainy day when you feel like making a major contribution to what we know about wine and air. You'll need to open up a fair amount of wine, so it might make sense to try it out on a day when you will be entertaining in the evening.*

*Choose any wine(s) you like, as many as you can afford, but as few as one will do. It would make sense to select a wine you would consider decanting – perhaps a very cheap red and a more expensive youthful one. You'll need three bottles of each, I'm afraid. Open one three hours before you plan to do your tasting and decant it into a decanter or a clean, empty wine bottle. Open the second bottle one hour before serving and simply let it 'breathe'. Open the third just before you taste a glass from each bottle, served to you blind by a kind-hearted accomplice. See if you can notice any difference between the effect of the three different preserving treatments.*

*This experiment is open to endless variation: with different wines, different lengths of time before tasting, and different sorts of 'decanter' (something with a wide mouth, such as a glass jug, would expose the wine to more air than a narrow-necked vessel).*

a bottle of wine into another container such as a decanter, you would aerate it and somehow telescope the ageing process into a few minutes by putting the wine into contact with a lot of air. The bouquet would be fanned into life by all this oxygen.

This view is still widely held, but the results of comparative tastings of samples of the same wines opened at varying intervals before tasting have been suspiciously inconclusive. Furthermore, some authorities argue that the effects of aeration can only be harmful; that by exposing a delicate bouquet to air you may make it evanesce, and that the interesting reactions between oxygen and wine are too complicated to be speeded up. All that can happen, they argue, is that the wine starts to oxidize too fast, and therefore deteriorates.

Many ordinary wine drinkers claim that some wines, especially cheap reds, taste much better if opened and left to 'breathe' for a few hours. This may have nothing to do with decanting or even aeration. After all, such a small proportion of wine, the area of the bottleneck, is in contact with air that only a tiny amount of oxidation would take place. A much more likely explanation is that with cheap wines there may be off-odours trapped in the gap between the surface of the wine and cork, and that this 'breathing' process allows them to evaporate.

It is true that the potential disadvantage of dissipating the bouquet of a wine by decanting it or allowing a half-full bottle to stand open can sometimes be an advantage. Some wines, full-bodied reds particularly, can be just too intensely flavoured when young. Rather than gaining extra flavours, the decanter allows them to lose some of their aggressive youth and mellow into a more palatable, if more vapid, middle age. This is especially true of some rich reds from California, Australia, Italy, the Lebanon, and the odd 'farm-yard' wine from Spain and the Rhône.

*B*ECAUSE THE *tap incorporates a one-way valve, wine boxes are designed to let wine out but no air in. When this self-deflating mechanism works perfectly, you can draw off as much or as little wine as you like without the problem of the wine inside being exposed to lots of harmful air. It is certainly true that an opened wine box guards wine for longer than an opened wine bottle, but it is important to realize that*

★ *by following the advice given opposite you can considerably prolong the active life of a wine sold in bottle; and*
★ *the process of filling wine boxes is still far from perfect and, at the moment, wine kept inside an unopened wine box deteriorates after a very few weeks, much sooner than wine kept in an unopened bottle.*

*See too the exercise demonstrating the harmful effects of air on wine, outlined on page 50.*

**Keep a collection of small bottles to decant leftovers**

A good set of rules, then, is to open cheap and full-bodied reds an hour or so before serving, to decant when there's a sediment to remove or a beautiful decanter to enjoy aesthetically, and otherwise not to get too exercised about the whole business.

## Wine leftovers

AS THOSE marketing wine boxes are very well aware, we don't always consume wine in exact bottle-sized portions. If a wine is left in a half-empty bottle the air will accelerate its deterioration. The lighter the wine the faster it will deteriorate. (Though, as outlined earlier, some very aggressively full-bodied wines can benefit from a bit of aeration.)

This wine course involves a great deal of comparative tasting, as it is chiefly by comparing different wines that we can learn about them. This is likely to result in many wine leftovers, fractions of a bottle that you will want to keep for future drinking. Do not despair! Wine from a bottle that has been opened can last for weeks, provided it is kept in conditions as near airtight as possible. On the other hand, the more air it is left in contact with, the sooner it will spoil.

The answer then is to keep a stock of small bottles into which you can decant leftovers. Half-bottles are useful for this purpose, as are the quarter-bottles served on planes, and here the funny half-litre flasks into which the Hungarians put Tokay really come into their own. Fill them right up to the top and then stopper them firmly with narrow corks (Italian ones are useful because most Italian bottlenecks are unusually small) or stopper corks saved from old Sherry and Port bottles. Of course the decanting process itself will mean that the wine loses a little bit of its initial freshness, but the leftover wine should still be perfectly enjoyable if kept in this way.

*T*RY DRINKING *wine out of the following drinking vessels and note how 'wrong' it tastes. Is it partly because you can't get a look at the wine before tasting it?*

*china teacup, pottery mug, pewter tankard, silver goblet, plastic beaker, paper cup (this, curiously, is probably the best of these, affecting the wine's flavour least)*

*Try swirling a sample of wine round in a glass without a stem. It will be much more awkward and liable to spill.*

*Muster as wide a selection of differently shaped glasses as you can, and pour a small, similarly sized sample of any single wine into each. Give each a short swirl taking a concentrated sniff from it immediately afterwards: swirl, sniff, swirl, sniff, etc. Notice how much lighter and more evasive the bouquet is on those samples in glasses whose shape encourages the volatiles to escape into the atmosphere, such as these –*

## Why you need glasses

MUCH MORE important than the exact temperature of the wine, and/or whether you've decanted it, is the sort of vessel you taste it from. Metal, and even pottery, goblets may look good on the shelf, but leave them there if you want to get the most from your wine. Glass is the ideal material because it is tasteless and doesn't impose any temperature on the liquid inside. You can easily warm up a glassful of wine by cupping your hand round it, if necessary, and you can savour the anticipatory pleasure of looking at a wine's colour.

We have seen how important it is to swirl wine around in order to release its flavour, and this is where the stem comes in. A glass with a stem can easily be rotated, but without necessarily warming the wine up at the same time. You will want to 'collect' the flavour in the space above the wine's surface, which means that the best shape for a wine glass is one that goes in from the bowl towards the rim. If you make sure the glass is not filled more than half full, there should be no danger of precious wine spilling out as you swirl and there'll be lots of room for the vapour to collect above it. The best wine glasses therefore are tulip- or near-spherical-shaped and have a stem. Coloured glass is rather frowned upon as it disguises a wine's colour; similarly cut crystal, the pride of glass departments throughout the land, for much the same reason. The best wine glasses are never the most expensive. Many off-licences sell glasses called Paris goblets for less than 50p each. These can hold as much as 8oz so that you can get a good noseful of vapour above a 2oz, or even a 3oz, sample. For tasting, it's important that glasses aren't too thimble-like, otherwise you won't be able to get the full impact 'on the nose', as professional tasters say.

*— as opposed to being stronger when trapped in more enclosed glasses,
such as these:*

There's an official tasting glass devised by the Institut National des
Appellations d'Origine (INAO), but quality seems to be variable.
Good sources of plain, well-shaped glasses which are made from
attractively thin glass include the following merchants:

Berry Bros & Rudd, 3 St James's Street, London SW1
Ellis Son & Vidler, 57 Cambridge Street, London SW1 and
        Hastings
Green's, 34 Royal Exchange, London EC3
The Wine Society, Gunnels Wood Lane, Stevenage, Hertfordshire

*Just to prove the point, next time you have some sparkling wine
open, compare the bubble and mousse in a thoroughly rinsed glass
and one that still has a slight coating of detergent. The fizz will be a
damp squib in the second glass.*

Remember that you don't need an enormous amount of wine in order to taste it, for it is the surface, rather than the depth, of the sample that releases the all-important flavour. An inch depth in an 8 oz glass would be ample. The standard number of glasses for *drinking* available per 75 cl bottle is between six and eight, but you could squeeze out up to twenty samples for tasting purposes.

You don't need a battery of different glasses for different wines. You could get by quite happily with a single sort, described above, though you should probably fill it only sparingly when serving fortified wines like Port and Sherry. The wine trade's single-mindedness over glasses does waver a little when it comes to sparkling wines and champagne. Approved glasses for bubbles are tall and thin, allowing only limited escape space for the carbon dioxide (not those saucers which encourage wines to lose their fizz fast), but the standard glass will be fine for *tasting* sparkling wines – possibly better for enjoying the flavour as opposed to the fizziness.

Thin, delicate glass is not necessary for tasting but it does add to the overall pleasure of drinking.

Do be careful when washing and storing glasses. You may well need to use detergent to get greasy fingermarks off, but be sure to rinse glasses well afterwards. The taste of Fairy Liquid does nothing for fine wine – and its traces play havoc with the mousse of a sparkling wine. Also make sure that you store them right way up, so that they don't trap a stale smell in the bowl, in a clean cupboard or box.

**Compare bubble & mousse in glass
that has thin coating of detergent**

*See sample tasting notes on pages 102–103.*

**Get into the habit of writing down
your impressions at the time of
tasting**

## Wine and words

IN ORDER to compare, discuss and remember wines we need some way of recording and communicating our reactions to them. A vocabulary consisting of the delighted yelp and disgusted moan just does not do the trick. I've seen some tasters use nothing but numbers (three for clarity, five for bouquet, seven for finish, etc.) but it's not very illuminating to have every wine described only by a sort of football formation. There are others who try to draw the impact of a wine's flavour on the palate.

Opposite is a wine that is very showy at first but then finishes short.

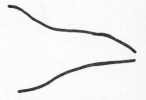

And here's one that's 'dumb' on the nose but opens up in the mouth.

Either or both of these 'languages' are fine to supplement but not supplant the most subtle method of communication that we can so far muster for flavour, style and so on: the written (and spoken) word.

The easiest way to learn about how wine tastes is to keep a record of your tasting experiences, to make tasting notes on as many of the wines you taste as you can. Knowing that you have to describe a wine helps enormously to concentrate your mind on it, and the notes provide a reference for you when building up the valuable experience of drawing comparisons. Quite how assiduously you keep the note-taking habit will depend on how much enthusiasm and thickness of skin you have. I don't make notes when friends ask me round for supper, but I know one or two professionals who do. They've never regretted it for a minute (their spouses may occasionally have, but not their publishers).

*Get into the habit of writing down your impressions of the wines you taste as soon as possible after you try them, at the time of tasting ideally, or perhaps when you get back home.*

*Try to develop your own special trigger words for different grape varieties and then for other more complicated aspects of wines. Throughout the second half of the course, specific examples are suggested. When stuck for a trigger word, try reading through old tasting-notes to see if any expression keeps cropping up in association with a particular factor determining taste.*

**You will learn five times as much
by comparing two wines**

The difficulty of choosing words to describe wines has been outlined in Chapter I, under 'Capturing the flavour'. There is an attempt at a brief glossary of tasting terms at the back of this book, though you will doubtless evolve your own terms for some sensations. The mose useful of these will be your 'trigger' words for various commonly encountered grape varieties. Once these are established, you should be well on your way to successful blind tasting. For some time I had used 'blackcurrants' for the claret grape Cabernet Sauvignon and 'raspberries' for red Burgundy's Pinot Noir, but was still searching around for a word I could use to pin together all my impressions of the Hermitage grape Syrah. Then someone volunteered their 'burnt rubber', and it has worked ever since. This story is told to encourage you to persevere if you find matching words and flavours a difficult exercise. As you will have gathered, the expression can be as absurd as you like.

The most important item on your tasting notes is the full pedigree of the wine you are tasting. Make sure you eventually get down its name, vintage, shipper and any other information, even if you start out by tasting the wine blind. A set of random wine descriptions is of little use to anyone unless each wine is fully identified. If you are organizing a wine tasting for friends, you will help them enormously if you write out tasting sheets beforehand.

Make sure you leave plenty of room between each wine's name as full-blown tasting notes encompass descriptions of each aspect of the wine's full assault on the senses, usually categorized as shown opposite. (Conclusions should probably be headed 'Brain'.) When starting out, it helps to be wordy rather than terse, so that you establish what sort of characteristics you normally associate with various groups of wines. As you get more experienced you can begin to omit the features you've come to expect and note only the most striking aspects of the wine.

| Wine | Eye | Nose |
|------|-----|------|
| Pinot Grigio 1981 DOC<br>  Santa<br>Margherita,<br>  Alto Adige | Very pale. Watery with greenish tinge. Slight sparkle. | Pronounced smokey perfume reminiscent of grape skins. |
| St Véran 1978<br>  Louis Jadot,<br>  Mâconnais | Pale yellow. | Great 'green fruit' attraction. |
| Château Giscours 1979<br>  Cru Classé,<br>  Margaux | Concentrated crimson (very like the 1978 tasted alongside). | Warm, rich, oaky – almost like a California Cabernet. |
| Wynns Coonawarra Cabernet Sauvignon 1978<br>  South Australia | Great 'legs'. Blackish crimson. Lighter than average for Australian Cabernet. | Some blackcurrant character together with lots of extract. |
| Bernkasteler Doktor Beerenauslese 1971<br>  Estate bottled by Deinhard, Middle Mosel | Dark, syrupy gold with tawny tinge. | Burnt petroly nose. Some acid evident already. Slightly musty at first, but this dissipated. |

10th July 1983

| **Mouth\*** | **Conclusions** |
| --- | --- |
| *Lots of acidity; shortage of mouth-filling fruit.* <br> *Short.* <br> *Lightweight.* | *Typical example of good modern white winemaking with low-temperature fermentation, but a bit short of character. Won't improve.* |
| *Perfect balance between acidity and pure Chardonnay fruit and body. Medium body.* | *Tastes much more youthful than a 1978 because of pronounced acid, but already drinking well.* |
| *Very powerful. Tannin very evident still, but not overwhelming.* | *Claret with a great future. Better than many other 1979s tasted and should mature within the decade.* |
| *A heavyweight. Warm-climate soft Cabernet with flavour fading to a short finish.* | *More elegant than many Coonawarra Cabernets but still not for the faint-hearted. Almost mature.* |
| *Very sweet at the front of the mouth but a dry finish. Layer upon layer of honeyed flavour during and after each mouthful.* | *Wonderful mature rich Riesling. A great treat.* |

\*Entries in this column tend to be confirmation of the flavour as initially sensed by the nose, together with notes on the cruder dimensions such as sweetness, acidity, tannin, body.

**It helps to give the wine a score**

$T$AKE A *mouthful of wine, taste it as instructed so far –
monitoring its effects on your mouth and brain – and then
spit it out. Compare the sensation with that of monitoring
the mouthful and then swallowing it. Is there really any difference in
taste? Okay, swallowing the wine might leave a few more volatiles
at the back of your mouth, well placed to waft up the retro-nasal
passage, but the difference is marginal. Notice how fully you can
experience the 'finish' of a wine even if you spit it out.*

If you do most of your tasting in a fairly structured way, usually at home and occasionally out with like-minded friends, you could keep all your tasting notes in one book. Such a written record of your drinking experience, if you persevere and taste a sufficiently wide range, you might find to be extremely valuable one day. Looseleaf binders are useful for those who taste more peripatetically, and those who enjoy fiddling about with cards and coloured pens could even develop a wonderful system of cross-referencing their tastings by type of wine. 'Now let's see . . . when did I last taste Louis Latour's Meursault?' A simple flick through an immaculate card index and you'd find notes on the 1979 to compare with the 1981 in front of you. What a *coup*. And of course the micro-chip opens up all sorts of possibilities.

Wines change with age so do try to date your tasting notes.

And when reaching conclusions about a wine take into account some assessment of how ready for drinking you think it is (the amount of tannin in red wines, and acid in whites, is a good pointer here) as well as how good it is. There is more on assessing wines below.

## The noble art of spitting

IT'S HEARTBREAKING but true: there are no tasting faculties in your throat, so you don't *need* to swallow wine to taste it. In fact, the less you swallow, the less clouded your perceptions will be by the haze of alcohol and the better you will be able to taste. You may think that only after you swallow a wine do you get a proper perception of its aftertaste. But that's not taste, it's an after*glow* – the simple and none-too-subtle effect of ethyl alcohol. If you spit out every mouthful, you will be amazed at how your tasting notes stay legible longer.

*Just a word of warning. Even if you carefully spit out every single mouthful, you will probably not escape entirely the effects of alcohol. Come what may, alcoholic fumes will travel around your mouth, up your nose and retro-nasal passage, and you may feel slightly light headed. In any case, you will find it extremely difficult not to swallow a single drop of wine – and all those fumes will further prejudice the results of a breathalyser. Because of their profession, French wine brokers are said to get special dispensation from 'l'alcotest'.*

*Practise spitting neatly in the bath. Put lots of force behind each spit, purse your lips and aim for your feet. You are not expected to spit in silence.*

I am not suggesting that you expectorate on social occasions. In fact, spitting out good wine seems as much a waste to me as it doubtless does to you. There are, however, some circumstances in which it is wise to spit out the alcohol, if possible.

★ When you want to keep sober, either because you're driving or because of other commitments after the tasting.
★ When you're tasting a dauntingly high number of wines, more than half a dozen, say.
★ When you're tasting very young wines that don't give a great deal of pleasure, and you are not in need of alcohol.

Losing inhibitions about spitting in public is one of the first things to be done by the embryonic wine taster. It is sad but irrefutable that wine, that wonderfully intriguing and uplifting liquid, contains a potentially dangerous substance. When it makes sense to spit, you should be proud rather than ashamed to do it. You may associate expectoration with rather seedy old men and pavements, but wine people have perfected the art of doing it with great style. 'Spit with pride' might well be the wine taster's motto. The stylish spit is forceful, an elegant trajectory with not the merest suggestion of a dribble, aimed dead centre of the spittoon.

Any old jug can earn itself the smart appellation of spittoon, though to avoid nasty splashes it makes sense to put some absorber like torn paper or sawdust into the bottom of it. A wooden wine case, such as those used by the better Bordeaux châteaux, filled with sawdust is a smart spittoon, though a spittoon with running water is even more efficient at disposing of the unsavoury evidence. If you can taste near a suitable sink then the business of spitting is easy.

*You will probably find that the number of different wines you can study seriously in one session will increase steadily and then reach a maximum – quite literally, saturation point. I would suggest that you start by comparing only two wines. The first exercise in specific wine tasting, contrasting two Chablis of different qualities (see page 120), is a good starting point. Quite soon you will find you are able to look in detail at three wines, still getting enjoyment out of them without feeling overwhelmed.*

*The bigger the group in which you taste, the more wines you can afford to tackle. You'll probably find, though, that twelve at a time is the absolute maximum. Many professionals try to limit themselves to even fewer, although I know the odd wine authority who seems to have infinite resistance to acid and alcohol and can still write a wonderfully neat tasting-note on wine number 113 (the greatest number I've ever seen tackled at one time – and they were all 1979 Beaujolais from a single producer, marathon-man Duboeuf). Try chewing a dry biscuit between mouthfuls of wine and notice how little it seems to affect the palate. Now try a mouthful of Cheddar and see how a fairly substantial red wine seems to give you the taste you want to complement the cheese flavour.*

*When planning what wines to serve with a meal (if it's the sort of occasion that warrants more than one wine), bear in mind the conventional sequence of wines. For more on this (actually very uncomplicated) subject, see Chapter 6, 'Wine, food and fun'.*

## Formal tastings

H ERE IS a brief description of a clinically formal tasting so that you'll know what to do if invited to one, or want to organize a particularly pukka wine tasting for friends.

Up to one hundred wines may be 'on show', though most tasters tackle only about thirty of them. An open bottle of each is set out on long tables covered with white tablecloths. If the organizer has been thoughtful, the tables will be sufficiently well spaced to allow good traffic flow. Spittoons should, similarly, be strategically placed. Many's the time I've spent most of a tasting with cheeks bulging as I jostle my way through the crowd to the lone spittoon in the far corner. There may be the odd jug of water to rinse glasses or palates, and some edible but not too distracting blotting paper in the form of low-flavour savoury biscuits. Carr's Table Water are fine, Bath Olivers show real style and little cubes of (English) cheese are likely to flatter the wines.

**It can be extremely tedious if you refuse to give any clues or encouragement**

In most circumstances, even at the dinner table, there is a conventional order in which wines are served or tasted, and it makes quite a bit of sense. 'White before red, dry before sweet and young before old' encapsulates it. As with serving-temperature considerations, 'white before red' is really a loose way of saying 'light bodied before full bodied', so that a wine is never overwhelmed by one that preceded it. It makes sense

**Make sure that glasses aren't too thimble-like**

You don't have to be a millionaire to indulge in one of these 'directional' tastings. Bordeaux's rather formal structure of ranked châteaux lends itself particularly well to the technique, but the wines don't have to be 'premiers crus'. Any collection of wines from a single vintage, no matter how humble the château or blended Claret, can give you a horizontal tasting, and will teach you something about that vintage.

You can attempt a vertical tasting of any wine with a vintage date on the label – though it might take quite a bit of scouting about to gather together much of a collection of different vintages. Most wine merchants sell, at best, two recent vintages of a given wine and only a handful can offer a good range of mature vintages. Try these mature wine sources:

Adnams of Southwold
Averys of Bristol
Berry Bros & Rudd, London SW1
Corney & Barrow, London EC1

not to put dry wines at a disadvantage by coating your mouth with sweetness first (though the French almost always serve something sweet as an aperitif and somehow seem to survive). The older a wine, in general, the more fascinating it is (true only of fine wine, though – don't try 'maturing' a cheap *vin de table*). It is therefore sensible to ascend to a peak of quality as a tasting climax.

At a tasting organized by a wine merchant, the choice of wines will be dictated by those he wants to sell to you. If you're organizing a tasting, you might well follow some of the suggested exercises in this course. Any tasting organized around a grape variety is always fascinating. It is relatively easy to find examples of, say, the Cabernet Sauvignon from all over the world, and by tasting each one you can learn a lot not only about the varietal but about the regions where they were made.

You could also taste the range of wines made by a single producer, to try to come to grips with each of them and his particular style. Some of the most fascinating and intellectual tasting exercises, however, are based on either a 'horizontal' or 'vertical' tasting. Tasting horizontally has nothing to do with reclining on Recamier couches but involves studying lots of similar but different wines of the same vintage – all of the 1978 Pauillacs, for example, to see how Château Latour 1978 compares with Châteaux Lafite and Mouton-Rothschild. Tasting vertically involves tasting different vintages of the same wine; vintages of Château Latour 1985 back to 1970, for example.

At a formal tasting you will usually be given your own tasting glass and be expected to make do with a fairly small tasting sample, up to an inch deep, of each wine, emptying any remains into a large 'dregs' jug or bottle with a funnel before starting on the next wine. Sometimes, if wines or

*Gerard Harris of Aston Clinton*
*Harrods, London SW1*
*Justerini & Brooks, London SW1*
*Luc Lacerre, Cardiff*
*Lay & Wheeler, Colchester*
*Laytons, London NW1*
*Milroy's, London W1*
*Reid Wines, Hallatrow, Bristol*
*La Réserve, London SW3*
*Philip Tite Fine Wines, London W4*
*Henry Townsend, Beaconsfield*
*La Vigneronne, London SW7*
*The Wine Society, Stevenage*

*T*HE SIMPLEST *way to 'mask' bottles (if they're shaped identically) is to wrap them in tin foil or to adopt the American technique of 'brown-bagging' them. For this, you need a collection of fairly tough opaque paper bags into which you can pack each bottle, either taping the bags closed round the neck or simply scrunching the paper up tightly. Remember to take all the capsules off completely so that there aren't any distracting identification signals. You'll need to give each bottle a number or a letter, either scribbled on the bag or swinging round the neck on a reusable cardboard label. Oh, and if you're using foil, it is of course much easier to open the bottles after wrapping, so the sequence should be: de-capsule, wrap, open, number, shuffle, taste, panic.*

glasses are in very short supply, there'll be a single glass of each wine placed in front of its bottle for everyone to taste from. I think any disease would have to be very rabid to manage to transmit itself from one taster to another via a glass rinsed in wine – alcohol being a strong disinfectant. If tasting as cosily as this, though, it really does make a bit of a stink if you leave the smell of cigarette smoke or perfume on the glass.

## Tasting 'blind'

ORGANIZING A 'blind' tasting is quite a lot of work, though the amount you learn can make it very rewarding. It is absolutely staggering how important a part the label plays in the business of tasting. If we know that a favourite region, producer or vintage is coming up, we automatically start relishing it – giving it every benefit of the tasting doubt. It took me five years of annual disappointing and puzzling blind Champagne tastings before I realized that I didn't actually like the *taste* of Bollinger, as much as its ethos and label.

You will need to ensure that no clues to identity are given. This may mean painstakingly decanting every wine into a set of anonymous bottles (the standard green Claret one is fairly easy to collect), though this would not be suitable for very delicate wines. Otherwise, you will have to employ one of the bottle-disguise methods outlined on these pages.

*Australia's most vocal wine man, Len Evans, has devised a more socially acceptable variation on the guessing theme. In his Options Game the host starts by asking of his wine: 'Is it Bordeaux or Burgundy?' Even if you get that wrong, you can all go on to the next question: 'Is it Médoc/Graves or St Emilion/Pomerol?' The Australians are so sharp they actually start at the next level of question, 'Pauillac or Margaux?' The host might then go on to, 'Is it pre- or post-1974?', '1976, 1975 or 1979?' And finally, 'Château Palmer, Issan or Lascombes?' All pretty tricky stuff, but it's a game that everyone can play right to the end.*

*Top quality Vouvray is hard to find in this country. O. W. Loeb, of London SE1, lists those of Foreau and, as I write, has a 1979 Sec at £4.86.*

*To find disappointing wines costing well over £5 a bottle (though you are unlikely to be that keen) you would be well advised to make a speciality of red Burgundy. See the section on Pinot Noir for specific names that can be trusted in this minefield of quality.*

If you really get the wine bug, you may want to let the bug eat into your social life by serving wines blind when entertaining. (It's easier then, because you can use decanters or a well-placed hand when pouring the bottle.) This can be great fun if everyone is equally interested in, and equipped for, making a guess. It can also be extremely tedious, especially if you refuse to give any clues or encouragement. Be wary of torturing your guests.

## Assessing quality

BLIND TASTING may be a fairly rarefied and not terribly useful skill, but some guidance on assessing a wine's quality can help you enjoy just a bit more every wine that comes your way.

This is particularly beneficial because price is no direct indicator of quality. There is no great wine available at £2.50 a bottle (though there is still some on sale for less than £5 and it's often called Vouvray). There are, on the other hand, some very disappointing wines that cost more than £5 a bottle, and there is an enormous variation in the quality of wines currently on sale for between £2.50 and £5. So it makes sense to learn how to judge quality in an educated and rational way.

The two most obvious pointers to quality – balance and length – have already been outlined on page 55. You can enjoy a fairly basic wine, such as a Muscadet or a Beaujolais, if it's well made. Look for the sensation in your mouth after you have swallowed or spat out a mouthful of the wine, as well as monitoring its flavour and how complex it is. A fine example of a Meursault or a Barolo is likely to be an obviously 'greater' wine, with more layers of flavour and intrigue, but there is a time and place for every sort of wine. There have been one or two periods of my life when I have

*Post-Robert Parker, most Americans now score out of 100. Else-where, some tasters score out of ten, some out of twenty, some out of five and some even out of seven. I find I need twenty points to allocate, and even then I find myself tempted into halves. The twenty-point scale is the one most often used by official judging panels and other medal-awarders. Practise adding a score to the conclusions in your tasting-notes. The most common problem with scoring is deciding whether to score an immature wine for current pleasure or its potential quality. You may have to invent your own symbol here. My tasting-notes are often littered with arrows to show likely future development.*

*Another problem with scoring and assessment is more philosophi-cal. If you're tasting a wine that gives you great pleasure and yet doesn't seem to you a typical example of what it's supposed to be, how should you score it? Very much an A-level question this, but one that might provide the subject of a post-tasting debate. And, you will find, the discussion afterwards is one of wine tasting's greatest pleasures.*

been lucky enough to taste nothing but great wines for days on end. I wouldn't say it was pure hell, but by the end this ungrateful wretch was aching for a simple glass of something straightforward and everyday. We need variety in wine drinking as much as in anything else. Don't think that it's not worth learning about wine if you can't afford to spend more than a few pounds a month on it. There is good and bad quality at every price level.

To concentrate your mind on assessing the quality of a wine it helps to give it a score, as well as making the usual tasting notes on it. This is particularly helpful if you're tasting a range of similar wines with a view to picking out your favourites. After all, one of the chief consequences of infor-mal comparative tasting should be to note the names of those wines, producers and vintages that give you particular pleasure.

Funnily enough, likes and dislikes, the one area everyone who doesn't know much about wine does invariably proclaim they know about, tend to recede with the gaining of knowledge and experience of wine (sounds much grander than just drinking it, doesn't it?). Most professional tasters end up with more or less the same concept of what makes a good wine.

Happy tasting.

'NOSE' ANY of the following wines and notice how like the taste of Muscat grapes they smell. 'Grapey' might be your first tasting note: Asti Spumante; Moscato; Spanish Muscatel; Moscatel de Setubal; any southern French Muscat from, say, Beaumes de Venise, Rivesaltes or Banyuls; Muscat d'Alsace. Arm yourself with a few grapes and a glass of wine to sip. Contrast the two flavours.

Peel yourself a grape. Taste the flesh. Then chew the peel, and nibble a pip. These last two exercises are an uncommonly unpleasant part of this wine course.

# 3 The raw material – white grapes

CURIOUSLY, ONLY one sort of wine actually tastes like grapes, and that is wine made from Muscat or related grape varieties.

In every other case, wine tastes quite different from grapes, even from those grapes from which it was made. Grapes have a simple fruity flavour, their lack of deviousness having caused wine folk to label it 'rather one-dimensional'. Wine on the other hand has a much more complicated taste, definitely two-, possibly even three-dimensional. There are layers of flavour here, different nuances, though underneath everything there should be the same basic fruitiness that grapes have. The winemaker's job is to transform his raw material, grapes, into something as interesting as wine, while retaining their common attribute, fruitiness.

Grape skins taste astringent. The pips when crushed taste bitter. Only the flesh, which is mainly juice, is suitable raw material for a fresh, fruity white wine. (Red wines may need a bit of astringency or tannin – see page 37.) The first stage in making a white wine therefore is to eliminate the skin and pips from the process by gently crushing the grapes and running off the juice. The harder the grapes are pressed the more astringency the resultant wine will pick up from the skins. Fine white wines are usually made from 'the free-run juice', i.e. the juice that can be drained from a vat of grapes

*Constrast the flavours of a good Chablis from a reputable producer such as Drouhin, Michel, Albert Pic, and a cheap generic Chablis bottled in the UK.*

*E*XAMINE AN *Alsace Gewürztraminer from a recent vintage. Léon Beyer are renowned for their very rich Gewürz, Trimbach make a very crisp one, and Hugel are dependable. Sainsbury's usually stock their own keenly priced example. Note the curious perfume and try to come up with your own description of it: lychees, mangoes, cachous? Notice how it suggests sweetness on the nose but is then followed by a dry but*

crushed by their own weight (though the doctrine of a little 'skin contact' has been gaining ground). In an area where a wine earns its right to an appellation by virtue of the grape type and where it was grown (e.g. most of France), cheaper versions often contain a high proportion of juice from very hard-pressed grapes.

The juice contains sugar because the grapes were ripe and this can now be fermented into alcohol, turning sweet grape juice into a much drier liquid that can be called wine. (This is why grape juice is always sweet. The only way to get it 'drier' is to ferment out the sugar. Those who insist on tinkering about with nature, and humanity's naturally greedy instincts, may sometimes then de-alcoholize the wine so that they may have dry grape juice.)

Yeast is the stuff that converts the sugar to alcohol. Yeasts occur naturally in the 'bloom' on grape skins (and are therefore mixed into the juice) in an established vineyard; or cultured yeasts may be introduced for even greater control over the process. When they've done their work they die, so wines very rarely taste 'yeasty'.

This fermented grape juice is now wine although, as demonstrated below, it is capable of extraordinary variation of taste.

## Gewürztraminer – the most recognizable grape

GEWÜRZTRAMINER may be one of the most difficult grape varieties to pronounce (Guh-*vurts-trah-mee-ner*) and spell, but it is probably the easiest to imprint on your palate memory for future recognition. It has a heady, almost perfumed, lychee scent. Some find it reminiscent of tropical fruit, without being too certain of which one. There's something definitely exotic about

*full-bodied taste. Try a bit on the tip of your tongue to test sweetness. Contrast the very powerful distinctive nose with that of a basic dry white table wine. Almost any other white wine will seem a very shy little flower indeed beside the orchid-like Gewürz.*

*Very few German (and, nowadays, even fewer Austrian) Gewürztraminers find their way to Britain. They have a rich golden colour, even in youngish examples, and note also the thick, almost oily texture. A number of California Gewürz have been shipped here, as well as one rather impressive one from Associated Vintners in Seattle, Washington State. Grand Cru of Sonoma has made California's most acclaimed. The grape is also grown in Yugoslavia, and one of the cheapest ways of tasting it is via Victoria Wine's Traminer, a rather coarse, flabby wine but with definite spicy Traminer characteristics in its aroma. Seek out examples of Gewürztraminer and note what they all have in common. Even light Gewürztraminers from Italy and New Zealand have that funny smell. Try to establish firmly your own 'palate picture' of the varietal.*

**Gewürztraminer may be one of the most difficult grape varieties to pronounce**

Gewürz (which is German for 'spiced', a fairly accurate description), though it can pall after a while. Connoisseurs claim to find it too obvious – a bit like scented cachous – after prolonged exposure to it, but it's a wonderful safe starting point for the wine taster.

The 'traminer' bit of its name is derived from the village of Tramin in the Italian Tyrol, and there are still some light, delicate Gewürztraminers made in the Alto Adige hills of north-east Italy. Most Gewürztraminer found in Britain, however, is from Alsace on the Franco-German border. Alsace is famous for its perfumed wines, which smell sweetish but actually taste dry (providing the exception to prove the rule that the palate usually merely confirms what the nose already suspected). Alsace Gewürztraminers are a force to be reckoned with as they ripen well, but all the sugar in the grapes is fermented out to make a dry wine high in alcohol, often as much as 13%. They smell lusciously pungent but have a dry finish. The grapes themselves are unusual in that many of them are pinkish, not white at all, and Gewürz can often be quite a deep-coloured straw yellow. Low acidity is characteristic of Gewürztraminer made in a fairly warm climate, and some of them go rather 'oily' with age.

In Gewürztraminer's homeland, Alsace, it's considered a very noble but rather tiring grape, and the winemakers themselves often prefer to drink Riesling. It is also grown across the Rhine in the warmish German wine regions of Rheinpfalz or the Palatinate, Rheinhessen and Baden (where it's usually left quite sweet), and in Austria where it can make delicious, deep golden, very sweet dessert wines. There has been considerable experimentation with the variety in New Zealand and in California, where wines are never quite as dry as in Alsace and can sometimes be as sweet as Austria's sweetest. Italian

*A–level: if you get the chance, try to taste a Gewürztraminer alongside a Muscat. The most revealing pair would come from the same Alsace producer and should reveal the added richness, spice and lesser grapiness that Gewürz has, compared with Muscat. La Vigneronne, London SW7 are Alsace specialists.*

T**O GET** to grips with the essential Sauvignon-ness of Sauvignon you could not do better than start with a Sancerre or Pouilly-Fumé from a good grower. Yapp Bros, of Mere in Wiltshire, could supply either, and the wines of Baron Patrick de Ladoucette or the rather more earthy Jean Vacheron are irreproachable. (These last two belong to that infuriating class of top-quality French wines that are easier to find on restaurant wine lists than on the shelf.) Sauvignon de Haut-Poitou, available from Lay & Wheeler of Colchester and elsewhere is another possible example.

**You will see how 50% more sunshine tastes**

Try to establish your own trigger words for the grape. Green fruit? Herbaceous? Gooseberries? Flinty? I find that a helpful way to recognize Sauvignon is first to realize that it hits your senses in a

Gewürz is the most underplayed. Some Gewürztraminers may be labelled simply Traminer.

The only possible taste confusion may be in Alsace with the grapey Muscat, as both are very aromatic and have a sweet, flowery smell.

## Sauvignon and what sunshine does

SAUVIGNON BLANC is another very distinctive grape variety and has great appeal for those who appreciate crisp, dry, uncomplicated wines. The piles of empty Sancerre and Pouilly-Fumé bottles collected from restaurants all over the world every morning testify to that. It is grown in all sorts of different wine regions, which is why I have chosen it to illustrate the effect of climate on taste, but there is not too much variation in its distinctive aroma. 'Cats' pee on a gooseberry bush' may not sound a very appealing description to you, but after a bit of exposure to, and consideration of, the smell, you may come round to agreeing with it. There's something very definitely 'green' about the smell; some people find raw gooseberries, others the smell of blackcurrant leaves. Just to smell the wine gets you ready for the whack of acidity with which it will cut the palate, and perhaps that is what has earned it the loose but evocative adjective 'flinty'. You're supposed to get a whiff of gunsmoke from a good Pouilly-Fumé and, indeed, as a ready victim of auto-suggestion, I often have, though I've never smelt actual gunsmoke. This is what tasting notes are all about – finding terms that match flavours most closely, even if only imagined.

Sauvignon is a grape made for our times, times of high interest rates. The wines should be drunk while they're young and fresh. Choose the youngest vintage available, for the

*very direct way, so that it's 'pointed' along the middle of your mouth
and nose rather than having a much broader fan-like flavour like that
of Gewürztraminer, or the Chardonnay examined below.*

*A-level: very much an optional-extra tasting at this stage, but good
examples of the richness that a bit of Sémillon can give to the slightly
lean flavour of the Sauvignon are Robert Mondavi's Fumé Blanc
and Joseph Phelps' Sauvignon Blanc from California (try The
Winery of London W9, Harrods and La Vigneronne, London
SW7); also, from Bordeaux, Pavillon Blanc de Château Margaux,
Château Laville-Haut-Brion and, more affordably, Domaine de
Chevalier and Château Carbonnieux.*

*Now try to contrast Sauvignons grown in different climates. One of
the wines mentioned above would be fine as your coolest representative, or a Sauvignon de Touraine from the middle Loire would be
cheaper and still noticeably acid and dry (if a little less pure in
flavour). A New Zealand Sauvignon is of a similar aromatic style,
though often has more apparent fruit.*

*A dry white Bordeaux would make a good example of a
temperate-climate Sauvignon. An increasing proportion of such
wines are now sold with the word Sauvignon on the label, though
the French have been much less concerned to specify grape varieties
than winemakers in newer wine regions such as California and
Australia. There's a Sauvignon Sec from Delor that is fairly well
distributed, but almost any white Bordeaux in a green straight-sided
bottle (often called Château Something) would provide an example
of the looser, rather less acid, style of a Sauvignon that has been
ripened by a bit more sunshine.*

*Cheaper (and, sadly, coarser) would be Victoria Wine's Yugoslav
Sauvignon from Fruska Gora. This wine tastes almost sweet and
demonstrates nicely the lower acids in a warmer-climate wine.*

*Most Sauvignons from California (where the clever Robert Mon-
davi revitalized the sales appeal of the varietal in the early 1970s by*

grape's fruit is not the opulent sort that develops intriguing complexity with age. It simply gets a bit stale and the initially high acidity starts to predominate. The wines are usually very pale straw in colour, except in the rare (and expensive) examples that have been given a period in wood, and have taken on a golden tinge. Acidity is the most pronounced characteristic of the wines and almost all are dry to bone dry. There will rarely be any great length of flavour, which tends to tail off swiftly after a rather dashing start. Some Californian and very smart Bordeaux producers blend in a bit of the Sémillon grape (see page 137) to give more weight and a longer-lasting flavour. Without this palate-filler Sémillon, Sauvignon is light to medium bodied.

Along with parts of New Zealand, where the grape has been particularly successful, the Loire Valley is the coolest place where Sauvignon is cultivated, and Loire Sauvignons will either be labelled with the grape name or with that of one of the Sauvignon-producing appellations such as Sancerre, Pouilly-Fumé, Quincy, Reuilly or Menetou-Salon. Sauvignon de St Bris, made in the far north of Burgundy, also demonstrates the cool climate style of Sauvignon that's dry, very acid and almost steely, it's so pure and tart. Sauvignon is also responsible for most dry white Bordeaux; the more temperate climate there on the Atlantic seaboard can be 'tasted' in the slightly less acidic, more open wines. Sauvignons from Yugoslavia also demonstrate how a bit more sunshine cuts down the acidity you can taste in a wine. The Sauvignons and Fumé Blancs of California show what happens when you transplant the varietal to a positively warm climate. The nearer the Equator any sort of grapes are grown and ripened, the less acid and more sugar there will be in the resulting must, and the less acid and more sugar or alcohol there will be in the wine – unless deliberate steps are taken, such as picking the grapes unusually early. This was already hinted at by the different examples of Gewürztraminer examined above; those

*restyling it and renaming it Fumé Blanc) are noticeably different from their cousins reared in chillier France. 'Grassy' is the word that lots of Californians associate with the varietal, and it certainly produces rather more florid wines over there. They are rarely bone dry and are noticeably different on the nose and tip of the tongue from cool climate Sauvignons. A similar 'warmer' wine is sent across the Atlantic from Chile by the Spanish wine firm Torres, which has a South American outpost there producing inexpensive white Sauvignon-based Santa Digna. South Africa is now also producing some relatively rich examples of warm-climate Sauvignon Blanc. Collison's of London SW1 should stock at least one good example.*

---

*T*O FORM *a satisfactory impression of Chardonnay you will probably have to taste it in three forms: youthful and carefree, mature and fascinating, and warm-hearted and rich. For the first, a good white Mâcon will do nicely. Georges Duboeuf makes fine examples of St Véran, Pouilly-Fuissé and Pouilly-Vinzelles, and his wines are imported by Berkmann Wine Cellars and stocked by Davison. This is the most straightforward and affordable way of experiencing the positive, smoky flavour of the Chardonnay, which at this early stage in its development has something a bit 'appley' about it. I'm always reminded of melons by a good Mâcon Blanc.*

*The second style of Chardonnay is to my mind the finest, though it is very much a high-day-or-holiday sort of purchase. At least dependably fine white Burgundy is easier to find than fine red wine from Burgundy's heartland, the Côte d'Or, and few bottles of Meursault, Montrachet and Corton Charlemagne are likely to disappoint. Louis Latour's Corton Charlemagne, Domaine Leflaive's Montrachets and Marquis de Laguiche Montrachet represent just*

made in the hotter climate of Austria have noticeably less acid than the Alsace versions. Of course, climate is only one of the many factors that affect the taste of wine. The differences you will taste in any range of Sauvignons could in part be attributed to things like their age, the age of the vines themselves, winemaking techniques or even the exact clone of the vine planted. (American Sauvignon always tastes distinctly more flowery than French to me and this may be the explanation.) We will be examining all these factors, but at this point try to concentrate purely on the softening effect of sunshine. What happened to the grapes can be tasted in the wine, whether it's a Sauvignon Blanc or any other grape variety. The more acid a wine is the less sunshine is likely to have ripened the grapes, and the cooler the climate it is likely to have come from.

## Chardonnay and the kiss of oak

UNLIKE Sauvignon Blanc and Gewürztraminer, which are designed primarily for a giddy youth, Chardonnay is a grape that produces wines capable of doing wonderful things in their middle and old age. Only the Riesling is a serious rival to Chardonnay's claim to be the greatest white grape in the world. Montrachet, which has its home in Burgundy, has done quite a bit for Chardonnay's reputation in the past. However, dazzling Chardonnays emerging from some of the world's newer wine regions are doing their bit to reinforce the glamour that surrounds the variety. It's capable of a wider variation of flavour and quality than either of the varieties examined so far, but is characterized by being dry, full-bodied and with a much 'broader' flavour than pointed, edgy Sauvignon. You can feel the weight of the wine immediately and know that this is no beguilingly aromatic aperitif, but a meaty, almost beefy, number that demands attention. Because of this weight and firmness, the acidity of a Chardonnay is not usually as notice-

*some of the pinnacles in the Chardonnay landscape. To appreciate what they really have to give, treat yourself to one that's at least five and preferably fifteen years old. These wines have accumulated so much flavour they demand rapt attention. Don't serve them with food that will spoil as it cools – and remember to serve all Chardonnays a bit warmer than most white wines because of their weight. In fact these are the wines that could be mistaken for red; they're so long they could cure a sore throat. 'Steely' and 'meaty' might both be used here.*

*California or Australia is the obvious source of the third kind of Chardonnay, the sort that's just bursting out of itself with flavour. Almost all such wines will state alcohol content on the label, as European wines will have to do eventually. Choose one that's at least 13° and, even if it is a youthful example, you will probably be rewarded with a very luscious, deep yellow, almost viscous liquid that tastes of a rather exotic fruit salad and is so rich it's almost sweet.*

*Somewhere floating around these three wines, in the flavour you absorb chiefly through your nose, is what Chardonnay is all about. My word is 'smoky' because Chardonnay seems almost to catch my throat, perhaps in anticipation of the spread of flavours that will constitute the finish of the wine somewhere in that vicinity, in contrast to the solely nasal appreciation of aromatic varieties like Gewürztraminer and Sauvignon. As it mellows, it takes on so much richness that it's almost 'buttery'.*

*To get some idea of the full range that the Chardonnay grape can offer, you could start at the basic level with a Bulgarian or cheap Italian example. These are unadorned wines made for early consumption, with only the faintest suggestion of Chardonnay flavour. Just up the scale are the Chardonnays de Haut Poitou from Caves de la Madeleine, London SW10, and Italian Chardonnays at about £4 a bottle. With the Mâcons and Pouillys suggested above, and Chardonnay de l'Ardèche, these represent the best-value way of tasting the pure fruit flavour of Chardonnay.*

**For more exotic Chardonnay-based wines, seek out the lovely golden**

able as in the lighter-bodied Sauvignon. But, however
opulent the Chardonnay seems to taste, it is always dry.
Admittedly the richer California Chardonnays hover towards
the brink of medium dryness because they're so alcoholic, but
the grape is fundamentally designed for dry wines. (The only
Chardonnay I have ever tasted that had been specially vinified
to produce a sweet wine was really rather unpleasantly flat.)

**If a wine is very alcoholic you may
well feel like avoiding naked
flames**

To form your palate picture of Chardonnay you will probably need to taste more examples of it than were necessary to
come to grips with the more obvious Gewürztraminer or
Sauvignon, but a certain 'smokiness' in the bouquet of any
Chardonnay is, for me, the grape's chief distinguishing mark.
Another very revealing characteristic of Chardonnay is that,
unlike the two varietal studied so far, its flavour seems to gain
intensity in the mouth. Any well-made example will have a
fascinating long finish that may seem more powerful than the
initial bouquet.

Chardonnay is traditionally thought to reach its apogee on the

*Australian and Californian Chardonnays, or put yourself at the mercy of the eclectic La Vigneronne of London SW7. Note that the most luscious and full-bodied examples come from the warmest regions, as was demonstrated with Sauvignons.*

*To get some idea of what oak ageing does to the taste of wine, arm yourself with a bottle of Chablis (perhaps the same trusty one as has already been used in two previous exercises). O. W. Loeb, of London SE1, stock the archetypal no-wood Chablis of Louis Michel. This represents Chardonnay at its purest and least adorned by the influence either of oak or of prolonged sunshine. There's a lean fruit flavour here that is almost steely. Its impact on the palate, if it's a youthful example high in acidity, can be close to pain – so dry is the wine. It is something like Sauvignon, except that the flavour*

Côte d'Or, the heartland of the Burgundy region, in wines such as Corton-Charlemagne, the Montrachets and some Meursaults. Not quite as great, but still good, white Burgundies can be found lurking behind labels saying Pernand-Vergelesses, Auxey-Duresses, St Aubin, Rully, Montagny and Bourgogne Blanc. From the southern, less smart, end of Burgundy come Chardonnays called St Véran, Pouillys of all sorts except Pouilly-Fumé, Beaujolais Blanc and Mâcon Blanc. Few of these will actually say Chardonnay on the label; nor will the only other two French wines that are traditionally based on Chardonnay – Chablis, made sixty miles north of the Côte d'Or, and Champagne. Most Champagnes contain about one third Chardonnay grapes, and those called Blanc de Blancs are made of nothing but. If you want to taste a still wine made from Chardonnay grown in the Champagne region, look for a Coteaux Champenois Blanc de Blancs.

Because the rewards can be so great, Chardonnay has been taken from its home base in north-eastern France and cultivated all over the world; and such wines will normally be more easily identifiable, with Chardonnay specified – nay boasted – on the label. Chardonnay has been an enormous success in California and Australia; they're winding themselves up to a similar peak in South Africa and New Zealand; it's all the rage in Italy now; and there are plantings from Catalonia to Lebanon, from Chile to New York State.

The flavour of any Chardonnay evolves considerably with maturation, and the most influential factor here is whether the wine is given any time in wood. Chardonnay and oak seem made for each other, and many winemakers with serious aspirations for their Chardonnays (and the cash to buy and maintain barrels) try to give them a bit of wood ageing. Sometimes, to add on a new layer of oak flavour, even the fermenting is done in oak rather than the more neutral stainless steel or other inert substance used in the 'fresh fruit'

*doesn't have that aromatic edge of cats' pee but hints at something broader.*

*At the other end of the scale of oakiness would be a California Chardonnay from a producer such as Robert Mondavi, Cuvaison and Joseph Phelps. These wines gain a sweetish, almost vanilla-like overlay of oaky flavours together with a golden hue and considerable weight; so much that it can sometimes be confused with sweetness. These wines are so rich that you may find them difficult to drink throughout a meal, though vintages after 1978 have been much less pronounced. For wines with this obvious oaky character, try Les Amis du Vin of London W1, Alex Findlater of London NW8, The Winery of London W9 and La Vigneronne of London SW7.*

**A-level:** *If you wish to progress to greater subtleties, you should try to pick out the much more subdued oakiness of the example of great Côte d'Or Burgundy you selected at the start of this Chardonnay exercise. Leflaive, Lafon, Sauzet and Louis Latour all use some oak barrels in the ageing of their top wines, but it is usually evident only in a suggestion of vanilla or toast on the nose and a very slight deepening of colour (sometimes also a certain buttery flavour).*

**S-level:** *And now for real enthusiasts, a few really contrary treasures – Chardonnays from newish wine regions that taste confusingly like the lightly oaked aristocrats of the Côte d'Or. Lay & Wheeler of Colchester may have some Tisdall Mount Helen Chardonnay from Australia; La Vigneronne and Adnams of Southwold may stock Acacia and Chalone Chardonnays of California, and the latter might even have some Stony Hill stashed away. Oak is doing its job properly when it's barely detectable. Some Mondais Reserve Chardonnays are very like the Burgundian prototype.*

technique of fermenting which emphasizes the fruitiness of the grapes.

Wines of any sort, red or white, that have been kept in wood definitely taste different, especially if that wood is fairly new (or newly shaved) with lots of oak flavour still to give, and if the barrels are small so that the wood-to-wine ratio is relatively high. As we shall see, wines such as Rioja and young Claret demonstrate very well the effect of wood ageing on red wines, but Chardonnay provides the best examples of how well wood and white wine can work together. A whole new range of flavours are introduced to make the wine much more complicated and rewarding, but they need time to meld together and produce a balanced wine. That's why wood ageing makes most sense for wines destined for a longish life. There would be no point in giving Sancerre a year in small oak casks as it's a wine that is made expressly to be enjoyed young and fresh – from the Sauvignon grape, which doesn't age well.

In the recesses of our subconscious, most of us probably associate wooden casks more with traditional winemakers than with those in what we rather patronizingly call the New World. Ironically, however, as an ever-higher proportion of Chardonnay made in France is denied the chance of lodging in oak, it is the Californians in particular who have been frantically shipping casks across the Atlantic from top French coopers to give added richness to their Chardonnays. Only a handful of Chablis producers, for instance, have any wood in their cellars, while most Napa and Sonoma wineries are stacked high with expensive barrels. Some of the new enthusiasts have rather overdone the oak, and we have seen a spate of Chardonnays weighed down not only by alcohol but also by all the rich flavours associated with oak and the

*To see what the grape itself tastes like, try to track down a youthful Semillon from Australia. Notice, even on a fairly young example, a low acidity and yellowish colour, with hints of the spiciness to come. Roll it round the mouth to feel the full weight of the wine. You might even note a certain creamy texture with the smoothness of lanolin. Sémillon, like Chardonnay, is not searingly aromatic and, with its relatively heavy body, it lumbers towards you rather than attacking you with a point of sharp flavour.*

marriage between oak and wine. Some of them can be enjoyable, if only in small quantities, and they certainly provide a superb opportunity to taste what 'oakiness' is like.

Some top Côte d'Or producers still put their best Chardonnays into oak for a while, but they tend to keep the oak flavour more restrained and in harmony with the fruit. This is the ideal to which producers of Chardonnay all over the world aspire; some of them show every sign of beating the Burgundians at their own game. 'Just a kiss of oak' is what some California producers are trying to give their precious, wildly fashionable Chardonnays. By looking carefully at the wide range of different styles of Chardonnay available today, you should get a good idea of the extra richness in colour, body and flavour that oak gives to a white wine. You will also have reinforced the lessons already learnt about the influence of climate on wine.

## Sémillon – a great rotter

SÉMILLON IS a curiously obscure grape. Even members of the dwindling ranks of Sauternes lovers are often unaware of the crucial role played by the varietal in its production. No serious wine drinker would ever confess ignorance of or aversion to Chardonnay, but such is the Cinderella-like state in which the grape languishes that the word Sémillon is hardly ever found on a wine label.

Only in Australia, and especially in the Hunter Valley, is Semillon (l's pronounced and no accent) taken seriously as a varietal, to be vinified by itself as a dry white worthy of ageing and labelling as Semillon (though, just to be cussed about it, they sometimes call it Riesling – crazy). Youthful Australian Semillons provide a rare opportunity to taste the grape unblended with its habitual Bordeaux partner Sauvignon. We have already seen examples of dry white Graves,

**You will be expected to make do
with a fairly small sample of wine**

*Try to get hold of an old Hunter Valley Semillon. As I write,
they're thin on the ground in Britain, although the Australian
specialists, Alex Findlater of NW8 and Ostler's of EC1 may be able
to help, and Averys of Bristol, who were early pioneers of wines
from Australia, might have a bottle or two lurking in their cellars.
Notice – in fact you won't be able to avoid it – the curiousness of the
old Semillon's flavour, as well as its deep colour and weight. That is
my volcanic twang: a taste almost of burnt earth, with lots of little
mineral trace elements close to the surface. There's something reminiscent of those black charcoal biscuits served in gentlemen's clubs.*

*You will get the most out of this tasting exercise if you arm yourself
with two bottles (or, preferably, the infuriatingly elusive half-bottle*

such as Domaine de Chevalier, made mainly from Sauvignon supplemented by the richness of Sémillon. Just down the road in Sauternes, Barsac and Bordeaux's less famous sweet wine districts, a bit of Sauvignon is often added to Sémillon to give the resultant blend a bit of extra acidity while keeping it predominantly Sémillon and sweet.

Sémillon is relatively low in acid, even weightier and more alcoholic than Chardonnay, and hence carries with it the suggestion of sweetness even when it is vinified dry. Some tasters find figs in its flavours, others cigars. It can sometimes have a slight edge of citrus and there's something almost waxy in its texture. Clues to the grape's identity are: a deep golden colour, lots of alcohol and low acidity.

As it ages it takes on an almost orange colour, whether it's a dry or sweet wine, and the mature dry Sémillons of the Hunter Valley are some of the wine world's most curious and under-appreciated treasures. They are, it must be said, an acquired taste. The wines seem to lose their early message of the grape and take on the character of the land itself. Any Hunter wine more than a decade old starts to display a curious minerally taste which I call a 'volcanic twang' (to hoots of laughter from Australians, of course). This applies to every varietal cultivated there, and is the most striking example I have come across to support the traditional European view that the actual composition of the soil and subsoil in any region determines the flavour of wine produced there. (Californians argue that it is important only that the land is well drained to encourage deep roots seeking moisture and therefore a complex root system.) There is a high proportion of volcanic soil in the best bit of the Hunter, just as there is in Madeira – this may account for my 'twang'.

To experience Sémillon's greatest contribution to wine pleasure it is necessary to look at sweet white Bordeaux,

*size) of good-quality Sauternes, one made in a botrytis-struck vintage and one from a growth in which botrytis was not encouraged to make its somewhat frightening appearance. (It makes the grapes look as though they're covered with thick grey cobwebby dust.) Good vintages for botrytis in recent years have been 1985, 1983, 1979 and 1975. Vintages in which good sweet white Bordeaux was made without the help of botrytis were 1981, 1978 and 1976. Find an example of a 'cru classé' château of Sauternes in each group, if you can afford it, but a less well known name for about £5 or £6 a bottle may well illustrate the point. Notice how the non-botrytis wines are very fruity and honeyed, but how the 'botrytized' wines seem if anything even sweeter, with an overlay in some of something that reminds me of slightly rotten cabbage and in others of luscious, unctuous spice.*

*Try out the oak-versus-inert-material-ageing exercise using different Sémillons. If you take an inexpensive sweet white Bordeaux, say a Ste Croix du Mont, Loupiac or simply a basic Sauternes or Barsac with no château name on the label (most off-licence chains can offer what's called a 'generic' i.e. common or garden, Sauternes), you will notice the sweet unctuousness of the Sémillon grape. There will not, however, be any of the extra layers of flavour, such as of botrytis or of oak ageing, which underlines the intensity of a superior 'cru classé' château-bottled wine from Sauternes. Notice the deeper, browner colour in the superior wine.*

*Or, to reduce the variables even more, compare a Château Doisy-Daëne with a wine from the same vintage and from a property that is of equal standing but keener on oak maturation, such as Châteaux Coutet, Climens, Suduiraut or Rieussec.*

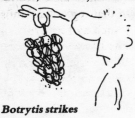

**Botrytis strikes**

especially the best wines from the communes of Sauternes and Barsac. (The first encompasses the second so that all Barsac is Sauternes but not all Sauternes is Barsac.) To make a great sweet wine you have to have grapes that contain an awful lot of sugar, so that even when you have fermented enough to produce the wine's alcohol content you are still left with lots of fruity richness.

The best sweet white wines in the world share a common helper towards this gloriously luscious state, in a rather unsavoury-looking mould. In certain warm, moist autumns, this attacks the grapes and – without breaking them and causing spoilage – shrivels them to concentrate their sugar content. *Botrytis cinerea*, also known as noble rot, *pourriture noble* and *Edelfäule*, gives a special honeyed vegetal quality to the taste of overripe grapes. It occurs only in vintages when conditions are just right, and only in certain places. For years California's vine growers did their best to eliminate it because they didn't realize what lovely things it could do for grapes such as Riesling, Gewürztraminer, and Sémillon. Vintages that are too dry can produce sweet wines, but they won't have the curious whiff of *botrytis* – to which Sémillon, with its thin skin, is conveniently prone.

*A-level:* You could at this stage see whether you can detect the difference in taste between a sweet white Bordeaux that has been given some oak maturation and one that has been fermented and aged in the vat. Most of the *cru classé* châteaux of Sauternes still use oak. Indeed, they sometimes use it for too long, but less famous sweet wines from that region and most of those from the 'lesser' neighbours, such as Ste Croix du Mont and Loupiac, are no great friends of wood. Château Doisy-Daëne is an unusual example of a classed growth Sauternes in which the influence of wood is minimal.

T O PROVE to yourself what a good judge of wine you are, get hold of any German wine with the word Riesling on the label and one of the following: any Yugoslav Laski Rizling or Riesling such as Lutomer, Cloberg or that from your local supermarket chain; or any Hungarian Olasz Riesling. Get someone to serve you a glass of each 'blind'. See how the racy acidity and pure, fresh perfume of one leaps out of the glass to encourage you to have another sip. The lesser wine (which according to EEC law should be called Rizling) will probably seem rather dull, even mousey, compared with the real Riesling.

The lesser Riesling is not a very easy wine to distinguish 'blind' because it's not strong on memorable characteristics. Not one of the wine world's greats, this, but a good illustration of the fact that wine's quality does vary greatly.

Now study, and try to memorize, the particular appeal of the real Riesling. Of course, the more you have spent on your German Riesling example, the stronger will be the Riesling characteristics and class. But even a fairly humble example should have the very appealing combination of high acidity (notice how the edges of your tongue start to crinkle in anticipation even as you smell the wine)

## When a Riesling's not a Riesling

A SIMPLE qualitative exercise is long overdue, one which is particularly apt to illustrate the strange case of the non-Riesling Riesling. Probably the first wine of which I was conscious was served to my grandmother and me at a sedate Somerset luncheon party, and we called it Lutomer Rize-ling. We were wrong on two counts. We should have pronounced it *reece*-ling of course and, furthermore, the wine wasn't 'proper' Riesling at all, but from an unrelated and much less aristocratic grape that goes by names such as Welsch Riesling, Italian Riesling, Olasz Rizling and Laski Rizling. The only characteristic that this Welsch Riesling has in common with the noble Riesling of Germany – called Rhine Riesling, Rheinriesling, Rajinskirizling, White Riesling and Johannisberg Riesling outside Germany – is that it tends to make slightly perfumed, medium dry wines with a fair bit of acidity. The difference in quality should be apparent.

The Austrians have managed to make some extremely good wines from the Welsch Riesling, including even some very sweet ones that earn the designation Trockenbeerenauslesen. And in the north-east of Italy there are also some light, fragrant Italian Rieslings. However, the 'lesser' varietal is most popular in Yugoslavia, Hungary and Romania, where it is encouraged to produce lots of rather undistinguished wine. Yugoslavia's Lutomer and Cloberg and Hungary's Pecs all derive from Laski Riesling.

Real Rhine Riesling is a much more finicky vine. It ripens late, so the vine grower always runs a risk that the crop will be lost, and it produces relatively little wine per vine (though the Germans are good at coaxing as much as possible from it). The entire German wine scene is centred on Riesling. Ninety-five per cent of Germany's fine wine is made from this single

*with a lovely smell that suggests fresh Alpine flowers. (There's nothing too exotic and heady about the Riesling, unlike the Gewürztraminer.) The lightness of body is a good giveaway for a German Riesling, as is a certain amount of sweetness following the lovely fruity perfume. Try to imprint this palate picture on your memory, for the aroma of the Riesling grape should be one of the most distinctive of all. Honey-and-flowers is a common tasting note.*

*The French tend to call their wines after the place they come from; the 'appellation contrôlée' system of designating the better wines enshrines Meursault and Sancerre rather than Chardonnay and Sauvignon. Newer wine regions, such as California and Australia, major on grape variety or varietal. The Germans also often specify the grape variety together with the place it was grown (e.g. Bereich Bernkastel Riesling), but their quality designation system revolves around the ripeness of the grapes when they were picked – and hence, usually, the sweetness of the resultant wine. This means that their most prized wines are called either Trockenbeerenauslese or Beerenauslese. They're very sweet, very rare and very expensive. To examine the effects of unusual ripeness on the Riesling grape in Germany, look instead for one of the next two rungs down, Auslese and Spätlese. There is usually noticeable sweetness on the tip of the tongue in such wines, and yet the balancing high acidity will stop them from being remotely cloying. See if you can detect any of the vegetabley, cabbagey smell of botrytis as already experienced with Sémillon.*

grape variety which, like Chardonnay, has been planted all over the world by winemakers aspiring to the exciting race and breed of the prototypes. Riesling, again like Chardonnay, changes considerably with age, but even in its early life it is marked by very zesty acid and a delicate flowery-fruit aroma which shouts refreshment. Within Germany itself there is great interest in the new wave of Trocken (dry) and Halbtrocken (half-dry) wines which they find go much better with food than the more commonly exported German wines which, typically, have considerable residual sugar thanks, in most cases, to adding Sussreserve (unfermented grape juice) to wines that have been fermented out to dryness.

In the world of wine, as in every other, what we have least of is what we want most. The winemaker in southern Italy or California tries desperately to keep the acidity level in his wines up under the powerful glare of the ripening sun. His counterpart at the northern limit of German vine cultivation lusts after more sunshine to ripen his grapes, and the most prized German wines are those highest in natural sugar. Only in the sunniest vintages is much sweet wine made there. But Riesling Beerenauslesen and Trockenbeerenauslesen, picked very late to trap every last ray of sunshine in the bottle, can provide more good examples of *botrytis* or *Edelfäule* – at a price.

A-level: *A good Sauternes and a 'TBA' or 'BA' are both extremely sweet and unctuous. They might also both have a whiff of botrytis about them. The way to distinguish between them is to look for the flowery fragrance of the Riesling grape, much more distinctive than the bouquet of rich Sémillon.*

*Germany has eleven distinct wine regions, of which only the Mosel-Saar-Ruwer (one region), Rheingau, Rheinhessen and Rheinpfalz (or Palatinate) send much wine to Britain. The regions are listed in increasing order of sunniness and richness of wines produced. Try to get hold of an example of even ordinary 'QbA' wine from each region (though the Rheingau specializes in top-quality wines) and contrast the weight and style of the wines. Mosel wines, in the green bottles, are lightweight and 'slatey' sharp. Rheingau wines seem to have the most judicious balance of Riesling fruit and northerly acidity. Rheinhessen wines tend to be a bit flabby and a huge proportion of them end up as Liebfraumilch, while the Rheinpfalz, with the most sunshine of all and some interesting soils and grapes, turns out Germany's spiciest wines.*

**Rhine Riesling ripens late so the grower always runs the risk that the crop will be lost**

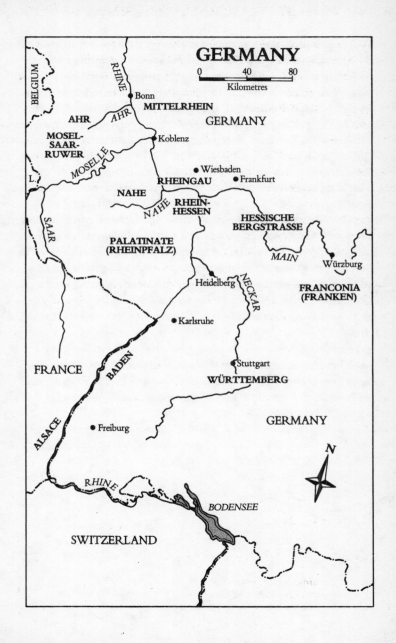

*Try to find an example of a mature Riesling in order to be impressed by how wonderfully this grape ages. Although in its youth it appears so frail and appetizing, it seems to gain strength over the years and adds all sorts of flavours to the initial grape aroma. Among recent years in which Rieslings suitable for ageing were made in Germany are 1985, 1983, 1976, 1975 and 1971. Wines of, say, Spätlese quality and above from these vintages should by now be fairly deep golden-green in colour, still retain lots of acidity and have developed a much more complex nose. Notice that curious 'old Riesling' smell that I associate with petrol or something more agreeably oily, at least.*

*Note that the most basic qualities of German wines, called 'Kabinett' or (even more basic) 'QbA' or 'Qualitätswein', are designed for early drinking. Ordinary German wine should be drunk just as soon as you can. Hang on only to wines of Spätlese, Auslese, BA or TBA quality. And 99 per cent of all the lesser Welsch Riesling made should be drunk in its youth.*

A-level: *It can be confusing trying to distinguish a Mosel Auslese, say, from a Rheingau Kabinett. The first will be relatively light in body but high in sugar, while the converse is true of the second.*

The very sweet Rieslings, *TBAs* and *BAs*, are usually fiendishly expensive. Curiously, however, wines that are only
medium dry to medium sweet, *spätlesen* and *auslesen*, can
often be good value – especially if they have a bit of age on
them, as standard German pricing practice seems to have
ignored inflation. Such wines can provide wonderful
examples of what happens to Riesling as it ages. Just like
mature Chardonnay and Sémillon, the wine takes on a more
intense colour, often a deep gold but in this case with a
greenish tinge, almost gamboge. The bouquet evolves into
something much more layered than the simple floweriness of
young Riesling. It is faintly reminiscent of petrol, though still
enticing and extremely pure in its appeal. A Riesling is often
steely but the fruity acidity is its most obvious distinguishing
mark. As it ages, this acidity becomes more apparent while
the sweetness seems to recede. When it is too old (either from
a poorish vintage such as 1978, or because it has come to the
end of what might be a very long run) the wine seems to taste
dry and too tart.

The effect of climate on taste is well illustrated even within
the fairly close wine regions of Germany. German wine is
sold either in green or brown bottles, the green ones coming
from the Mosel and its tributaries, the Saar and Ruwer, and
the brown from Rhine river regions such as the Rheingau,
Rheinhessen and Rheinpfalz. Because they are even cooler
than Rhine vineyards, those on the steep slopes of the Mosel
produce lighter, crisper wines. Some of them may have only
about 7° of alcohol, while those of the Rhine are at least one
degree stronger and taste noticeably more substantial. Travelling upriver past the Rheingau to Rheinhessen (for Liebfraumilch) and Rheinpfalz, one encounters increasingly fuller-
bodied wines that have gained intensity and ripeness with
more sunshine.

*Try out an Alsace Riesling. Hugel wines are quite easy to find, but any producer will do. Notice how the wines have the same pure flowery Riesling smell and the suggestion of lots of refreshing acidity on the nose. When you test out the sweetness on your tongue, however, you will see that the Alsace wine is almost bone dry. It is certainly much drier than any German Riesling, other than one of the newfangled 'Trocken' or 'Halbtrocken' wines designed for the diet-conscious German market.*

*See if you can distinguish blind between an Alsace Riesling and a Mosel Riesling. The key is in the weight, or body, of each. Many Alsace wines are almost double the alcoholic strength of some Mosels.*

*An Australian Rhine Riesling can provide an excellent, if rather accelerated, example of what happens to the grape with age. Australian Rieslings are characterized by great vibrancy, a little bit of 'spritz' and not that much sugar. Try Alex Findlater and Ostler's.*

*Les Amis du Vin of London W1, The Winery, W9, and La Vigneronne, SW7, are possible sources for California Johannisberg or White Rieslings (same thing). Most California examples are well balanced even though much fuller bodied than German wines. Note the flowery Riesling smell overlaid with extra west-coast ripeness. Many of California's Rieslings seem to me to have the rather exotic edge of lime (added citric acid?) on a honeyed Riesling flavour.*

Riesling is the most respected wine cultivated in Alsace just across the Rhine from Rheinpalfz, cheek by jowl with the rather richer Gewürztraminer grape. It should be easy to distinguish an Alsace Riesling (which in some ways gives a particularly clear picture of the aroma of the Riesling grape) from most German wines because Alsace winemakers ferment all the sugar out to make dry wines. They still have the perfumed floweriness on the nose, but are dry on the palate. Now, however, there is a vogue for dry wines in Germany and these *Trocken* can sometimes be confused with Alsace wines, though they're usually lighter.

The grape they call the Rhine Riesling has been very successful and popular in Australia, especially in the Eden Valley and Clare. Being from Southern Hemisphere vineyards harvested in February and March, such a vintage-dated wine always has a good six months' greater age than European equivalents. Moreover, Australian Rhine Rieslings seem to age very rapidly. Even after as little as three years, they are deep yellow and busy giving off all sorts of interesting petrol-like signs of age.

California has also had unexpected success with the grape they call the Johannisberg or White Riesling. The wines have much more body and alcohol than their German counterparts, but careful winemakers have kept acidity levels well up. They can be very attractive, flowery medium dry wines that, like Beaujolais, are so obviously gulpable that they are strong candidates for that rather puzzling epithet 'real drinking wines'.

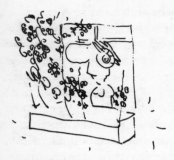

*Because Müller-Thurgau has no great cachet in Germany, not too many labels specify it. Most Liebfraumilch is substantially made up of Müller-Thurgau, however, even though it may be tarted up a bit with something like Morio-Muskat (see below). Well over a quarter of Germany's vineyards are planted with this grape variety.*

*Perhaps the easiest way to taste unadorned Müller-Thurgau is to find an English example. Lamberhurst Priory in Kent make an attractive, if dry, one, as they do nearby at Spots Farm. English wines are, in the main, made from Germanic grapes and tend to taste like German wines, only much drier. This means that there are strong similarities between English wines and Germany's new 'Trocken' and 'Halbtrocken' wines. A good place to buy British is the English Wine Centre of Alfriston.*

*New Zealand winemakers often manage to make from the Müller-Thurgau something a little more vibrant than their Northern Hemisphere counterparts. Try Peter Dominic, Victoria Wine, Waitrose, and Fine Wines of New Zealand of London NW5 for examples of their light, fruity and often slightly 'spritz' style.*

*Look for character in an Alsace Sylvaner and notice how difficult it can be to find it. Trimbach can sometimes make an example that's so racy it is just like a Riesling, but most others are simple crisp dry wines with just a faint whiff of Alsace pungency.*

## German commoners

GERMANY ALSO produces a wide range of wines from grapes less aristocratic than the Riesling. Most of them are modelled on it, some exaggerating its aromatic qualities to the point of obviousness, others being too pale a shadow. They tend to be cheaper than Rieslings, so it pays to develop a taste for what they have to offer.

Müller-Thurgau is Germany's most widely planted grape variety, a century-old crossing inspired by Riesling but without such refreshingly high acidity and with a much softer, grapier aroma. The crossing was developed to be a much less risky, earlier-ripening grape than the Riesling, and this is translated into a much less interesting range of flavours in the resulting wine. Its advantage is that it has a high yield and can flourish in spots where Riesling can't, but don't expect greatness from it and drink it young. For much the same reasons as in Germany, the Müller-Thurgau is popular with grape growers in England and in that other wine region far from the Equator, New Zealand, where they rather naughtily call it Riesling Sylvaner.

Sylvaner is a straightforward grape grown extensively in Germany and Alsace which has pronounced acidity and usually not much else.

German grape breeders have more recently been at work on varieties with even more obviously aromatic appeal – partly because they are useful for converting duller base wine into something that tastes faintly Riesling-like. (It is well known that lots of very ordinary Italian wine is 'Germanized' in this

*You will almost certainly have drunk some Morio-Muskat, if only as a small part of a cheap German blend. Victoria Wine and Asda sell a perfectly creditable, very spicy medium-dry litre from the Rheinpfalz.*

*We will probably see more and more wines labelled Scheurebe. Watch out for examples in the Spätlese category and above, and look for a certain blackcurrant-leaf flavour.*

*To experience plain, unadorned Loire Chenin Blanc, try any white wine labelled Anjou, Saumur or Vouvray. Notice the fruity, appetizing nature of the wine. There is lots of acidity and some honeyed, almost peachy flavour but noticeably more body and 'breadth' than the Riesling grape would give. Most off-licences can offer an everyday example of one of these wines, and Yapp Bros of Mere, Wilts., specialize in examples with lots of character. 'Damp straw' is my trigger expression.*

*Palpably better quality, and often ludicrously underpriced, are the wines of Savennières, Quarts de Chaume, Bonnezeaux and those of quality-conscious Vouvray producers such as Gaston Huet, A.*

way.) Morio-Muskat is one of the most aromatic grape variety crossings, and has strong Muscat, i.e. grapey, characteristics. Many inexpensive German QbA and Tafelwein bottles (the lowest quality level) contain a bit of Morio-Muskat. Very scented cachous.

Scheurebe is one of the most promising new crossings. When the grape is ripe it can make very fine dessert wines with some of the elegance of Riesling. When it doesn't ripen fully, however, it can be quite unpleasantly catty.

## Chenin Blanc and a bit of cloning

CHENIN BLANC is unusual in that it is grown extensively throughout the world's wine regions, with enormous variation in the taste of the wine it produces. It makes fairly ordinary wines in the main, but is clearly capable of greatness.

The home of the Chenin Blanc is the Loire Valley and, in particular, the long middle stretch upriver from Muscadet country towards the distant vineyards of Sancerre and Pouilly Fumé. It is the basic grape of Anjou Blanc, Saumur (still and sparkling) and Vouvray (still, sparkling, sweet and dry). Even within the confines of the tiny appellation Vouvray, the versatility of the grape is demonstrated. There it makes wines of all degrees of sweetness, fizziness and potential. Basic Loire Chenin Blanc has a faint honey-and-flowers smell, not totally unlike Riesling but with less distinction and more body. Like any Loire wine, these basic Chenins have lots and lots of acidity – remember the Sauvignon exercise with latitude?

There are little pockets of vineyards on the Loire, however, where the Chenin Blanc can produce honeyed wines that can last, if not for ever, certainly for half as long. When they're

*Foreau, Marc Brédif and Daniel Jarry. Try Yapp again, O. W. Loeb of London SE1 and Caves de la Madeleine, SW10. These are wines with real honey (especially if, as in some Bonnezeaux, Quarts de Chaume and Vouvray in 1976, botrytis has struck) and a gold colour. Acidity will always be high but the richness of the wines gradually builds up. There is a superior Anjou, Moulin Touchais, whose 1959 appears to be ubiquitous (try any 'proper' wine merchant) and to be a good fifteen years younger than the date on the label. I have never tasted a Loire wine of this type that seemed over the hill – and I have tasted several wines from the 1920s.*

**Climate is only one of the things that affect the taste of wine**

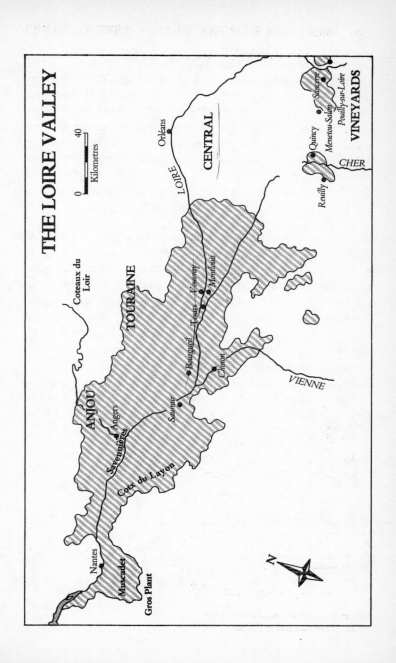

*A California Chenin Blanc should not be too difficult to find (The Winery of London W9 specialize in California). It will probably be a soft medium dry wine with none of the bite and 'wet straw' of the Loire example. Collisons of London SW1 or the Cape Wine Centres of W1 and Edinburgh will have a score of South African Steens or Chenin Blancs. Notice the appetizing, slightly 'spritzy' quality of these wines. Their positive, almost smoky character to me can be more reminiscent of a slightly sweet, very youthful basic Mâcon (Chardonnay) than an Anjou (Chenin Blanc from the Loire). Try to taste at least two of these three possibilities together so as to get an accurate idea of the contrasts between them. Look out for Chenin Blancs from other parts of the world and see how they shape up to the Loire model.*

young, they have so much acidity that it is difficult to believe
they have much sweetness in them at all. But, as they mature,
they develop a lovely, round, almost 'gummy' character that
takes them closer to the golden syrup mould. Wines such as
Vouvray and Montlouis are usually made in a wide range of
degrees of richness, from *sec*, through *demi-sec* to *moelleux*.
After a decade or two the colour takes on a wonderful golden
lustre; but the key to a Loire Chenin Blanc, however old and
however sweet, is very high acidity together with some
honey and a suggestion of summer flowers.

Chenin Blanc is grown widely in California, Australia, South
Africa (where it is very popular and usually called Steen) and
South America. What is puzzling is how unlike Loire Chenins
these wines taste. Standard California Chenin Blanc is pretty
neutral, used for straightforward medium dry inexpensive
wines that provide a good base for the winemaker's skill.
South African Steens are different again, with a bit more race,
character (and *spritz*) to them. The explanation for these wide
variations may lurk in that science-fiction word 'clone'. A
single cutting of a vine type can be responsible for the future
of that varietal in a new wine region. The Australian wine
industry owes its existence to a handful of vine cuttings taken
out there by the first settlers, for instance. It is possible that
the Chenin Blanc of California and the Steen of South Africa
stem from clones of the varietal that emphasize characteristics
rather different both from each other and from the original
Chenin Blanc of the Loire. Just a slight variance from the
original plants could well have become exaggerated over the
years. Clonal selection, choosing a particular plant because it
has the characteristics one wants, plays an increasing role in
the world of wine. Germany leads in this technique of making
sure you have the sort of vines you want by planting only
selected clones of them. You can choose plants for a high
yield, high quality and resistance to all sorts of pests, diseases
and conditions.

*T*AKE A *black grape and peel it. Do the same to a white grape and notice that they are almost indistinguishable.*

*As further evidence of how a white wine can be made from black grapes by carefully running the juice off the skins before ferment-ation, you need only consider Champagne (better still – drink some). Well over half the Champagne vineyards are planted with the black-skinned Pinot grapes. The Californians also made lots of wines called Blanc de Noirs when they had vineyards full of black grapes, and there was a fashion for white wines. Some of these wines were made by careful separation of skins and must, others even by charcoal 'bleaching' of the wine.*

*Notice how pale the Grenache-based reds of Lirac and Tavel can be, as can many red Burgundies. Claret (Cabernet Sauvignon) and Hermitage (Syrah) tend to be very deeply coloured, however. We shall be considering this in more detail. Look out for the colour of different vintages of Bordeaux, another subject to be studied in more depth later.*

# 4 *The raw material – red grapes*

## How to make wine red

THE PRINCIPLES of making a white wine were out-lined on page 119. If you followed those steps with a black grape you would end up, amazingly enough, with a wine that was white – possibly very pale pink. The flesh of all but a handful of obscure grape varieties is the same colour: sludge green. Colouring materials, pigments, can be found only in the skin of the grape.

This means that to make a red wine, or rather to make a wine red, it is essential to keep the grape skins in contact with the must so that the pigments will be attracted out of the skins and into the resultant wine. Conveniently, the heat generated by the fermentation process puts everything into a stewing state, and this hastens along the colour-extraction process. Otherwise fermentation happens just as with white wines.

On page 59 we examined some of the factors governing how much colour a wine has. Some grapes are higher in natural pigments than others, as we shall see below. Grenache is a pale grape, as are some clones of Pinot Noir, while Cabernet Sauvignon and Syrah are very thick skinned and therefore great potential donors of colouring matter to the must. Some years encourage thicker skins than others. The weather pre-ceding the Bordeaux vintages 1980 and 1977 was wet, and diluted the colour as well as the quality of the Clarets of those years.

*One of the hallmarks of top quality Claret, a classed growth wine (one that says 'cru classé' on the label and was included in the 1855 classification of the Médoc and Graves), is that the wine has been given a fairly long 'cuvaison', time for the must to macerate on the skins. Compare the colour of a wine such as this with one from the same vintage but from an ordinary property, a 'petit château' that is not 'classé', or a blending vat.*

*To examine the fruity charm and deep colour given by carbonic maceration and allied techniques, arm yourself with a Beaujolais, a cheapish Côtes-du-Rhône or a Vin de Pays from a reputable wine merchant. What all these very different wines have in common is a very low-tannin, supple attraction in which the fruity character is emphasized, and there to be enjoyed only months after the vintage.*

*I*T'S SAD *but true that to experience the real taste of Gamay at its best you should avoid British-bottled Beaujolais. Some bottlers over here manage to retain the essential freshness, but too many somehow let it escape as they rumble the wine across the Channel in tankers. To form your impression of Gamay look for Beaujolais that has been bottled in the region. Straightforward Piat de Beaujolais, easy to find, would give you the flavour. So should any wine from Georges Duboeuf (available from Davisons Berkmann Wine Cellars), Loron, Dépagneux and from the only Beaujolais specialist in this counry, Roger Harris of Weston Longville in Norfolk. Notice the colour and distinctive smell,*

By leaving the skins in contact with the must for a protracted period, the winemaker can give extra colour to the resultant wine. However, he has to be careful not to overdo it, as bitter tannic elements will seep out at the same time as the pigments. The must may be left 'on the skins', as they say, for anything from a few days to three weeks. Extra colour and tannin can be obtained by pressing the leftover skins and adding that 'press wine' to the original wine that was pumped from or run out of the fermentation vat.

Another means of making red wine and extracting a lot of colour out of the grapes quickly is carbonic maceration or 'whole grape fermentation'. Beaujolais is made by a version of this technique, which involves fermenting the grapes without breaking them. The heat builds up inside them and by the action of carbon dioxide in the absence of oxygen another sort of alcoholic fermentation happens naturally. This makes very supple fruity wines that are not designed for a long life, because they don't contain lots of tannin, but are very deeply coloured. (The grapes at the bottom of the vat are crushed, which means they ferment in the traditional way.)

## Gamay the gulpable

GAMAY, the grape responsible for Beaujolais, is for most tasters the easiest varietal to recognize in a red wine. Even the colour is distinctive: crimson with a definite purplish tinge, making Beaujolais one of the 'bluest' wines in the world. The smell is even more tell-tale though, and even more difficult to describe than that of other grapes. Gamay is always high in refreshing acidity (these wines are really 'white' in function if not in hue) and just one whiff will have your tongue crinkling. Then there's a smell that I describe as 'juicyfruit', sometimes with a slightly inky edge. The standard tasting note on Beaujolais is always 'fresh

*definitely an aroma and not a bouquet (see Glossary). One good example should be enough to imprint that Gamay character on your memory.*

*Remember that a light-bodied red wine, such as the sort of Beaujolais the Gamay produces can take a certain amount of chilling if you want a drink for refreshment. In any case the Gamay is not a grape that gives off so many fascinating nuances of flavour that you need to encourage this vaporization by warmth. Standard practice in the region itself is to serve Beaujolais 'cellar cool', at about 52°F. Beaujolais is the perfect wine in circumstances in which you can't govern serving temperature too strictly, such as on a picnic. It can bear a wide range of temperatures, so if you chilled it before setting off you would probably still enjoy it at the much warmer temperature it reached by the end of your picnic.*

*Look for the following names on the label to enjoy superior Beaujolais from these 'crus': Fleurie, Chiroubles, St Amour, Chénas, Juliénas, Brouilly, Côte de Brouilly, Morgon, Moulin-à-Vent. A wine labelled Beaujolais-Villages will usually taste a little firmer and jucier than a straight Beaujolais, while these 'cru' wines have positive character of their own.*

and fruity', the freshness being that acidity, and the fruitiness the very simple but undeniable appeal of the Gamay grape. You know when you smell it that it's not a great wine, but it's so eminently gulpable that any genuine well-made example will woo you into the glass.

Gamay usually produces fairly lightweight wines but you may come across examples that seem medium or even full bodied. In many cases this will be because of a mechanical-sounding winemaking technique called chaptalization, the adding of sugar to the grape must (*not* to the wine) and then fermenting it out so as to make the resultant wine stronger. This is perfectly legal in France and, if carefully done, does nothing to the flavour of the wine, but simply adds body. It is usually beet sugar that is added though there are moves within the EEC to turn some of its wine lake into concentrated grape must that could be used instead.

Gamay-based wines are very rarely suitable for ageing. Their chief purpose is to refresh and give gulping pleasure while still youthful – sometimes still in the nursery, like all that Beaujolais Nouveau. A *cru* Beaujolais, from one of the nine special villages, can gain depth and interest for about five years after the good vintage, and the wines from Moulin-à-Vent can age into an almost Burgundian state of maturity.

Other Gamay-based French wines are usually called Gamay on the label (Beaujolais very rarely is) and are made in Touraine on the Loire, in the Ardèche and the Côtes d'Auvergne, du Forez and Roannaises. However, these are rarely as interesting and lively as Beaujolais.

To form an impression of what Cabernet Sauvignon tastes like when reared in its original Bordelais setting, look for a bottle of Claret, as fine as you can afford. The standard Claret bottle, with straight sides and a narrow neck, is easy to recognize and it often even has a label proclaiming a château name. The key to likely quality is the 'appellation' specified on the label. 'Bordeaux' is the most basic 'appellation' and might not present a very distinctive model for your palate picture of Cabernet Sauvignon. 'Bordeaux Supérieur' is the same quality level and merely means that the wine is slightly more alcoholic, say 11° as opposed to 10.5°. Most really good Claret carries a more specific 'appellation'. Try to find one from some territory that is respected as a producer of the finest Cabernet Sauvignon in the world: St Estèphe, Pauillac, St Julien, Margaux, Haut-Médoc , Médoc or Graves. Specific châteaux whose vineyards are planted with a high proportion of Cabernet Sauvignon, and whose wines are therefore very good examples of the varietal's characteristics, include (you should be so rich) Latour, Mouton-Rothschild, d'Issan, du Tertre, Pouget and La Louvière. Cabernet should, however, dominate in the blend of any wine with the 'appellations' specified above.

Notice in your sample of fine Bordeaux Cabernet the intensity of everything; colour, flavour and length are all very pronounced. The only ingredient in which Claret is relatively short is alcohol. Smell the wine and try to register that blackcurrant flavour. This grape

## Around the world with Cabernet Sauvignon

CABERNET Sauvignon is the grape variety before which lovers of fine wine should genuflect. Pinot Noir may be responsible for a few thousand bottles of great red Burgundy every year, but the Cabernet Sauvignon is the main ingredient in millions of bottles of wine with enormous ageing potential made all over the world. It has the winning combination of producing top quality wine and adapting well to a wide range of climates and soils, while retaining its basic character.

Not to put too chauvinistic a point on it, it's rather like the English language. From its home base Bordeaux (which at one time was ruled by the English crown) it can now be found in a similar form but with different accents throughout the globe – particularly in America, South Africa, Australia and New Zealand. With the emphasis on 'varietal labelling' in these newer wine regions, it is very easy to pick out wines made from this – the greatest – red grape variety. In its homeland Bordeaux, however, less than one per cent of all the wine made from it will actually specify Cabernet Sauvignon on the label. This is partly because red Bordeaux (or Claret, as we British call it, after the light *clairet* we used to ship from western France in the Middle Ages) is made from a mixture that consists mainly of Cabernet together with some other grapes. The other factor is the French *appellation contrôlée* system's concentration on geography. If you see any of the words listed opposite on the label, then the predominant grape variety in a red wine is almost certain to be Cabernet Sauvignon.

Bear in mind that, contrary to popular opinion, the Cabernet Sauvignon is not the most widely planted variety in Bordeaux. Most red wines carrying the general *appellation* Bordeaux will be made in the Cabernet Sauvignon style, even

*aroma may be overlaid with the flavour of oak, something we shall
examine in more detail, if the wine has been given pronounced wood
ageing. For the pure grape aroma, try a Pierre Coste Graves from
Adnams of Southwold or Lay & Wheeler of Colchester. He produces
some fine examples of Bordeaux Cabernet without any oak
influence. See page 185 for more on oak.*

*To get a suitably well-informed impression of Cabernet, you should
probably force yourself to sample the huge range of wines made from
the grape around the world. Outside Bordeaux, but still in France,
surprisingly little Cabernet is grown – only in the outlying regions,
such as Bergerac and Buzet, and in tiny pockets planted by the
quality-conscious, as at Mas de Daumas Gassac in the Hérault and
Château Vignelaure in Provence. Further afield there are delicious
Cabernets made in California, Washington State, Argentina and –
especially delicious – Chile (though much of the Cabernet there may
be the lesser Cabernet Franc, according to Miguel Torres,
winemaker extraordinaire of Catalonia and Chile). New Zealand
and Australia have substantial Cabernet plantings, with Coonawarra Cabernets winning greatest acclaim. South Africa specimens
are beefy but definitely Cabernet, and there are plantings in Lebanon
(Château Musar), Greece (Château Carras), Bulgaria (cheap and
now available as part of the Hirondelle range), Yugoslavia (variable), Italy (soft and good value in the north-east and a great asset for
noble wines in Tuscany) and Spain (in Catalonia, to best effect in
Jean Leon's wines and Torres Gran Coronas). Try to extract the
Cabernet character from each of these wines whenever you have the
chance to taste them. Probably the cheapest way to experience
Cabernet fruit is in one of the less expensive California varietals.
But there is a very alcoholic snag, as detailed in the next section.*

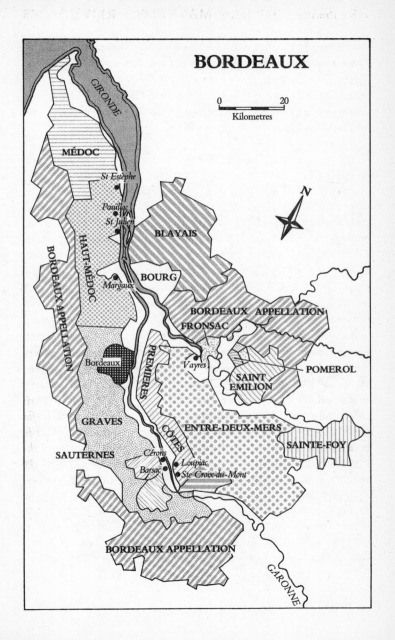

YOUR FIRST *example of Claret, as suggested in the previous exercise, will do admirably to demonstrate Cabernet from a temperate climate. Notice that you find it really rather appetizing. Another glass with food would be pretty nice, though the high level of tannin in youthful Claret means that it's difficult to drink without food, and seems even tougher if served too cool. Claret has been described as the ultimate beverage wine. Almost any wine merchant or licensed outlet should be able to offer Clarets by the score. Traditional City and St James's Street merchants make a speciality of it. New Zealand Cabernets such as Cook's or Montana are often so light and dry they can be almost weedy, and you may have to hunt the flavour.*

though they may contain a high proportion of other Bordeaux grapes, its less emphatic country cousin Cabernet Franc (see below), the Merlot of St Emilion and Pomerol in the north-east of the region, or the less distinguished Malbec grown on the Bordeaux fringes.

The Cabernet grape itself is small and blue, grows tightly clustered and, when pressed and fermented, usually has lots of tannin and colour to give to the must. The keynotes of youthful Cabernet are a very deep purple ink colour, the aroma of blackcurrants (not totally unlike the related Sauvignon Blanc) and, usually, lots of acidity and tannin. Claret, unlike some hot-country Cabernets, is only light to medium bodied, but its flavour is very intense and there is often a very lingering finish. A good Cabernet is capable of ageing superbly and many, with their high level of tannin, demand it.

## Cabernet and climate

BECAUSE Cabernet Sauvignon is grown in so many different settings it is very useful as an illustration of the effect of the climate of an area on the style of wines produced there. The Cabernets of Bordeaux, in a temperate climate on the fairly chilly Atlantic seaboard, display the quintessence of the variety with lots of fruit, but they are low in alcohol and have marked acidity. Cabernets produced in New Zealand, with a climate at least as cold, are even lighter in body and are also often drier and more acid. Washington State Cabernets and some of those produced in the cooler parts of north-east Italy represent the slightly fuller, fruitier style of Cabernet that results from, among other things, rather hotter summers than are usual in Bordeaux and New Zealand.

*Most California Cabernets will prove the point about the difference a hottish climate makes to the richness of the wine made there. Choose your example by the alcohol content on the label. Cabernets of 14° are by no means uncommon in California. You will notice, as well as the viscosity and the burn in the finish of such a high-alcohol wine, much less acidity than in your Bordeaux example and a richness that tastes almost sweet. Watch out for the distinctive minty, eucalyptus flavour in some more expensive California Cabs, made famous by Heitz Martha's Vineyard. Some California Cabernets can, however, be confused with some Clarets. A youthful very concentrated Claret from a ripe year that is high in extract because it has had a long 'cuvaison' can seem very like the deep-coloured, intense wines of California – especially since top producers in California use exactly the same sort of barrels as the Bordelais (sometimes even from the same cooper). Look for the lower alcohol level, as a good indication that the wine was made on this side of the Atlantic.*

*The Château Musar wines show great spicy character with surprising finesse. Try the 1970 if you ever get the chance. Try Collison's for Cape Cabernets, of which Meerlust's blend Rubicon with classic Bordeaux grapes is the best I've tasted. Australian Cabernets are now, happily, relatively easy to find and Penfold's and Lindeman's produce reliably good examples.*

To see the most dramatic examples of the impact of unmitigated sunshine on a red grape variety in general, and on Cabernet Sauvignon in particular, it is necessary to look at one of California's heavyweights. Full-bodied, ripe-to-the-point-of-plumminess Cabernets are not difficult to find there; indeed, it takes a great deal of ingenuity to produce a California Cabernet that is not too high in alcohol, and everything else too. Look at the depth of colour in these (often inexpensive) wines. When you look down into it, you will probably find it difficult to locate the bottom of the glass through the wine. The smell will be so strong, it'll have blackcurrant and practically every other fruit you can imagine. Many sought-after Napa Cabernets even have a hint of mint or eucalyptus overlaid on all this. In fact, a certain mintiness is a good giveaway to a California Cabernet. A feeling of faint-heartedness in the taster when offered a second glass is another indication that there is a wine made from grape ripened to a merciless level of potential alcohol by the relentless Californian sunshine.

Other examples of hot-country Cabernets, with concomitant effects on colour and alcohol levels, are Château Musar (though Cabernet is here blended with Rhône grapes) and many Australian and South African 'Cabs'. A common sight in wines from these two countries, both of whose reds often taste very hot, is a blackish tinge – almost as though the flavour has been steamed out of them. Although I rarely aspire to pinpointing the exact region in each country, I can usually tell a South African Cabernet from an Australian because the former is sweet and chocolatey, while the latter has a more minerally whiff about it – often with notable acidity (which has often been added) and a distinct blackcurrant note. Coonawarra is one of Australia's most established areas for Cabernet.

***Here is a grape ripened under the
relentless Californian sun***

For pure, unblended Cabernet Franc try to taste a red Loire such as
Chinon, Bourgueil, or slightly more intense and long lived, St
Nicolas de Bourgueil. There's a certain juiciness, though it's less
fruity than Beaujolais. My trigger word is 'pencil shavings' for the
distinctive aroma of these wines – and I mean the wood bit rather
than the lead. I hope you can find something less recherché. Yapp
Bros of Mere can supply good examples, and Peter Dominic list a red
Saumur, though it's a less pure specimen.

Northern Italian Cabernets are becoming increasingly easy to find on

## The other Cabernet

ALTHOUGH 'blending' is seen as a dirty word by so many wine drinkers, the most famous wine in the world, Claret, is very much a blended wine. Almost all Bordeaux estates, usually called Château Quelque-chose, are planted with a mixture of grapes. Even those such as the top Médoc and Graves wines, which are predominantly Cabernet Sauvignon, will have a bit of something else planted alongside and blended into the final wine.

The most common 'other grape' is Cabernet Franc. It is often rather contemptuously dismissed as a lesser version of the Cabernet Sauvignon, but it can't be all that bad. Château Cheval Blanc, the top property of St Emilion whose wines sell at the same price as Château Lafite-Rothschild, is made up of two thirds Cabernet Franc. Cabernet Franc is known as Bouchet in St Emilion and nearby Pomerol, the two communes that complement Médoc and Graves on the other side of the Gironde to make up Bordeaux's top red wine area. (Cabernet Sauvignon ripens later than Cabernet Franc and can't ripen well in St Emilion/Pomerol.)

Cabernet Franc tastes similar to Cabernet Sauvignon, but is usually even more herbaceous, almost weedy. And because the grapes themselves are bigger, the wines are less tannic and are lighter coloured. The grape is planted extensively in the middle Loire and in northern Italy, where it produces luscious fruity wines with an edge of acidity and grassiness. They are rarely designed for a long life, however, and most Cabernet Franc wines are simple and gulpable, in the style of Beaujolais. (Cheval Blanc produces wines that are an exception to this, blending with rich Merlot grown on unique land and given rigorous small-oak-cask treatment.)

If you see the word Cabernet on an Italian wine label, then it

British shelves, and they're very good value too. Note that they seem rather sweeter, or at least less acid, than Loire Cabernets, because they're ripened by a bit more sun. These are red wines that can be drunk with great relish in their youth.

Try to taste one of the Loire or Italian Cabernets alongside a Cabernet Sauvignon of the same age, a young Médoc or Graves perhaps. Taste the Claret second because its much higher tannin content will pucker up your mouth, leaving a coating of astringency all over it. Notice how much more body and colour the Claret has too – and surely it seems drier?

The Torres red Santa Digna from Chile is an interesting example of a South American Cabernet Franc, available from La Vigneronne of London SW7. Compare it with a Concha y Toro Cabernet, also from Chile, and see if you can discern the different characteristics of a Cabernet Sauvignon in the second wine. Also look at a wine labelled Cabernet Sauvignon from NZ. See how Cabernet Franc-like the distance from the Equator makes it.

---

*I*T SHOULDN'T be too difficult to find a good, toothsome example of a Merlot-based Claret. Any St Emilion would do, as indeed would any wine that has St Emilion on the label in any form (there are all sorts of complicated and tiny 'appellations' such as Montagne-St Emilion, St Georges-St Emilion, and various other hyphenated communes). A Pomerol would be even better, being likely to contain a higher proportion of Merlot, as explained below. Most off-licences should be able to offer a 'petit château' (i.e. not reckoned officially 'grand' in terms of quality, but perfectly sound). Corney & Barrow of London EC1 specialize in top quality properties from St Emilion and Pomerol; you could even buy yourself a Château Petrus from them.

Notice the greater viscosity and slightly higher alcohol content in a

is almost certainly predominantly Cabernet Franc, planted much more widely there than Cabernet Sauvignon. Friuli and Trentino, up to the far north-east, turn out very good-value wines of this type.

There are many similarities between them, but you should be able to recognize a Cabernet Franc from a Cabernet Sauvignon by its lower tannin, colour and body. When Cabernet Sauvignon is cultivated in a very cool climate, however, it starts to taste remarkably like Cabernet Franc (see New Zealand).

## Merlot the fruitcake varietal, and yields

MERLOT IS to St Emilion and Pomerol what Cabernet Sauvignon is to Médoc and Graves. The varietal that predominates on this 'right bank' is a wonderfully attractive supple sort of grape which, when properly vinified, turns out rich, spicy wines with all the plummy sort of appeal of a rich fruitcake. So appealing can it be, in fact, that Pomerol's Château Pétrus, made almost entirely of Merlot, qualifies for the dubious distinction of being the world's most expensive wine.

It ripens easily and produces wines that taste quite sweet. This counterbalances what tannin there may be to make them seem much softer than would an equivalent Cabernet Sauvignon.

*Merlot than in a Cabernet Sauvignon. There's a warm, sunbaked sort of flavour that is reminiscent of very ripe fruit, almost a plummy fruitcake. The tannin seems less marked than in Cabernet Sauvignon, and there's much more richness than in Cabernet Franc.*

*Look out for Merlots from Stag's Leap, Newton and Duckhorn in California, Château Ste Michelle in Washington and Sokol Blosser in Oregon . La Vigneronne, The Winery, Alex Findlater and Lay & Wheeler of Colchester may be able to help. The California vintages I have tasted – fairly early in the west-coast career of the Merlot grape – are very high in tannin, but this may well be reduced by winemakers during the 1980s. Washington and Oregon Merlots are softer, gentler and designed for much earlier consumption. Notice the same sweet fruity nose, however.*

*Compare your St Emilion or Pomerol standard Merlot example with an inexpensive Italian specimen. Many licensed supermarkets and unexciting off-licences stock one, often in a big screwtop bottle. You can tell just from the colour that the Italian specimen is much thinner and paler. It will taste that way too with pronounced acidity spun out over a rather watery taste. A pale (red) colour, often rather dull, is an indication that the vine yield was too high for quality.*

*Good, exciting Italian Merlots can be found with 'DOC' on the label (the Italian equivalent of 'appellation contrôlée') from all over northern Italy. Victoria Wine may have one from Villa Ronche in Friuli.*

A good Merlot-based wine often has a sort of rich velvety texture with a heady, complex aroma that some have variously described as gunshot, pheasant and gamey. I'm spirited more to the spice shelf than the game parlour myself.

Merlot reaches its apogee in St Emilion and Pomerol. However, plantings are increasing dramatically on the US west coast as Californian winemakers are realizing what the potential is for a rich alternative to their darling Cabernet Sauvignon. Further north and east in Washington is one of the very few wine regions that have taken to Merlot in a serious way and the state is turning out very attractive supple examples, some of them vinified in Oregon.

Merlot, like Cabernet Franc, has long been planted in the north of Italy, with very variable results. It is almost inconceivable that Château Pétrus should emanate from the same varietal as some of Italy's cheaper 'two-litre' Merlots. Comparison of St Emilion/Pomerol with such a wine illustrates well the result of asking too much of a vine in terms of grape production. There are stringent controls on most French *appellations* as to exactly how much wine each acre of vines may produce. A good property may well do an additional summer prune to further restrict yield (*rendement*) to make only, say, 30 hectolitres of wine per hectare (about 2½ acres). An Italian Merlot designated *vino da tavola* may have been made to about three or four times this yield, and the taste is obviously 'stretched' accordingly. The result is a much thinner, less exciting wine, although there are also likely to be variables other than yield of course – climate and clone being the two obvious ones. There are good Italian Merlots; look for the DOC ones of the north.

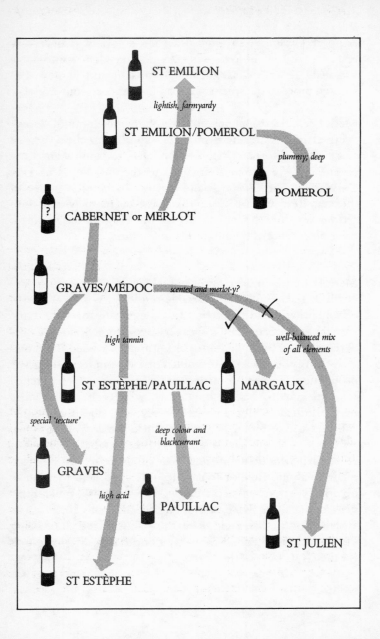

## Claret – a geography lesson

BORDEAUX is a very obligingly well-ordered wine region, which is why it is such a favourite with those who enjoy blind tasting. It's divided into separate estates or châteaux which don't change (much) from year to year. Each region – Médoc, Graves, St Emilion, Pomerol and the lesser ones – is divided into neat communes, each of which should have their own characteristics just as each vintage puts its own stamp on to the wines it produces. This is particularly true in the biggest top-quality Claret region, the Médoc.

When tasting a Claret blind, the taster would first of all decide whether he was faced with primarily Merlot (St Emilion/Pomerol) or Cabernet (Médoc/Graves). If he smelt the rich plumminess of Merlot, he would look for great intense spiciness that suggested *lots* of it – with a deep colour – and that would lead him to Pomerol. If the Merlot seemed to have been mixed with a noticeable proportion of Cabernet Franc (alias Bouchet) producing a lightish-hued, slightly farmyard-smelling wine, then this would suggest St Emilion.

In a wine that seemed predominantly Cabernet Sauvignon he would look for the distinctive 'texture', a sort of dry, sandy, almost earthy taste that is characteristic of Graves. If he didn't find it, he should in theory start trying to work out which of the Médoc communes or parishes the wine could come from. (In practice, most blind tasters are casting about wildly by this stage. Could be Italy? California perhaps? Oh for a logical brain and cool soul in these circumstances!) Neatly, the most northerly commune, St Estèphe, produces the wines highest in acidity. (The Napa Valley plays a nasty trick on wine tasters, with its coolest vineyard and most acid wines in the south nearest the Equator, but also nearer the cooling influence of San Francisco Bay than the warmer vineyards to the north.)

Wines from St Estèphe can be hard and very tannic when young. Pauillac is the most famous commune, with three of the four Médoc 'first growths' classified in 1855. Its wines tend to be very concentrated and blackcurranty with lots of tannin. Margaux is quite a way to the south and wines made there tend to be more delicate and slightly more Merlot-y. St Julien contains lots of second-growth châteaux and, typically, makes wines that come somewhere between Pauillac and Margaux – 'just enough of everything' is the convenient description, though a certain cedarwood flavour is associated with the commune.

This amount of detail is given here because Claret guessing games are the most common and can, believe it or not, be great fun. I suspect that those who indulge in them have more faith than I in just how likely they are to be right. I've seen it rarely, but it's the getting there that's fun.

## Vintage and age

IF GUESSING-the-commune seems a dazzlingly skilful dinner-party trick, guessing-the-vintage assumes almost mystical status. Contrary to popular belief, there are relatively few sorts of wine in which such a feat makes sense. All the dry, crisp whites we drink with relish when they're young tend to follow the same path towards a stale unexciting state with years, so that guessing the vintage for most whites equates with guessing the age. The same is true of many of the less exciting reds that are sold in huge volumes to be drunk as young as possible.

Guessing the vintage is significant only for wines that develop

interesting characteristics with age, i.e. those that mature
rather than simply age, and are made in regions where the
weather varies sufficiently from year to year to give each
vintage its own character. This means that vintage-guessing is
a widespread exercise only for white wines based on Chardonnay, Riesling and Sémillon and reds from Cabernet Sauvignon, Merlot and most of the other varietals discussed below.
We touched on the great years for the three white varieties with
ageing potential, but it is with Claret, again, that most fun can
be had with vintage guessing. California Cabernets do vary
from vintage to vintage (the question being whether they were
made in a drought year or a year immediately post-drought,
rather than in a wash-out), but the much more temperate
climate of Bordeaux fashions the most dramatic vintage variations.

There is no shortage of literature on how the different vintages
are evolving, and the monthly magazines *Wine* (55 Heath
Road, Twickenham, Middlesex) and *Decanter* (St John's
Chambers, 2–10 St John's Road, London SW11) regularly
print up-to-date assessments of characteristics of wines as they
develop. It is important to realize, by the way, that vintages
evolve. A vintage such as 1975 was hailed as 'vintage of the
century' as it was being picked. Before it was ten years old,
doubts were being expressed about it being just too tannic for
its own good. Doubtless there will be a change of accepted
opinion, for better or worse, by the end of this century.

However, it is worth studying a specific example of just how
different two consecutive vintages can be. We have seen that
red wines lose colour and start to go browner with age, but
there is much more to identifying Claret vintages than guessing age. The 1980 vintage, for instance, was a poor thin thing
set between two very useful, fruity, well-coloured ones.
Looking at a 1980 compared with a 1979 you might be tempted
to think it was older, so pale will it be in comparison. Look at

the actual hue. The 1980 is still fairly purplish and therefore can't be all that old. When you taste it, however, you see that it is very light in body and low in tannin. The 1979 wine is much more concentrated in both colour and flavour, often still with noticeable tannin. Even though it is a relatively 'forward' vintage, the 1979 still has a few years to go.

Still talking Claret, if you find a wine with very deep colour indeed it is likely to be one of the following: 1985, 1983, 1982, 1978, 1975 or 1970. If the wine is very pale, it is either very old (if it's browny or tawny) or (if it's still definitely red) it will probably be from the 1980, 1977 or 1973 vintages.

Remember that, with red wines, tannin and depth of colour are an indication of youth, while complexity of flavour and fading of hue suggest maturity. If you have bought a quantity of the same wine, a case of a dozen bottles for instance, you will want to monitor its progress so that you don't drink it too soon. With a moderate quality Claret, the wine might be ready to drink within three to five years of the vintage, while the most revered names can take three decades to mature. Generally speaking, the better the wine, the longer you will have to wait before it can prove it. The sadness is, of course, that you can never know when a wine has reached its peak of quality until it has passed it. Again in general terms, Cabernet Sauvignon wines take longer to mature than those based on Merlot and/or Cabernet Franc.

Also bear in mind that your Claret sometimes goes through a stage they call 'dumb', meaning that it doesn't say anything much to your senses, particularly your nose. Especially when recently bottled, about two years after the vintage and/or at certain periods over the next decade or so, good quality Claret can seem very closed up, as though it's turning in on itself to concentrate on knitting together all the various elements inside the bottle. Don't write off a Claret that is very deep coloured and tannic but without much bouquet. It's probably merely youthful and getting ready to reveal its charms.

## Red wine + oak = Rioja

OAK MATURATION is much more common for red wines than for whites. Many producers of red wines would like to have rows of neat new small oak casks in their cellars for the extra dimensions of flavour they could add to their wines. What prevents them is the cost of the casks themselves, and the work involved in keeping them in good shape. Wine evaporates fast when it's kept in a porous wooden container, and cellarmen have to work constantly keeping each cask topped up so that air won't get to work on the wine and spoil it to the point of oxidation. Wood also encourages the natural precipitation of the bits of solid matter left in suspension in the wine after fermentation. A good thing – except that the wine has to be regularly pumped, or 'racked', off this deposit to stop it taking on a stale taste. This means that wine in a well-kept cellar is regularly moved from one cask to another, leaving behind casks that need careful cleaning and reconditioning. No wonder the coopers of France are turning to California as the most obvious place to find winemakers spurred on by fanaticism to such hard work.

The alternatives to wooden casks are large vats made of stainless steel and other inert substances, which are free from the dangers of evaporation and much easier to clean. Wines kept in such vats for the period of settling and 'marrying' after fermentation taste simpler and much more obviously fruity than those which take on the layer of oak flavouring offered by wood storage. There are some wines that are much better

*You can use your 'standard Cabernet Sauvignon' example to illustrate the combination of oak and red Bordeaux. Choose any wine from the Médoc or Graves, from a specific château. To contrast with this, try to track down one of Pierre Coste's youthful Clarets, sold by Adnams of Southwold, and Lay & Wheeler of Colchester. Notice that the second wine, which has been kept in an inert material, is very fruity and the tannin is hardly noticeable. The first wine, unless so old it will have cost you well over £15, is much more tannic, and probably also has a much more complicated flavour. Underneath the cedary oakiness of the first wine is the straightforward fruitiness of the second, but the two wines are as dissimilar as Barolo and Beaujolais.*

*Perhaps a cheaper way of 'tasting oak' on red wines is via a bottle from Greece. A high proportion of the red wines exported from there have a distinctive oaky flavour as a result of their treatment.*

*Try to compare a 'cru classé' Claret with a slightly more impoverished château, described as 'bourgeois' on the label – i.e. one rung down from the 1855 classes. You will note much more flavour on the superior wine, with an intense tannic flavour brought about by its newer and more vigorous oak lodgings during infancy.*

*Examine a red Rioja. An example shouldn't be difficult to find. (Only beware of the very young Riojas that have been shipped to this country in recent years.) Make sure it has a vintage date of more than three years before, and have a look at the seal on the back of the bottle. They seem always to be changing the regulations, but at the last count 'vino de crianza' wines must have at least one year in wood, 'reservas' at least two and 'gran reservas' between two and*

suited to this sort of treatment though, and they would be rather overpowered by oak. Beaujolais and other light fruity wines, such as Valpolicella, are obvious examples.

Claret, as usual, provides an excellent illustration of the effect of oak ageing. All classed growth properties will put their wines into small oak casks, the traditional Bordeaux 225-litre *barrique*, as will many châteaux which although not *classés* is making serious wine for a medium to long life. The better regarded the property, the newer the casks they can afford, the more intense oak flavour will be picked up, and the longer we have to wait until the wine is drinkably mature. There are some Clarets that are specifically designed for a vivacious youth rather than an august old age. They and wood are kept firmly apart so that the fresh fruit quality of the wine is emphasized and the liquid is ready to drink only a year or so after the vintage. Compare one of each type to study the effect of Bordeaux's eighteen months or so in small oak casks.

The number of times an oak cask has been used before affects the final taste of the wine, as outlined already in Chapter 1. The newer a cask, the more flavour and tannin it has to give to the wine. The lesser properties of Bordeaux put their wines into casks that have perhaps already been used by several smarter châteaux, and the effects of keeping wines in wood like this are therefore much less obvious.

The exact provenance of the oak also has a great bearing on the flavour of any wine kept in cask. Limousin and Nevers are the standard sorts of oak used in Bordeaux. You can taste their rather taut, dry, rigorous flavour in your standard Cabernet Sauvignon example. Californians have exhibited awesome enthusiasm in experimenting with different sorts of oak (and different depths of char, *and* different sorts of stave).

*five years. In practice, CUNE and La Rioja Alta produce particularly good Riojas, though some supermarket Riojas will do to illustrate the point. Notice the pale red colour with a slight tawny tinge. There should never be any sediment in a Rioja, so often has it been racked off its lees. Now take a sniff. There's warmth, sweetness and vanilla there (and sometimes even a slight suggestion of vomit, I'm afraid, though not on the better examples). Take note of how different this opulent vanilla American-oak smell is from the taut cedar French-oak flavour on a fine young Claret.*

**Wine from the wood definitely tastes different**

*Marques de Murrieta and white Tondonia Lopez de Heredia are good examples of the traditional white Rioja style, while Marques de Caceres exemplifies the new crisp one. Spanish specialists include Laymont & Shaw of Truro and the Sherston Wine Company. Being both dry and rich, the traditional whites resemble some mature dry white Graves.*

They have found that there is a great difference in flavour between the native American oak and various imported French varieties. Most top wineries try to use small oak casks for their top Cabernets, though the much cheaper American oak gives an easy, sweet vanilla flavour to lesser wines.

**In a well kept cellar wine is always kept moving from one cask to another**

We in Britain are obviously rather keen on American oak. Rioja, the warm red wine from northern Spain, has been a great success here and its chief flavour component is American oak. All red Rioja with the *crianza* seal on the back has spent some time in small American oak casks – usually two years or more, and certainly usually long enough to give the wine the very distinctive sweet vanilla smell. Red Rioja must be one of the easiest wines to recognize – not because of the grape, for most Riojas are made of a blend of several local grape varieties, but by the American oak flavour that is its keynote. Another good clue to a Rioja's identity is its relatively light colour, made paler by the Riojan practice of moving wine from cask to cask, or 'racking', even more often than in most wine regions.

Some white Rioja is given a similar American oak treatment, though an increasing proportion is now made without any wood so that it tastes like a cross between a Muscadet and a Mâcon Blanc. The 'traditional' white Riojas demonstrate well how white wines gain rather than lose colour with oak ageing, and can have an interesting mixture of the vanilla bouquet and fairly high acidity. Again, they are made of a mixture of local Spanish grapes.

FOR THE taste of true Pinot fruit you would be well advised to go for one of the lesser 'appellations' of Burgundy. Not only do they cost a fraction of the big names, they are also usually more reliable (at their quality level). These aren't wines for great development, but the well-made ones offer good simple Pinot flavour. Plain old 'appellation' Bourgogne (French for Burgundy from any reputable merchant ('négociant') or individual grower ('domaine') is a good one to head for.

Notice that the wines are fairly light and have a very fruity nose – it reminds me of raspberries, other people of strawberries or violets. There's something soft and sweet about the wine, and little tannin (though there may be quite a lot of acidity in a not-so-good vintage, because the region is so far north).

Probably the cheapest way of tasting Pinot Noir is via a bottle of sweetish red Bulgarian or Yugoslavian. The flavour won't be the purest, but it's a start.

## The fabulously fussy Pinot Noir

JUST AS Cabernet Sauvignon is responsible for most of the great red wines of Bordeaux, Pinot Noir is solely responsible for all the great red Burgundies. No red grape other than Pinot is allowed into such *appellations* as Gevrey-Chambertin, Chambolle-Musigny, Clos de Vougeot, Romanée-Conti, Nuits-St-Georges, Aloxe-Corton, Beaune, Pommard and Volnay. When grown in the finest vineyards of the famous Côte d'Or, the 'golden slope' of Burgundy, in a good year and vinified by a careful winemaker, it can produce fabulous wine. 'Ethereal', 'soft and velvety', 'iron hand in a velvet glove', 'rich and scented' are all descriptions of great red Burgundy. 'Overpriced', 'thin and mean', 'ludicrously light' are all descriptions of bottles of red Burgundy that have disappointed.

It is a sad fact that red Burgundy offers more disappointments more expensively than any other wine type. This is partly because too many wines have been made by men who are good at growing vines but not necessarily at making wine; partly because some very poor clones of Pinot have been planted; partly because the region produces much less than world demand, so can get away with offering poor value; and partly because the Pinot Noir is such a finicky grape. The Cabernet Sauvignon has travelled happily all over the world, with some stupendous results. But winemakers and vine growers from Napa to New Zealand try each year to make a presentable Pinot – and usually fail dismally. Good Pinot can be so exasperatingly great that attempts will continue to be made (and with any luck quality in Burgundy will rise) so it is worth getting your palate trained to recognize the grape.

Good Pinot is slightly sweet and definitely more gently perfumed than the rather uncompromising Cabernet. Tannin is much less marked, for Pinot is much less 'pippy' and the skins

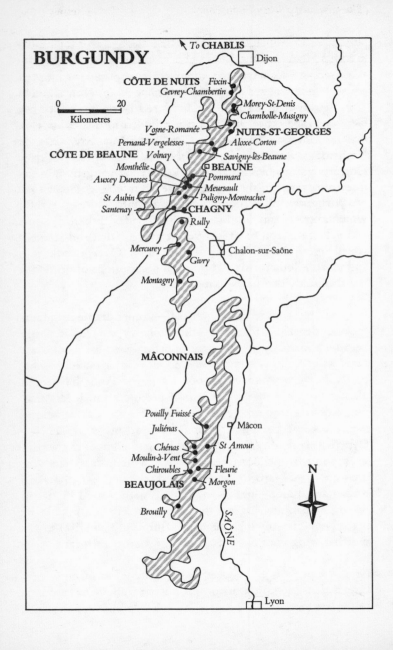

# BURGUNDY

To **CHABLIS**

Dijon

**CÔTE DE NUITS** *Fixin*
*Gevrey-Chambertin*

0       20
Kilometres

*Morey-St-Denis*
*Chambolle-Musigny*

*Vosne-Romanée*
**NUITS-ST-GEORGES**

*Pernand-Vergelesses*    *Aloxe-Corton*

**CÔTE DE BEAUNE**   *Volnay*    *Savigny-lès-Beaune*

*Monthélie*    **BEAUNE**
*Auxey Duresses*    *Pommard*
*Meursault*
*St Aubin*    *Puligny-Montrachet*
*Santenay*    **CHAGNY**

*Rully*

*Mercurey*    *Givry*    Chalon-sur-Saône

*Montagny*

**MÂCONNAIS**

*Pouilly Fuissé*
*Juliénas*    Mâcon
*Chénas*    *St Amour*
*Moulin-à-Vent*
*Chiroubles*    *Fleurie*
**BEAUJOLAIS**    *Morgon*

*Brouilly*

*SAÔNE*

**N**

Lyon

are in general much thinner. This also accounts for the Pinot's relatively light colour (though very serious places, such as the ultra-pricey Domaine de la Romanée Conti, ferment the wine on the skins for so long that they manage to extract quite a good depth of colour). Most Pinots have less body than the average Cabernet and their appeal is perhaps more subtle. It is easy to see why Claret was always described as masculine and Burgundy as feminine, however much one resists such facile descriptions. Some tasters describe the scent of Pinot as boiled beetroot, others as dead game. In young Pinot there's the very definite smell of raspberries, while in middle age it takes on definite vegetal overtones.

**For years Britons have been accustomed to Burgundys that are heavy and syrupy**

*Only a handful of wine merchants in Britain treat Burgundy really seriously, but it is gradually becoming easier to find top quality examples of Côte d'Or reds. The following should be able to help you spend your money wisely: Adnams of Southwold, Averys of Bristol, Corney & Barrow of London EC1, Domaine Direct of London WC1, Ingletons of Maldon, Essex, Laytons of London NW1, Lay & Wheeler of Colchester, O. W. Loeb of London SE1 and Henry Townsend of Beaconsfield.*

*The most exciting provenance of Côte d'Or Burgundy is the individual 'domaine', provided it is one that is quality conscious. The route to them is through one of the British wine merchants listed above. Most of Burgundy's output is, however, bottled by the shippers or 'négociants' and they have very varying reputations. Here are some of the more reliable for red wine:*

*Bouchard Père et Fils – good vineyards around Beaune.*
*Joseph Drouhin – extremely rigorous, the best of the new methods grafted on to traditional techniques.*
*Louis Jadot – rich and firm.*
*Jaffelin – sound, owned by Drouhin.*
*Moillard – good on recent vintages.*

*Peter Dominic and Justerini & Brooks have made a speciality of the Chalonnaise wines, especially the ones of the excellent producer Delorme. Notice that they are definitely lighter and leaner than fine Côte d'Or wines, in terms of style and quality a halfway house between the Côte d'Or and the Hautes Côtes.*

The Côte d'Or is made up of the northern part, the Côte de Nuits centred on Nuits-St-Georges, and the southern Côte de Beaune dominated by the town of Beaune. Traditionally, the wines of the Côte de Nuits are visualized as firmer and longer lasting than the softer, lighter style of the Côte de Beaune. In practice, the name of the producer is a much better guide to likely style and quality than even the name of the *appellation*. All of these wines are expensive, but if you have lots of money and patience you can build up your own impressions of the different producers. The briefest of brief outlines of mine are shown opposite.

Much cheaper than those from the Côte d'Or, and usually rather light and tart, are the wines from its upper hinterland, Hautes Côtes de Nuits and Beaune. Rather better examples of affordable red Burgundy made from the Pinot grape come from the Côte Chalonnaise to the south. Rully, Givry and Mercurey are the names to look for here. Any further south and you are into Gamay country. The grape that makes such luscious wines in the Beaujolais region turns out some very ordinary stuff under the name of Mâcon Rouge, geographically between the Côte Chalonnaise and Beaujolais. The explanation may be partly clonal.

Vintages for red Burgundy are even more variable than for red Bordeaux, and indeed considerably more variable than for white Burgundy. Chardonnay is a much less fussy vine than the delicate Pinot Noir. So far north is Burgundy that the Pinot ripens there satisfactorily only about one vintage in

*Try Doudet–Naudin wines for a reminder of 'old-style' Burgundy.*

*Very little Alsace Pinot is imported into Britain, so keen are the German tourists who flood the region to take home a bottle of red wine. However, Sancerre Rouge and Rosé is now quite widely stocked. Most examples demonstrate a bit of Pinot scent, and a very light colour. They are usually chaptalized fairly heavily to bring them up to a toothsome alcoholic strength. If you ever find a Champagne that is described as a Blanc de Noirs (Bollinger occasionally make one from their intense and ancient Vieilles Vignes of Pinot) it will be pure Pinot, as is the irresistibly named Bouzy Rouge.*

three, and until recently rot has been a severe problem. The 1975 vintage, for instance, was a memorial to the poor colour and stale flavour that can affect the resultant wine after rot has struck grapes in the vineyard. However, in a fine vintage, such as 1978, the grapes ripen fully to produce lots of sugar (and therefore alcohol and body), colour and flavour. Pinots in general are ready to drink long before Cabernets, owing to their lower tannin content and lighter weight.

True Pinot is usually a fairly light wine, but many readers may be surprised by this description. For years Britons have been accustomed to Burgundies that are heavy and soupy, with a dark ruby colour and so much weight they could be described as positively gutsy. This is because it was not until 1973 that the laws prohibiting the addition of fuller wines from the south had to be obeyed in this country. Long after the French had accustomed themselves to true Burgundy without the prop of Algerian and, later, Rhône and Italian blending wines, we were being sold these *mélanges* as 'Burgundy'. When controls became more stringent prices rocketed, and cheap 'Volnay' and 'Pommard' disappeared.

Some Pinot Noir is grown in other parts of north-eastern France: in Alsace (where it produces a dark rosé, illustrating well how difficult it is to get a deep-coloured Pinot even in a region whose white wines regularly notch up 13° alcohol); in Sancerre, where it is responsible for all those Sancerre rouges and rosés; and in Champagne, where it constitutes about one third of the blend that goes into the sparkling wine. Pure Pinot is available as a still wine of Champagne sold as Coteaux Champenois rouge, and the villages of Bouzy and Cumières are famous for it. The Pinot Noir grown there is supplemeted by the rather fruitier but less distinguished Pinot Meunier, rarely encountered elsewhere – though I have tasted as a 100 per cent varietal Pinot Meunier made by Great Western in Australia.

*La Vigneronne of London SW7, The Winery of London W9 and Les Amis du Vin of London W1 carry a wide range of California wines. Notice how rich and plummy most of these Pinots are, reared in California sunshine; in some cases the vegetable flavour is so ripe it's almost rotten but there's no shortage of sugar and (rather brownish) colour. Averys have occasionally had stocks of Tyrrell Pinot, which to me has that volcanic twang of Australia's Hunter Valley. In the Torres wine, on the other hand, notice how the oak treatment has rather overwhelmed the fruit, and that the smell of Pinot is followed by something just a bit too much like matchsticks and not much like raspberries.*

*Note, in all these examples, the effect of climate on the highly susceptible Pinot Noir grape. In the cool north of Europe it seems so much lighter and more acid than when reared in the sunshine of California and Australia.*

*Collison's of SW1 should have a few examples of Pinotage. They have the same sweetness as Pinot Noir, plus something that's almost inky. But these are rugby players – true Pinot can play nothing tougher than the violin.*

The most successful Pinots produced outside Burgundy have been grown in very cool micro-climates within much warmer regions. The Chalone winery, 2,000 feet up in the Santa Lucia mountains of California, together with Saintsbury, Calera and Acacia, has produced that state's best examples to date, and there is no shortage of seekers after the sublime Pinot there. The cooler climes of Oregon to the north have been tipped to rival Burgundy eventually, and the Eyrie Vineyards have made great progress towards that goal. Less successful American examples are too obviously 'hot climate' and are too plummy and full-blown to benefit from the delicacy that Pinot can give. The same criticism can be levelled at most attempts in Australia, though Tyrrell's (much to their surprise) won acclaim at the Paris 'Wine Olympics' of 1979.

St Helena make a very attractive Pinot in New Zealand, where the climate perhaps most nearly duplicates that of Burgundy. Other Pinots which can give a great deal of pleasure and help to imprint the flavour of the grape at not too great a price come from Italy and Spain. Torres make Pinot Noir the dominant character of their rather hefty, oaky Santa Magdala, and certainly there's a good Pinot scent, even though the wine could hardly be described as delicate. The Pinot Nero of northern Italy is also based on Pinot Noir, called Blauburgunder in the Tyrolean part of the country where it is most successful – just as it is in both Austria and Germany, where it turns out very thin stuff indeed. It is also grown in Hungary, where it's best as 'Villanyi Burgundi'.

Common in South Africa is a beefy red grape called Pinotage which is a cross between Pinot Noir and Cinsaut, the rough and vigorous southern Rhône grape. In my view, the Cinsaut is now by far the dominant strain, and the Pinot leaves only certain residual sweetness to remember it by. The wines are good value, though, for those who want a hearty alternative to Châteauneuf (*not* to Chambertin).

YOU CAN *do this exercise with any Claret and any red Burgundy, though it makes sense to choose a pair of roughly the same age and quality. If you know you're faced with a Château Mouton-Rothschild 1961 and a supermarket's non-vintage (NV) Burgundy, you really are making life a bit easy for yourself. Any of the wines suggested so far would do; your example of Pinot and Cabernet would make a particularly good pair. A brace of '82s would make the point. (You might find Merlot-based Clarets more difficult to distinguish from Pinot because both grapes are quite sweet.)*

*Here is a crude outline of your deductions in the order you're likely to make them:*

| | | |
|---|---|---|
| Colour | **pale**<br>*Pinot, or Cab in poor year* | **deep**<br>*Cab, or Pinot in very good year* |
| Viscosity | **low**<br>*Pinot* | **high**<br>*Cab or heavily chaptalized Pinot* |
| Flavour | **raspberries/vegetables**<br>*Pinot* | **blackcurrants**<br>**cedar/herbaceous**<br>*Cabernet* |
| Sweetness | **sweet**<br>*Pinot, or Cab in opulent year* | **dry**<br>*Cabernet* |
| Acidity | **marked**<br>*Pinot, or very young<br>(or ancient) Cab* | **swamped by fruit**<br>*Cabernet* |
| Tannin | **low**<br>*Pinot, or very mature<br>Cabernet* | **high**<br>*youthful Cabernet* |
| Body | **light**<br>*Pinot, or very poor Cab* | **full**<br>*Cabernet, or Pinot from<br>exceptional vintage* |

*Note that it helps here, as so often, to have an accomplice to feed you an unidentified glass of each. It is wise to keep the glasses in the same relation to each other, so that your accomplice knows that the glass on*

## A milestone tasting exercise

HERE FOLLOWS an exercise so important it deserves a section all to itself. Outsiders might think that telling Claret from red Burgundy is absurdly simple – until you've blindfolded them and proved they can't even tell red from white. One friend of mine marked her newly won status as Master of Wine by identifying a Burgundy as a Claret at the celebratory dinner. Famous gastronome André Simon (or was it Harry Waugh?) offered comfort to us all with his reply when asked when he'd last mistaken Claret for Burgundy. 'Oh, not since lunch,' he smiled.

If you can master this classic test of wine expertise you should be justly proud of yourself.

Now you could try to distinguish between a St Emilion or Pomerol and a red Burdundy. The Merlot-based wine will also have sweetness, but it's a plummy sort of richness in a full-bodied tannic wine with lots of colour, whereas red Burgundies are more likely to offer a raspberry sort of fruitiness in a wine that is lighter in both colour and body.

the left, say, is always the Claret. Or they can mark the glasses with
a felt-tip pen. If you have (or prefer) to perform this feat solo, you
can do it by switching the glasses round and round so that eventually
you forget which is which. The trouble is that you can't top up in the
middle of the exercise, and you need to have learnt enough to be able
to match each glass to the contents of the bottles when the work is
over.

*A* FIRST-CLASS and not too expensive way to acquaint
yourself with well-made Syrah would be to get a bottle
of Crozes Hermitage from that impeccable North Rhône
producer Paul Jaboulet Ainé. Any Jaboulet wine or example from
Yapp Bros of Mere is textbook stuff and the UK importers are
O. W. Loeb of London SE1, though you can find the wines widely
stocked elsewhere. Notice how intense the colour and flavour are.
The tannin is marked but combined with a flavour quite unlike
Cabernet Sauvignon. There's nothing here that would remind you of
blackcurrants. The nearest fruit would be mulberries perhaps, but it's
surely more mineral than vegetable (only Pinot is animal!). You
could probably find a Syrah de l'Ardèche even cheaper. Made often
from vines too young for a grander 'appellation', this will be thinner
and without the rich fruit of a full-blooded Syrah.

Good examples of South Rhône wines helped by Syrah are superior
Côtes-du-Rhône reds such as Lay & Wheeler's Château de Grand
Moulas, also stocked by Adnams of Southwold, Tanners of Shrews-
bury and Balls Bros of London. The Chantovent wines from the
Château and Domaine de Gourgazaud in Minervois show that it
can be a good thing in Midi wines too. The Syrah qualifies as one of
the varieties officially designated 'cepage ameliorateur' and certainly
adds colour and depth of flavour to these wines.

**Take time to 'monitor' just how
you feel after swallowing wine**

## Syrah, black as night

IN EUROPE the Syrah grape is largely confined to two small strips of steep vineyard on the banks of the northern Rhône just south of Lyons, where it produces wines called Hermitage, Crozes Hermitage, Côte Rôtie, St Joseph and Cornas. It's reassuringly easy to recognize by its very dark, almost black colour and its high level of tannin. The wines are concentrated and chewy and have a distinctive 'essence-of-something' flavour that I now associate with burnt rubber, though some people think of tar or ink. (It is a measure of how difficult it is to match words with flavours that so many of the expressions we use to describe wines we like seem uncomplimentary.)

The Syrah is also grown in the southern part of the Rhône Valley and by quality-conscious producers throughout the vast acreage of vineyards in southern France, 'the Midi'. It is very much a 'noble' grape, being designed for a long life and able to add firmness and an intriguing spiciness to blends of other grape varieties. You can tell a Châteauneuf-du-Pape or Côtes-du-Rhône from the southern Rhône Valley that has been toughened up by the addition of Syrah. It will have the blackish tinge and a certain amount of astringency not com-

*Specimens of Viognier are difficult to find and expensive when you do. Yapp Bros of Mere stock a good range of wines made from both Syrah and Viognier, as well as offering more than half a dozen examples of Côte Rôtie. They list Château Grillet as well as Condrieu, of which Les Amis du Vin of London W1 have a good supply too. Condrieu is better value than Château Grillet, but both have the fascinating aroma of this rare grape. An A-level exercise if ever there was one, but you could try to find the Viognier aroma in the bouquet of a Côte Rôtie.*

*Averys of Bristol, Alex Findlater of NW8 and Ostler's of EC1 are good sources of Australian wines, of which Shiraz (often pronounced 'shir-ah') is probably the best value. Notice the obvious warmth in the flavour. These are wines made with a lot more sunshine than even the annual average in the Rhône Valley. Take note of the provenance of your Australian Shiraz, for Australia can't be regarded as a single wine region – it's about as big as Europe, after all.*

monly found in other grapes of the Rhône and Midi. The Syrah produces wines that desperately need food to accompany them, so hard can they be, and they should not be broached for as long as you can bear to wait. The 1961 Hermitage La Chapelle from Paul Jaboulet Aîné has years ahead of it still, and, because it was such an exceptional year, tastes disconcertingly like a great 1961 Claret.

Côte Rôtie is different from the rest of the north Rhône reds listed above in that the good producers, of which there are but a handful, add a little of the local white grape, Viognier, to give the wine more delicacy and scent. The Viognier is very difficult to grow and is hardly planted anywhere outside the Côte Rôtie *appellation* and two neighbouring all-white ones, Condrieu and Château Grillet. (Although Joseph Phelps of California, a great lover of Rhône wines, grows some in the Napa Valley.) It has an intriguingly musky peach or apricot smell, is vinified to produce medium dry wines with lots of body because it is cultivated so far south, and is one of the most haunting white grapes there is. If you catch a whiff of this scent in a red wine, it will almost certainly be Côte Rôtie.

Rhône wines are currently very good value, and unlike Burgundy to the north the Rhône Valley has experienced very few disappointing vintages recently. It is strange that the Syrah grape is not cultivated more widely when it's capable of producing such thrilling, long-lived wines.

Even more bizarre is that the only country which does claim to grow a great deal of the grape, makes wines so unlike the greats of the north Rhône. The Shiraz, supposedly the same as the Syrah, is Australia's most widely planted wine grape and produces a great range of sweetish wines that are often brownish-red with no great intensity of anything – quite different from Hermitage. You may well find it difficult to see the connection between these two grapes. Nevertheless,

*Petite Sirah is bottled in California as a varietal, but a few examples find their way to this country, often for good reason, though Ridge's is excellent. Much more interesting, and a worthy American cousin to good Hermitage, is Joseph Phelps' Syrah, available from Les Amis du Vin.*

some of Australia's Shiraz is great value at the moment, for they still have a glut of red grapes and no shortage of sunshine to ripen them. Try to memorize the hot, baked flavour of the typical Australian Shiraz. Those from the Hunter in New South Wales have my volcanic twang (others even describe the flavour as 'sweaty saddle'), while some of the richer ones from South Australia and Victoria can have a chocolatey flavour to them. They are all relatively sweet (even if labelled 'dry red') and high in alcohol. There is often a lot of flavour to begin with but it can fall off leaving a thin, watery finish. Blends of Shiraz and Cabernet are quite common and often attractive because the Cabernet fills in the hollow of taste at the end.

In California, only Rhônophile Joseph Phelps and Estrella River offer much Syrah as a serious varietal, but there are extensive plantings of a grape they call Petite Sirah and which they thought for ages was a clone of Syrah. It is, in fact, Durif, a lesser and more obscure Rhône grape, but some winemakers there are quite enthusiastic about it. Petite Sirah has lots of tannin but a much coarser flavour than Syrah. It can be useful in blends to bone up the much less tannic Zinfandel. In sum, there's nothing petite about Petite Sirah.

## Grenache and other rosés

WHILE SOME of the beefier Châteauneuf-du-Papes and other southern Rhône wines may contain a bit of Syrah, Grenache is the most commonly planted grape there. It is distinguished by an unusual combination of paleness of colour and high alcohol, and has a sweet, fruity flavour that is a bit like a very strong mixture of Beaujolais and a good Pinot Noir – but with a bit of herbiness. It is widely grown in Provence and seems to pick up a bit of that region's lovely scent of lavender and wild thyme.

*The Winery of London W9 or Les Amis du Vin of London W1 may just be able to supply an example of the famous and expensive Martha's Vineyard.*

*Each time you taste a Châteauneuf-du-Pape, try to assess how much Syrah it contains. If you don't taste much Syrah, then the predominant grape variety is probably Grenache. The average Châteauneuf contains about 10 per cent Syrah, 65 per cent Grenache and a mixture of other local grape varieties, though some Châteuneufs are made without any Syrah at all, and the wonderfully complex Château Rayas (available from O. W. Loeb of London SE1) is made from nothing but Grenache. It has a deep colour from long fermentation and exceptionally low yields, but does have the ripe spiciness of which this grape is capable. Notice how sweet Grenache is.*

*Any Tavel or Lirac and most Provence rosés will demonstrate the Grenache as a rosé. Notice that a rosé can be quite as full bodied as a red wine, and have just as much acidity as a white. See if you can smell Provençal herbs in these wines.*
*   Contrast these 'proper' rosés with a cheap blended one – anything at the bottom end of the price range will do (so, I'm afraid, may many of the famous brands). See if you can tell whether the wine was a late-stage blend.*

*Take a glass of any two whites and make full note of their flavours and attributes. Blend them together in a third glass and compare the result. It won't be nearly as exciting. The blending process seems to result in the lowest common denominator of each wine. Contrast this with your memory of a fine Claret, for which the different vats were blended well before bottling and probably three or four years at least before you enjoyed the wine.*

*See if you can spot the Cabernet scent of a Cabernet d'Anjou. It can also taste a bit like a Sauvignon Blanc, nicely establishing the family link between that white grape and the Cabernet family.*

(If you think this must be complete fancy on my part, try Heitz Martha's Vineyard Cabernet and note how it picks up the eucalyptus flavour of the trees round about that patch of vines.)

Most Châteauneuf and other south Rhône wines are made from a mixture of grapes and it can be interesting to taste them knowing this. See if you can notice that they, like another blend, Rioja, taste more soupy – more like a mixture of different flavours than one dominant one. There are properties, however, that specialize in making a wine from Grenache only. This provides a good opportunity to come to grips with the flavour of this grape, which – as Garnacha – is an important ingredient in the typical red Rioja blend.

Because of its light colour, Grenache is in great demand as chief ingredient for pink wine and predominates in the taste of the powerful rosés of Tavel and Lirac. Notice the high alcohol content, pale colour and a certain lusciousness, even if the wine is basically dry. Most rosés are made in the same way as red wines, except that the must is run off the skins after a much shorter time so that much less colouring matter is absorbed. A few wines are made pink by fermenting red and white grapes together on the skins. Some cheap rosés are made by simply blending together red and white wines, but their flavour is likely to be fairly unharmonious as the ingredients can bear little relation to each other, and won't be given time to 'marry'. Any blending in winemaking should be followed by at least one year's settling time and preferably more, but that is a luxury that the blenders of inexpensive table wine can ill afford. You can see for yourself that if you blend two wines the result tastes much duller initially than the sum of the components.

Rosés are not generally thought of as 'serious' wines. All the

SWITZERLAND

AUSTRIA

FRANCE

*Riesling*

*Bardolino*

*Pinots*

Turin

Milan

*Valpolicella*

*Cabernet*

**PIEDMONT**

*Soave*

Venice

YUGOSLAVIA

**N**

*Barbaresco*

Genoa

*Barolo*

Bologna

Florence

Rimini

*Chianti*

*ADRIATIC SEA*

*Brunello di Montalcino*

**TUSCANY**

CORSICA

Rome

SARDINIA

Naples

Bari

*TYRRHENIAN SEA*

*IONIAN SEA*

Palermo

**ITALY**

SICILY

0          100

Kilometres

more reason to get lots of fun out of them by establishing which style you like: dry and herby as in Provence rosés or slightly sweet and herbaceous as in Cabernet d'Anjou, the superior neighbour of Rosé d'Anjou that doesn't actually have to have Cabernet in it.

## Nebbiolo, the foggiest

ITALOPHILES wake up. Your time has come at last. The great wines of Italy have not been mentioned so far because they tend to come from (red) grapes that are rarely encountered outside Italy. For years Italy was an island in terms of wine production and appreciation, though the 'classic' grapes of the rest of Europe have been gaining ground – quite literally – all over the country and especially in the north-east. These 'new' Cabernets, Pinots, Rieslings and Chardonnays apart, most of the grapes grown in Italy are foreign in name and taste to most non-Italians. Only the workhorse white variety Trebbiano, grown in quantity all over central Italy, is seen much elsewhere, and this is only as the rather undistinguished Ugni Blanc used as base wine for Cognac. The very high acidity level and low level of character are desirable for distillers, and can be useful for makers of white wine in climates as hot as many parts of Italy.

Italy's greatest wines come from pockets of cooler vineyards, usually by virtue of altitude, and its most famous fine wine region is Piedmont. Here the Nebbiolo grape is king, and the locals claim for their most famous wine (as others have done elsewhere) that Barolo is the 'king of wines and wine of kings'. Nebbiolo gets its name from the mist or *nebbia* that can shroud the vineyards of these Alpine foothills in the autumn, and is grown throughout the region to produce its longest-living wines. It can be easy to confuse Nebbiolo with Syrah, certainly in appearance and structure if not in flavour.

*Italian specialists include Luigi's of Parsons Green and Millevini of Stockport, Cheshire. The Market, Le Provençal, Harrods, Adnams, Ostler's and Les Amis du Vin should also list some good examples. Names to look for among producers of Barolo and Barbaresco include Borgogno, Ceretto, Aldo Conterno, Fontanafredda, Franco-Fiorina, Gaja, Bruno Giacosa, Pio Cesare, Alfredo Prunotto, Renato Ratti. Fontanafredda wines may be some of the easiest to find, being stocked by Peter Dominic among others, but are not the most exciting. Gaja's are the most unusual and least typical, some of them being very juicy indeed. Notice how strong, dry and tannic the wines are, but try to get to grips with their amazingly intense scent. You may be able to find violets or even the local Alban truffles there – if you've been lucky enough to taste these delicacies.*

*A-level: Compare a Syrah-based wine with one made from Nebbiolo of about the same age and quality of vintage (see below). Notice that the Nebbiolo is slightly stronger, probably slightly bitter and with a more voluptuous smell.*

*If you can compare a Barolo and Barbaresco from the same producer you will see that the latter is lighter in colour and body. You can broach most Barbaresco after about five years, but have to wait for eight with many Barolos. It is difficult to find the other Nebbiolo wines here except for a few rather coarse Spannas and some interesting, approachable wines labelled simply Nebbiolo.*

*Producers who have made modifications to the traditional way of making Barolo and Barbaresco include: Ceretto (whose wines are often marketed under the individual vineyard name – surprisingly rare in Italy – such as Bricco Rocche and Bricco Asili), Franco-Fiorina, Gaja (whose wines are very juicy indeed), Alfredo Prunotto and Renato Ratti. Look out for their wines at any of the stockists mentioned above. Try to compare one of their recent vin-*

The Nebbiolo is a very tannic grape that translates into very tannic, dark-coloured wines – though new techniques in the vineyard and cellar tended to lighten the colour of wines made since the mid-1970s. The hallmark of Nebbiolo is its bouquet, one of those smells that have non-wine-drinkers screeching with incredulous mirth when they read the classic descriptions: violets, truffles and liquorice are all common terms of appreciation for this very dry, full-bodied tannic wine. There's usually more obvious fruit and scent in a good Nebbiolo than in most youthful Syrah-based wines, and I sometimes find the great Italian Piedmont grape tastes rather pruney.

The trouble with wines made from Nebbiolo is that, although they all come from this corner of north-west Italy, there can be enormous variation in quality and style. Barolo and its rather lighter neighbour Barbaresco are the most famous, but Boca, Caramino, Carema, Fara, Gattinara, Ghemme, Lessona, Sizzano, Spanna and wines labelled as Nebbiolo are all based on the grape. Barolo is fashioned to last the longest, but a good Barbaresco can be less of an assault on the senses. Most of these wines are very strong; Barolo must reach a natural strength of 13° at least.

Traditionally winemakers in Barolo and Barbaresco would ferment the grapes on the stalks as well as with the skins for a protracted period, and then keep them for years in large and ancient chestnut casks – sometimes until the sales order was received, so that a wine might spend twelve years in wood and no time in the bottle before being sold. This tended to make a wine that was naturally very tannic, even drier and

*tages with a more traditionally made wine. Pio Cesare makes wines of great quality that have not been swayed by the wind of change in Piedmont. Some other producers have been responsible for some pretty nasty, tough wines. Notice how much more obvious the fruit is in the 'new' wines, and how much more noticeable the tannin is in the 'old' ones.*

*Try London's The Market, Le Provençal, Winecellars Warehouse or Adnams of Southwold for Barbera and Dolcetto. Notice how soft and fruity they are.*

ANY OF the Italian specialists listed on page 212 should stock a good selection of Chiantis. The Chianti region is in a transitional stage as I write (early in 1987) as it adapts to having, to the amazement of some, been awarded the

leaner of fruit flavour. Only in exceptionally fruity years could the wine be drunk rather than chewed. Things are changing now, however. Many winemakers have bought new casks and stainless-steel vats in which to ferment and extract maximum fruit from the grapes (without the stalks to emphasize the astringency). The wines are now kept in cask for a much shorter period (though the DOC laws still insist on a minimum of two years – even in lean vintages), and producers purposely give them extended bottle age to soften them, before putting them on the market. You can taste an enormous difference in different styles of these wines.

The gentle revolution in winemaking techniques makes recommending recent vintages a dangerous business, as the exact producer and their policy on 'modern' winemaking has a great influence on the likely taste of the wine. However, this is a general guide for Piedmont vintages of red wine.

Piedmont is also the home of two more definitely Italian grape varieties: Barbera and Dolcetto, not often enough available in Britain. Barbera produces dry, acid reds not unlike the red Vinho Verde wines of Portugal though medium bodied. These should usually be drunk young and slightly chilled, and with a completely different frame of mind than that required for the great Nebbiolo. Dolcetto is even more frivolous and gulpable though not sweet, despite the name. It is dry, very fruity and often rather inky. Its aroma has a certain smooth grapiness about it.

## Sangiovese by Jove

THE OTHER great red wine grape of Italy is the Sangiovese, named after Saint Jove. It is grown all over central Italy but is primarily responsible for Chianti. The Chianti laws are very strict as to exactly what

*coveted DOCG status, a distinct notch above its old DOC rating. The 1985 vintage is the one to head for and the 1984 the one to avoid. Chianti Classico is more concentrated and worth ageing than most straight Chiantis, and its badge of office is a black cockerel and seal on the back of the brown straight-sided bottle. Try to make your own palate picture of the Sangiovese. Note the relative paleness, bitterness, high acid and an intriguing knit of different elements in the nose.*

**Guessing the vintage is only significant for wines that develop interesting characteristics with age**

proportions of different grapes are allowed into the blend, but Sangiovese always represents the major contribution, between 50 and 70 per cent by law but often more in practice. White grapes, including the unprepossessing Trebbiano, comprise most of the rest of the blend (unusually for a red wine) so that most Chianti is quite pale in colour.

Sangiovese is one of those grapes of which many different clones have been planted, with widely varying results. The best way initially to come to grips with 'typical' Sangiovese is to taste a well-made Chianti, probably a Chianti Classico that comes from the heartland of the Chianti region, and preferably a *riserva* that has had time to soften and show at its best. Much of the Sangiovese planted in Chianti is quite pale (though the Sangiovese Grosso described below is very deeply coloured) and ripens late. Other characteristics are marked acidity and a certain rustic flavour.

My tasting notes for Chiantis are littered with the word 'farmyardy' – though I like them a lot. As with so many Italian reds, there is also often the suggestion of bitterness. The main distinguishing marks of a Sangiovese-based Chianti are therefore: pale red, going brownish after only three or four years; a smell of old vegetation (or old animals); lots of acidity; some bitterness and a certain coarseness of texture. Some youthful Chiantis may feel very slightly sparkling. This is because they have been made with the traditional *governo*, the addition of dried grape must to re-ferment in the wine after the initial alcoholic fementation.

As it ages, the wine gets paler and more brown in colour and, I think, reaches a peak at about five to eight years. After this the wines start to dry out as the initial fruitiness of a Chianti blend, containing as it does some rather neutral-flavoured white grapes, is not high.

*A good quality assessment exercise would be to try to distinguish blind between an inexpensive Sangiovese di Romagna and a fairly young Chianti Classico. There should be much more flavour in the more expensive wine to illustrate what the cheaper one lacks.*

*You will usually have to go to an Italian specialist for Brunello, and the wines of Biondi Santi – which represent the pinnacle of Brunellosity – are very difficult to find. If you do manage to taste the wine (and I don't recommend it as good-value drinking) you will notice an enormous amount of colour and tannin. The wine is very dry but, if you can find it, it should have lots of fruit in there lurking behind the tannin, waiting for it to move off. Alivini of London EC1 import Il Greppo – a less expensive way to try embryonic Brunello.*

*Most of the Italian stockists listed on page 212 should have one vintage of Tignanello, as do Corney and Barrow of London EC1 and many other specialist wine shops and even the biggest off-licence chain in Britain, Victoria Wine. This is a delicious well-balanced wine that you should try to compare with a well-made Chianti Classico. Notice the much deeper, more blueish colour of the Tignanello and how even a small amount of Cabernet is apparent on the nose. You may also find the flavour of oak and, if the wine is young, the tannin will be more pronounced on the Tignanello. Tignanello 1978, for instance, is a great, concentrated wine built to last for twenty years.*

*Windrush Wines of Cirencester, Glos., should have a Carmignano in stock. Those of the Villa di Capezzana are particularly good and taste slightly more traditionally Italian than Tignanello.*

*Try the Italian specialists again for Sassicaia. Remember this is all*

Sangiovese is grown all over Romagna and Umbria as well as Tuscany. Its most ordinary manifestation widely available in this country is as poor quality Sangiovese di Romagna that should be drunk as young as possible. It reaches its most famous and expensive peak in Brunello di Montalcino, made exclusively from a strain of Sangiovese Grosso and probably Italy's (the world's?) longest-living wine. The firm of Biondi Santi has done much to boost the price and reputation of these wines, and they are unpalatably tannic and concentrated when young. Biondi Santi's Il Greppo *vino da tavola* is lighter and made of younger vines.

In the Chianti region there has been a similar sort of revolution to that in Piedmont. Some of the more progressive producers have successfuly fought for a reduction in the amount of white wine officially required in the blend, and some of them have been quietly omitting the Trebbiano (that was only ever written into the laws because there was a surplus of it and it is particularly easy to grow). Some have even been experimenting with small oak cooperage as in Bordeaux, an alternative to the much bigger Slovenian oak casks traditionally used. This tends to produce much more elegant wines capable of longer life and well suited to subsequent bottle-ageing. Antinori have been pioneers of this and their Tignanello represents the effects of small oak, no white grapes and the addition of up to 10 per cent Cabernet Sauvignon to the traditional Chianti blend. Now much-copied, it's a fascinating example of the power this Bordeaux grape has to shape flavour even in small quantities. Also in Tuscany, the 250-year-old tradition of adding up to 10 per cent Cabernet to the Carmignano blend demonstrates that this has made sense for years.

Other examples of Cabernet's more recent invasion of Italy

*Cabernet and try to relate it to other Cabernets you have tasted. A comparison of Sassicaia with a Claret of the same age and price and a California Cabernet in the same range would be fascinating. The Sassicaia may well taste more like the American than its fellow European, for the micro-climate at the Tenuta San Guido, just south of Livorno, is hotter than the Médoc – much more like sunny California.*

(and also under the Antinori auspices) – are Sassicaia, grown
on the Tuscan coast from 100 per cent Cabernet Sauvignon
and given similar cellar treatment to Tignanello, and the
fabulously-priced Solaia from hillside vineyards. This wine
shows that Italy is eminently capable of producing delicious
wines from imported grapes, though you will probably find
it easy to distinguish it from a Claret.

M OST Burgundy shippers offer a Bourgogne Aligoté. They taste best from ripe vintages, and Adnams of Southwold have one of the best.

Palaçio de Brejoeira is 'the' Vinho Verde and an Alvarinho wine, though most Vinho Verde should have a little bit of the perfume. Hurlingham Wines should stock it. Laymont & Shaw of Truro have a fascinating Castel do Fornos made in Galicia from Albariño.

Any wine called simply Pouilly-sur-Loire will be Chasselas (as opposed to the Sauvignon-based Pouilly-Fumé). Luxembourg wines are rarely exported, but London's Swiss Centre has a good stock of Swiss wines.

Most good wine shops have Tokay in various forms – the most basic Tokay Furmint, Tokay Szamorodni, or the rich and gold, almost sherry-like Tokay Aszu which comes in increasing 'puttonyos', or degrees of sweetness (five is the richest).

I wouldn't search too hard for Gros Plant.

# 5 *Further tasting*

## More white grapes

ALIGOTÉ: the 'other' white grape of Burgundy and not nearly as noble as Chardonnay. Light, very tart, pale and not capable of long life. Best from Bouzeron.

*Alvarinho:* the best grape that goes into white Vinho Verde, and grown as Albariño just over the Spanish border in Galicia. Its fragrance can be almost Viognier-like in its rich peachiness, even though the wines are very high in acidity and usually vinified very dry.

*Chasselas:* unusually, a wine grape that is also found in the fruit basket. It's responsible for common table wines in the middle Loire and, as Elbling, for almost all of the light, dry and acid wines of Luxembourg and for the most ordinary wines of the Mosel. In Switzerland it is called Dorin or Fendant, and occasionally takes on an attractive light smoky character.

*Furmint:* Hungary's slightly spicy white grape that usually produces dry wines with a certain amount of body. Makes the wonder-wine Tokay, with the even more obscure Hárslevelü.

*Gros Plant:* the less fruity grape of the Muscadet region, it is

*The Austrian wine-faithful include the West End Wine Centre of London WI.*

*There can be few wine shops, and even fewer restaurants and wine bars, where at least one Muscadet is not stocked. Perhaps it's so popular precisely because it's so bland; and its dryness and acidity feel clean, as though they are doing you good. Lorne House Vintners of Cranleigh specialize in mature Muscadet.*

*The grape produces excellent well-balanced wines in Alsace, where the name Pinot Gris is taking over from Tokay (nothing to do with the great Hungarian wine of the same name). An Alsace Pinot Gris and an Italian Pinot Grigio should not be too difficult to find. Note the extra body of the French wine.*

*Most English wines state the main grape variety on the label. Spots Farm of Tenterden in Kent have produced particularly toothsome examples – the combination of cleanliness and fruitiness can be quite hard to track down. The English Wine Centre of Alfriston is a good place to buy British.*

*Any white Rioja will do, but I have found the Solar de Samaniego Blanco, imported by Arriba Kettle of Birmingham and listed by Laymont & Shaw of Truro, to be an especially good demonstration of the floweriness of the Viura's bouquet. CUNE now produce a 'Viura Blanco'.*

responsible for wines with marked acidity and very little charm; though it must be said that they are refreshing.

*Grüner Veltliner:* Austria's native grape with a lovely racy spiciness to it. Wines usually have this aroma with at least medium body, but enough acidity to keep them well balanced.

*Muscadet:* the name of the grape and the wine, produced at the mouth of the Loire around Nantes. Very crisp and fairly neutral in character, though exceptional vintages produce fruity wines which can mature. Otherwise, it is to be drunk young as an uncomplicated lubricant.

*Pinot Gris:* a grape of many names – Tokay in Alsace, where it can make almost Burgundian full-bodied dry whites; Ruländer in Germany and Austria, where it makes 'bigger' wines than usually encountered in either of those countries; Pinot Grigio in north-east Italy, where its wines are crisp and dry but with a slight hint of smoky fragrance.

*Seyval Blanc:* a popular hybrid (between the European wine-producing vine *vitis vinifera* and wild native vines) grown in England to produce clean, dry whites with a certain suggestion of German *Trocken* about them.

*Viura:* the white grape of Rioja, though I've found it difficult to isolate its characteristics. New-style white Rioja seems denuded of flavour, and traditional stuff tastes mainly of oak and age.

*A* VERY CHEAP red 'vin de table' will probably demonstrate the rather inky, dank flavour of the Aramon grape.
There's something faintly reminiscent of foxgloves
about it.

Carignane varietals are available from California and many in-
expensive California reds may contain more than a dash of the grape.
It's the major ingredient in southern French reds, or try to sift the
Garnacha out of Tres Torres to see what's left.

Lebanon's Château Musar wines provide a good example of the
influence of Cinsaut (and lots of sunshine) on Cabernet-based wine.

Torres Coronas from Penedes is chiefly Ull de Llebre and shows, in
comparison with their Tres Torres blend of Garnacha and Cariñena,
how much higher in acidity and how much paler and more 'serious'
this grape is. Most red Riojas will demonstrate the same thing.

Ridge take Zinfandel more seriously than most, and their wines,
available from Les Amis du Vin of W1 and others, demonstrate how
noble the grape can be if given the Bordeaux treatment of small oak
ageing. The Winery of W9 and La Vigneronne of SW7 should carry
a wide range of California wines.

## More red grapes

ARAMON: until recently widely planted throughout the Midi, where it produced oceans of cheap, thin, unexciting wine. This high-yielder was one cause of the European wine lake. The authorities are encouraging its grubbing up and the replanting of superior varieties.

*Carignan:* called Carignane in California, it is also grown extensively throughout the Midi, where crossed with Cabernet Sauvignon it is responsible for the vibrant juicy Ruby Cabernet. Another Midi staple grape, as well as being found in the southern Rhône and many other hot wine regions around the world, where it produces alcoholic wines with lots of colour but little subtlety. Often lake-filling.

*Cinsau(l)t:* another southern Rhône grape, but with an attractive spicy character added to its colour and alcohol.

*Tempranillo:* you will rarely have the chance to taste this grape unblended, but it is the principal ingredient in the typical red Rioja blend. It is also found, as Ull de Llebre, in the Penedes. I have found a flavour of tobacco about this grape, inasmuch as I have been able to isolate it.

*Zinfandel:* a very important grape in California and capable of being vinified into all sorts of different styles of wine, from jammy Beaujolais-like to intense and rigorous long-life Pomerol-like. Its distinguishing mark is a smell of hot berries and a deep colour. It is probably related to the much less common Primitivo grape of southern Italy.

*A*DEGA WINES *of Bristol and A. O. L. Grilli of Staple-hurst, Kent, specialize in Portuguese wines, and Oddbins have traditionally carried a wider range than most. Try other Portuguese reds too and you will probably note similar characteristics.*

*Camden Town and the Greek Islands, in reverse order, are the best hunting grounds for Retsina.*

*Bull's Blood* – Mainly *Blaufränkisch*

*Branded claret* – Mainly *Cabernet Sauvignon* and *Merlot; famous names include Mouton Cadet, Harveys No. 1 and La Cour Pavillon.*

*Hirondelle* – Most are mixes of grapes, but their Bulgarian *Cabernet Sauvignon* provides an inexpensive way of sampling this noble variety.

*Laski Riesling* – The less noble Italian or *Welsch Riesling*, usually branded Lutomer, Cloberg or Pecs.

*Liebfraumilch* – There are hundreds of brands of this commonplace German blend, which usually demonstrates only very loosely the *Müller-Thurgau* type plus a dollop of a new aromatic

## Wines without great grape genealogy

THERE ARE wines whose flavour is not fashioned by one predominant grape variety. Red Rioja is one of these and has already been examined in the section on red wine and oak. Châteauneuf-du-Pape also usually contains a mixture of grapes, though Grenache usually predominates. Most Portuguese reds, and the most famous Dão in particular, are made up of a mixture of grape varieties, with Tourigo, not encountered elsewhere, the most important. Dão can often be distinguished by its high glycerine content, which makes it very viscous, and a sublimation of pure fruit to quite a high tannin content which can give a rather astringent end-taste. Dão is deep in colour and in some cases needs about ten years to soften.

Perhaps the most obvious example of a wine style which is recognizable by some characteristic other than grape variety is Retsina, the resinated family of Greek wines. They smell of pine or floor polish, depending on whether they're drunk in a beach taverna or in the bleak British midwinter, and you should need little guidance to recognize them.

The cheap table wines and famous brands are rarely based on a single grape variety. There is masses of Carignan in most red *vin de table* (as well as a hefty dollop of Italian *vino da tavola* to give it colour), and in various parts of the world the good old Sultana is responsible for gallons of white table wine. The best known brands which exhibit varietal characteristics are summarized here, and can be a good first step in learning.

*variety; Blue Nun, Black Tower and Crown of Crowns are
some of the most popular.*

*Mateus Rosé – If you can detect any positive varietal character in this
wine, you're a better taster than me.*

*Piat d'Or – ditto.*

*Schluck – Austria's Grüner Veltliner.*

*Ungrafted territory:*

*All of Chile (taste how ripely
fruity Chilean Cabernets are).*

*Much of South Australia and
New South Wales*

*Most of New Zealand.*

*Monterey County in California.*

*Washington State and much of
Oregon.*

*Much of the Mittelrhein in Germany.*

*Round the Neuseidlersee in Austria (Rust, Apetlon, etc.).*

*Colares near Lisbon.*

*Listel and SICAREX wines from the sandy shores of the
Mediterranean.*

---

*T*WO ESTATES *in the southern Médoc provide good
examples of what a difference new plantings can make.
Château La Lagune was a run-down property in 1958, when
bought and revitalized by extensive new plantings. Its early 1960s
vintages, while good, probably contained a lot of young-vine wine,
which slowly mellowed and deepened throughout the decade. Its
neighbour Château Cantemerle was bought in 1980 and new plant-*

## More A-level exercises

### Grafted v. ungrafted

IN THE second half of the nineteenth century the vineyards of Europe were devastated by a little bug, the *phylloxera vastatrix* (vastatrix indeed!) which, having been imported by accident from America, munched its way through the roots of European *vitis vinifera* vines. All sorts of solutions were sought, and in the end the only effective one was found to be grafting *vitis vinifera* cuttings on to rootstock of wild native American vines that had developed a resistance to *phylloxera*. To this day, about 90 per cent of the world's vineyards are planted with these 'grafted' vines. There are little pockets of land where vines are 'ungrafted', either because there seems to be no danger of *phylloxera* striking (the louse hates sand) or because, by chance, it has never struck (as in Bollinger's tiny Vieilles Vignes patch in Champagne). You can taste the difference between the wines produced by these ungrafted vines and the rest. The flavour seems much more positive and full blown, sometimes almost pushily so. Here are some examples of ungrafted wines that you can afford. Next time you drink an early nineteenth-century wine, though, bear in mind that it too would have been produced from pre-phylloxera vines.

### Age of the vine

THE STATE of maturity of the individual vine plays an important part in determining the flavour of the wine it produces. In quantitative terms the vine starts producing a sensible amount of wine in its third year and reaches a peak at about fifteen to twenty years, decreasing steadily so that at fifty years it is scarcely economic to cultivate such an aged plant. The quality of the wine produced steadily increases

*ings have already begun as part of a ten-year programme to extend the vineyard by about 200 per cent. New vintages of Cantemerle may demonstrate the young-vine character too, though Bordeaux châteaux often sell off the produce of their younger vines rather than alter the character of the 'grand vin' that carries the château name.*

*Perhaps better examples are the wines of the Hautes Côtes of Burgundy where vines were planted in the late 1970s and the wines coming from there (in which Geisweiler specialize) have still been a little thin in flavour. Look too at Chardonnays coming from anywhere in the world that does not have a Chardonnay-growing tradition. Italy, Spain and Portugal provide particularly good examples.*

---

*L*AY & Wheeler of Colchester and O. W. Loeb of London SE1 *should be able to provide some excellent German examples of the nearby vineyards, encapsulated in affordable bottles by the same producer of the same vintage. Or you could try the experiment with different Grand Cru Chablis. O. W. Loeb, again, usually stock a wide range of the different 'premier cru' vineyards of the top quality Chablis producer Louis Michel.*

*You could of course stray into the minefield of the Côte d'Or, but there are so many variables here, I think you'd better play safer and cheaper elsewhere.*

---

'*M*ODERN' *dry white Riojas such as Marques de Caceres, Viña Leonora, Solar de Samaniego, and indeed nowadays almost all white Rioja apart from Marques de Murrieta and Tondonia from Lopez de Heredia.*

*Viña Sol and most dry white Torres wines.*

with age, however, so that really dedicated winemakers search out very old vines, however uneconomic their crop, to add depth and complexity of flavour to their blends. The older the vine, the deeper its roots and the wider the range of elements it can give to the wine. Wines from newly planted vineyards can taste rather thin and simple, while those from ancient vines have many more layers of flavour. You can seek out new plantings and old plantings, such as those suggested here, and compare the differences in character.

## Different vineyard sites

IN A SENSE, all fine wine tasting proves the extraordinary point that different vineyard sites, even adjacent ones, produce wines of quite different character. To demonstrate (though not necessarily explain) the phenomenon to yourself, taste any selection of Clarets chosen using Hugh Johnson's invaluable *World Atlas of Wine* (Mitchell Beazley) as a guide, or any set of wines from the Rhine and Mosel. The lesson is particularly apt if the wines have both winemaker and vintage in common. I can think of no better example than a range of wines from the great Mosel winemaker J. J. Prüm. His adjacent Wehlener Sonnenuhr and Graacher Himmelreich clearly show how much more sunshine the former attracts simply because it's oriented a few more degrees towards the sun on the banks of the river.

## Low-temperature fermentation

THERE ARE certain cellar techniques which leave a very strong stamp on the character of the resultant wines. Carbonic maceration is one that we have studied already in its effects on red wines. Low-temperature fermentation has had the strongest impact on white wines made today. The principle

*The varietals of Friuli in north-east Italy, especially Pinots Bianco and Grigio.*

*Many other Italian dry whites, including Victoria Wine's Bianco di Custoza.*

*Vin de Pays des Côtes de Gascogne.*

*Vin de Pays des Charentes.*

*Listel dry whites.*

*Many South African, Australian and New Zealand whites; Brown Bros in the State of Victoria sometimes ferment their whites for weeks on end.*

---

*C*OMPARE *the development of a fairly mature and (I'm afraid) fairly grand wine in different bottle sizes. Cheap wine isn't made to develop anyway, so there's no point in monitoring progress; it will always be downhill.*

is that by controlling the fermentation and making it happen very slowly at low temperatures, you keep everything very clean, pure and fresh. (For fine wines you're also in danger of failing to make an interesting enough cocktail of the potential flavours, but that's another story.) Some of the less expensive examples of this technique shriek 'modern winemaking' at me, much more loudly than they do their origins. Here are some examples of such wines. Look for their purity of flavour, high acidity and a characteristic that is almost steely but perhaps just very slightly dull.

## Bottle size

WINES KEPT in different sizes of bottle are thought to mature at different rates. Half-bottles encourage the wines to mature rapidly, perhaps without picking up quite such interest along the way as a standard bottle size or, reckoned to be most satisfactory of all, the magnum (containing 1.5 litres or two standard bottles). This is why a magnum of fine wine usually costs more than two standard bottles. Bottles even bigger are often sold more for their novelty value. They terrify me. Just think of dropping a jeroboam of Château Latour.

*Whatever you like your general
approach will probably be to ram
as much into your system as
possible*

*Next time you're having wine with a meal, notice how you consume
the solid and the liquid constituents. You'll probably find that you
take a mouthful of the wine before you actually eat anything, which
is a very good moment at which to taste it as consciously as possible.
Thereafter you use the wine as lubricant for the solid matter you are
taking in – just as you would use a glass of water in fact.*

# 6  *Wine, food and fun*

WINE AND food make a difficult subject for a book. All the relevant guidelines can be given in a short chapter such as this, or it demands a lifetime of research and dissatisfaction. If you are a purist, you could probably – after many disappointments – find the single wine that would best accompany each food or dish you allowed past your lips. You might match a hearty beef stew, for instance, with Châteauneuf-du-Pape because it too is made up of a maceration of different flavour components. If the stew were to be served with carrots you might choose a wine that depended heavily on the Grenache grape, to complement the sweetness in that vegetable. And if the accompanying potatoes were little new ones, you might be swayed towards a Châteauneuf of recent vintage, while older baked potatoes would suggest a more mature example. See what I mean? You can let the business of matching solids and liquids get out of hand. In general terms, you *can* enjoy almost any wine with almost any food.

This is particularly true since, in practice, we tend to enjoy food and drink at discrete intervals. We rarely find ourselves with a mouth of food and wine mixed up together – only if we're feeling particularly greedy. What usually happens is that we consume what's in front of us, or rather we take a selection of the food on our plate and then, when we're feeling thirsty, a mouthful of wine. So long as what we've just eaten doesn't completely destroy our tasting faculties, we can enjoy almost any wine, whatever its character.

*Try to monitor what effect the food you eat has on the taste of the wine you're drinking. Compare the sensations given you by that first mouthful savoured before you tasted the food and the mouthful of wine immediately after your first eating session.*

*Take some wine that you don't value too highly – or preferably two of very different styles, one light-bodied white and one full-bodied red. Now try the wines before and after mouthfuls of the following, all high in different sorts of acidity:*

*lemon juice (citric);*
*vinegar (acetic);*
*natural yogurt (lactic).*

*Try to monitor how much each affects the flavour of the wine, making sure that you get all of your mouth well rinsed in each substance. Notice how much more acid the wine tastes after the vinegar, though less markedly so after the lemon juice and yogurt. Might this suggest a modification to your salad dressings when serving wine? Notice too that the lighter-bodied wine is more affected. Strong-flavoured, full-bodied wines don't seem to mind the acid distractions too much.*

*Now try the apple and cheese trick. See how different a wine tastes after each – especially a young wine, the sort that was most frequently bought and sold and therefore gave rise to the adage.*

*Next time you're eating artichoke or asparagus, try out this surprising theory about wine taken with them. Don't you find your mouth left with a distinctly un-winey flavour if you try to drink wine just after a mouthful of either vegetable?*

In Chapter 2 substances that distracted from the business of wine tasting were discussed, and there are a few specific foods that might be served at a meal which would make it more difficult for you to appreciate wine. This is not to say you should never again eat chocolate or mint sauce, simply that it is unwise to serve your guests a very special bottle of wine when at the same time asking them to rinse their mouths with such distracting flavours.

*Acids:* anything *very* high in acidity makes a fine wine a bit difficult to taste afterwards (though it can flatter a slightly tart wine). 'Buy on an apple and sell on cheese' is an old wine-trade adage, illustrating the flattering nature of cheese – it softens the palate and makes it ready for a gulp of wine – and the much less flattering effects of the acidity in apples on wine tasted immediately afterwards. Some acids seem kinder on wine than others. A squeeze of lemon juice isn't going to ruin a wine, but a vinaigrette too high in *vinaigre* is no fun for any wine – or for any palate for that matter.

*Artichoke:* globe artichokes have a strange taste that makes any wine taste metallic. It contains an odd compound, cynarin, that makes great wine wasted on the magnificent globe. It's got so much liquid in it that you probably won't want any lubrication anyway.

*Egg yolks are probably the least serious offenders in keeping you from wine-inspired pleasure. Nevertheless, try a glass of red wine with your next soft-boiled egg and notice how difficult it is to taste the wine properly.*

*Ditto chocolate. Can you really judge a mouthful of wine after one of Dairy Milk? Incidentally, few of these tricky foods impair your smelling or 'nosing' abilities. You can still get most of the flavour of the wine, but you can't judge aspects such as sweetness, acidity and tannin properly, for which the inside of your mouth needs to be in prime unsullied tasting condition.*

*Tea and kippers are made for each other. Prove it by trying them with wine instead of tea.*

*Bendicks Bittermints and After Eights are double-killers of wine, of course. Don't try them till you know you don't want any more wine though a very rich Port would probably get through the menthol and smear of cocoa butter.*

*With curries, chilled beer can be deliciously refreshing – but if you really want to drink grape rather than grain, try the full-bodied, dry, but rather spicy wines of Alsace. You'll probably want something refreshingly cool, but it'll need lots of body weight to stand up to the spice.*

*After trying any of the 'danger' foods above, neutralize your mouth with either bread or water and see how much better you can taste the wine afterwards. However, curries and mint are too aromatic and affect the nasal passages as well, so they need more than bread and*

*Asparagus:* almost the same applies as for globe artichokes.

*Egg yolk:* a soft yolk seems to coat the mouth and leaves your taste buds defenceless and dulled. But then how often do you have wine for breakfast?

*Chocolate:* very similar effect to soft yolks – again because of its texture. However, a lightly chocolate-flavoured mousse would not play havoc with your palate.

*Kippers:* they're very oily and salty. I suspect it's the oiliness that prevents you from properly savouring a wine, for much the same reason as egg yolks and chocolate are barred from the company of fine-for-wine foods. These and other very oily foods seem best countered with a very tannic wine.

*Mint:* just as peppermints are not the best preparation for a wine tasting, very minty puddings or salads and (especially) a mint sauce that combines mint with vinegar are pretty poor accompaniment to fine wine.

*Spices:* subtly spiced dishes can be lovely partners for fairly full-bodied wines, but a vindaloo, it must be admitted, is not great with wine. Your mouth is left stinging and in no shape to measure the acidity, sweetness, etc, of a wine. You can still 'nose' a wine, but even your nasal passages are likely to have been heated up by the curry spices.

There is a simple solution to the tricky problem of eating unsuitable food and enjoying wine at the same time. You can swiftly 'neutralize' your mouth after a mouthful of food by chewing something bland and absorbent such as bread, or

*water – they need time – before you'll be on good wine-tasting form
again.*

*Almost any wine shop has at least one Fino. Tio Pepe and La Ina
are unusually good, as can be La Guita Manzanilla, Tres Palmas
and San Patricio. All Finos should be drunk as soon as possible after
being bottled. Oddbins stocks particularly interesting Sherries.*

*All these red wines should be fine with fish, especially fish that is full
in flavour and robust in texture.*

*Almost any wine made by a version of 'macération carbonique' (and
therefore low in tannin) such as Beaujolais, many Côtes-du-
Rhône and juicy young Cabernets.*
*Red Loire wines: Bourgueil, St Nicolas de Bourgueil, Chinon,
Saumur-Champigny.*
*Most reds from Germany, Alsace or Austria.*
*South Tyrol (Alto Adige) reds.*
*Bardolino, Valpolicella, most light Italian Cabernets and some
Chiantis, Barbera.*
*Red Burgundy from early-maturing vintages.*
*Most red 'vins de pays' from the South of France, Coteaux du
Tricastin, Côtes de Ventoux, Côtes du Luberon.*
*Light 'clarete'-style Riojas in their youth.*
*Many New Zealand reds.*

*You could take equal enjoyment from any full-bodied white wine
with many meat dishes. Again, it's body that matters more than
colour.*

simply swilling round a rinsing mouthful of water. A mouthful of bread after a sharply dressed salad or artichoke soon scrubs the mouth clean and ready for a taste of delicious wine.

There is one type of wine that is particularly useful for 'difficult' foods because it is full bodied, clean, dry but forceful enough to stand up to almost any solid. The driest Sherries, Fino and Manzanilla, are widely under-rated, and indeed underpriced. Because they are very good at stimulating the appetite, they're excellent first-course wines and would go happily with any salady dish, eggs, lots of spicy things and even the dread artichokes and asparagus. Fino with chocolate is not advised, however. Try milk.

So heretically sceptical am I about the business of wine and food that I don't even accept the rule that constitutes most people's knowledge of wine as a subject: white wine with fish and red wine with meat. I suspect what gave rise to it was the fact that most fish cries out for a bit of acidity to bring out its flavour – lemon juice, capers and even vinegar are standard accompaniments to fish – and white wines are usually higher in acidity than reds. In fact, this is only marginal. There are lots of red wines high in acidity that are delicious with fish, especially with fish that is stronger flavoured and relatively firm such as salmon, salmon trout, turbot, John Dory, sea bass, halibut and brill.

It is true that tannin, in which some red wines are high, does not go happily with delicate flavours of any sort and tends to leave a sort of inky taste. But light-bodied, low-tannin, high-acid reds such as those cited here would be fine with most fish dishes, especially those with a fairly rich sauce. These are wines you could serve coolish too if you want refreshment.

Serving temperatures of wine make a difference to how they

**You can chill wine by putting it in
the deep freeze or ice box for
twenty minutes**

---

*T*HESE ARE *some tried and tested combinations of food and
wine that you might not ordinarily think of.*

Madeira with clear soup: *a dry Madeira – Sercial or Verdelho –
can be beautifully 'nutty' with a meat- or fish-based consommé or an
even richer soup.*

Foie gras and sweet wine: *sounds disgusting, doesn't it? In fact,
any rich livery mousse is delicious with an unctuous sweet wine (it
must be fairly full bodied, which rules out the Germans but not the
Loire), provided there's lots of acidity.*

Blue cheese and Sauternes: *another strange-sounding combination
that works very well, based on much the same principle of sweet and
salty as ripe melon and Parma ham.*

*Cheese and wine are commonly accepted as ideal partners, being
honoured to the extent of having a social function named after them.
We naturally enough tend to think that French cheese will be an ideal
match for French wine. But next time you have a ripe Camembert or
Brie in the house, try it with a mouthful of wine and just see how the
ammoniac quality in the cheeses wars with the flavour of the wine –
making it taste bitter too. This does not apply to soft fat French*

taste, as we have seen, but the temperature at which you serve food is important too. Bear in mind that you won't be able to taste anything if you scorch or freeze your mouth. I may sound like an officious nanny, but don't expect to go wine tasting after a piping hot soup. Ice-cold sorbets are none too good either, I'm afraid, for they have a numbing effect on the inside of your mouth. Best to wait till you've finished eating a sorbet or ice cream before attempting to taste wine, perhaps a very cold and not-too-grand sweet white such as Monbazil-lac, 'country Sauternes'.

Much more important than temperature is the question of 'weight'. Even though you can enjoy all sorts of different flavours interleaved – a mouthful of poached halibut followed by one of youthful Claret can be lovely – mixing different weights of food and wine is usually a waste of the 'lighter' one. An avocado mousse is likely to be overwhelmed by a wine as strong as a Hermitage or Barolo, just as a delicate Mosel would be overpowered by the richness of jugged hare. With a subtly flavoured food it makes sense to serve a wine that's not too full bodied. With very strongly flavoured food, you would be foolish to expect a delicate wine to give much more pleasure than would a glass of water. Examples of wines that are particularly light and full bodied are given on page 43. Foods that are very 'full' and rich include anything that is highly spiced – which takes in curries and most dishes inspired by the Orient – very rich foods such as well-hung game and strongly sauced meats; strong cheeses, especially blue ones; rich meat pâtés, foie gras, mousses and terrines; and smoked fish, unless tempered with lots of bland cream and/or egg white.

With these guidelines, you will doubtless be able to come up with some delicious and exciting combinations of food and wine. If it's a casual family meal, then your choice of wine may be dictated by which bottle happens to be open – in

*cheeses in their youth, nor to the rather neutral Cantal, but certainly to many strong-flavoured French 'fromages' – not to mention 'formaggi' such as Gorgonzola. England, so berated by most gastronomes, produces cheeses that are perfect partners for wine. Good farmhouse Cheddar is surely the most marvellous accompaniment to all but the most delicate wines. It is firm and offers no strong competition to the flavour of the wine, but still has its own character. Stilton is a bit more difficult. It can be so powerful, and so salty that, like Roquefort, it calls for something very sweet and strong. Port makes sense in the circumstance and proves that I'm not trying to be iconoclastic, merely sensible.*

*Always remember that, in matters of gastronomy, no matter how hard some people may aspire, there are no ultimate rules or arbiters. No one can point a finger at you and say, 'Thou hast sinned by serving me a Mâcon Blanc with Shepherd's Pie!' If you don't enjoy it, you've only yourself to blame, but your guests should be far too grateful that someone else is taking the trouble to give them a meal to criticize.*

which case you might well learn all sorts of interesting things about unusual combinations of food and wine.

If you are trying to plan a selection of wines for formal entertaining, however, or simply to maximize informal enjoyment, it's worth bearing in mind the basics of choosing an order for wines: dry before sweet, light before full and young before old. Remember that four or more of you are likely to open at least a couple of bottles. It can be great fun, and very instructive, to serve two wines at the same time. This has the disadvantage of extra washing up, and possible accusations of pretension, but everyone will be surprised by how different two wines can seem when tasted together.

You can always take your lead for choice of wine from what's being cooked. With pasta you have a cast-iron excuse for an inexpensive Italian, or a better quality Chianti Classico Riserva. *Saucisson* suggests Beaujolais. Moussaka or kebabs allow you to introduce your friends to some of the better Greek wines such as Castel Danielis or Château Carras. None of these are expensive. And if you do feel duty bound, honour bound or perhaps promotion bound (when entertaining the boss) to spend a bit of money on wines for a special dinner, make sure you don't lash out on a wine that's not yet ready to drink. Trust in your nearest 'serious' wine merchant. You can judge how serious they are by the length of their replies to your questions, and they'll be delighted to advise on something more exciting than the price of the cheapest quarter-bottle of Scotch.

# Glossary

## Some useful words for wine tasters

I WOULD not call this the definitive wine taster's vocabulary, for such a thing does not exist. The descriptive terms included here are just some of the words you'll find helpful to describe sensations caused by wine in *you*. Some, indeed most, of these words are quite commonly accepted. Others (marked*) are, quite frankly, humble but mine own. 'Blackcurrants' is, for instance, a far-from-unusual description of the Cabernet Sauvignon aroma, but I haven't heard anyone else call the ripe Chenin Blanc of the middle Loire 'gummy'.

Evolve your own vocabulary if it helps you, though a wide range of possible terms has been included here in the hope that specific flavours may lead you to specific grape varieties. Also included are some of the wine world's most abstruse bits of jargon, just so you can hold your own in vinous conversation.

**acetic** a wine gone *vinegary* by overexposure to air.
**acid** a wine described as 'acid' will have too much acidity.
**acidity** vital component in wine that gives 'bite' and life.
**appellation** name of the (usually French) wine. *Appellation contrôlée* wines are France's top ones, representing about 25 per cent of her production and usually named after the place they were made.

**appley** some young Chardonnays smell like this, though the smell of unripe apples signals an excess of malic acidity.

**aroma** that part of the smell of a wine that comes straight from the grapes (cf. *bouquet*).

**aromatic** very strongly perfumed, e.g. Sauvignon and Riesling grape varieties.

**astringent** the tactile sensation that an excess of tannin leaves on the insides of the mouth. Used especially for white wines (see *tannic*).

**attenuated** smart-sounding term for a wine that is drying out, i.e. losing fruit and charm because of age.

**aura★** my own word for the 'personal bouquet' surrounding the bodies of each of us.

**baked** a smell of heat and, usually, high alcohol. The flavour is often, but not necessarily, cooked out. Very hot grapes.

**balance** vital relative measuring of different elements in a wine, especially sweetness, *acidity*, fruit, tannin and alcohol. Any good mature wine should be well balanced, though a youthful one may still be 'out of balance'.

**beefy★** lots of body and quite a bit of tannin.

**berries★** warm berries is the giveaway smell of Zinfandel.

**blackcurrants** aroma of Cabernet Sauvignon, called *cassis* in French. The related Sauvignon Blanc can smell of blackcurrant leaves.

**blowsy** a wine that has a lot of flavour at first, especially on the nose, but has no *length* and few indications (tannin if red and acid if white) that it will keep. Almost too much *fruit*.

**body** the measure of a wine's *weight*, a mixture of sugar, alcohol and extract.

**boiled beetroot** some people smell this on Pinot Noir.

**botrytis cinerea** a sort of rot that attacks grapes, shrivelling them and – if they're sweet and white – concentrating their lusciousness to good, and sometimes wonderful,

effect. Red wines lose colour and are ruined if attacked by this mould, variously known as *noble rot*, *pourriture noble* and *Edelfäule*.

**bouquet** the smell in a wine that derives from its fermentation and, most importantly, maturation (cf. *aroma*).

**burnt rubber**★ smell I associate with the Syrah grape.

**breathe** (v.i.) what a wine's supposed to do if you leave the bottle open for a bit before serving. This practice at least gives time for off-flavours to dissipate.

**buttery** the sort of richness (and colour) acquired by mature Chardonnay, traditionally associated with Meursault.

**cachous**★ I find something of the scent of these pastilles on very aromatic grape varieties such as Gewürztraminer and Morio Muskat.

**carbonic maceration** way of making red wine by fermenting the uncrushed grapes. Tends to make full-flavoured, deep-coloured, low-tannin wines.

**cardboard**★ my smell of stale materials that comes from poor treatment, often over-used filter pads.

**cats' pee** there's something of this in both Sauvignon Blanc and the intensely aromatic Scheurebe.

**cedarwood** traditional smell of a Claret given rigorous oak maturation; special characteristic of St Julien.

**chaptalization** commonplace (especially in France) practice of adding sugar to grape must in order to make the resultant wine stronger (though not sweeter).

**château** literally 'castle', but often the name for much less grand wine properties, especially in Bordeaux.

**chewy** very *astringent*.

**chocolatey**★ a flavour I find in the often rather sweet reds of Australia and especially South Africa.

**cigar box** synonymous with *cedarwood*.

**cigars** some tasters smell cigars on Sémillon.

**Claret** what we British call the red wines of Bordeaux, often labelled Château Something.

**classed growth** one of the sixty or so châteaux arranged in

1855 into the top five classes from the Médoc and Graves, or included in subsequent classifications of Bordeaux properties. *Cru classé* in French.

**clean** no off-flavours.

**clone** particular groups of vines produced from one cutting. Usually chosen in 'clonal selection', for one particular attribute such as high yield, disease resistance or even high quality.

**cloying** too sweet for the *acidity*.

**coarse** rough and ordinary without much interest.

**commune** French equivalent of a parish. Lots of wines are called after the commune in which they were made. A Gevrey-Chambertin is a commune wine, for instance.

**complex** lots of different well-married flavours that make a wine interesting, to the point of being fascinating.

**concentrated** lots of *fruit*, flavour and, often, colour too.

**corked/corky** wine with a definitely disgusting flavour, mouldy and rotten. Due to a poor cork usually, but even great tasting-gurus are not too clear about exactly how it happens. This is a flavour that's much more horrid than that of simple oxidation.

**crisp** a complimentary term for a white wine with refreshing *acidity*.

**cru** literally 'growth'. A *cru classé* is a classed growth, while a *grand cru* is a great growth.

**cuvaison** the extra period wine is left on the skins after fermentation to extract more from them.

**damp straw\*** my trigger expression for Chenin Blanc, though many others prefer *honey and flowers*.

**delicate** rather air-fairy term meaning light bodied and without very strong flavour, but well balanced.

**dumb** very little *nose*, common in youthful greats.

**Edelfäule** see *botrytis cinerea*.

**eucalyptus** cough linctus smell common in some concentrated California Cabernet Sauvignons.

**farmyard\*** smell I associate with Chianti, especially aged

Chianti, with some mature St Emilion and the odd
rustically made Châteauneuf-du-Pape.

**fermentation** the vital process of turning grape juice into
wine is the primary or alcoholic fermentation. The
secondary fermentation, encouraged in cellars far from
the Equator, is the malo-lactic fermentation that converts harsh malic acid into softer lactic acid.

**figs** another of those smells that other tasters associate with
Sémillon.

**finish** important part of a wine's impact on the senses. What
sort of impression it leaves at the end of the tasting
process. A wine with a poor finish fades away to
nothingness, and has no *length*.

**firm** not *flabby*, i.e. with sufficient *acidity*, and not in danger
of falling apart because of age or acetic danger.

**flabby** too low in *acidity*.

**flat** dull and boring flavour often without enough *acidity*, or
not sparkling if it's meant to be.

**flinty** confusing but oft-used term usually meaning *crisp* with
a certain suggestion of cold stones. Sauvignon Blancs
are often called 'flinty'.

**flowery** very fragrant in the way that flowers can be; floral
scents.

**forward** a wine is described as forward if it tastes more
mature than one would expect for its age.

**fresh** appealing because of its youth and *acidity*.

**fruit** very important component in the flavour of wines,
especially young ones, deriving from the grapes themselves.

**fruitcake\*** how the Merlot grape, especially in St Emilion,
strikes me.

**fruity** wine with lots of appealing *fruit*.

**full bodied** wine with lots of *body* as opposed to one that is
medium bodied or *light*.

**gamey** wines that smell pungent in a ripe animal sense, such
as a rich **Syrah** and **Merlot** (especially **Pomerol**).

**geraniums** unpleasant chemical smell, often associated with too much sorbic acid additive.

**golden syrup★** smell I associate with rich sweet whites, especially those affected by *botrytis*, and particularly Rieslings.

**gooseberries** 'green' sort of smell associated with Sauvignon Blanc.

**governo** technique still used in parts of Italy, especially Chianti, to add the prickle of a second fermentation to young wines by the addition of dried grape must to the wine after first fermentation.

**grapey** wine that smells of grapes, usually a Muscat.

**green** young wine with too much *acidity*.

**gummy★** the richness that very ripe Chenin Blanc grapes can bring to a wine.

**gunshot★** smell of rich mature Merlot, especially Pomerol. (Just one step ahead of *gamey*, after all.)

**hard** wine with too much tannin.

**harmonious** well balanced.

**heavy** too much alcohol and too little *acidity* for the fruit and sugar levels. According to EEC rules, heavy wines are those with an alcohol content of more than 15° (i.e. Sherry, Port and other fortified wines), as opposed to *light* wines.

**herbaceous** smell of grass and weeds, often found in the Cabernet family wines, especially Cabernet Franc.

**herby★** smell of thyme, lavender and pine sometimes found (perhaps fancifully) in the Grenache wines of Provence and the Midi.

**hock** German wines grown on the (sometimes outlying) banks of the Rhine. Wines from such regions come in tallish brown bottles as opposed to the green-bottled Mosel wines.

**hollow** wine with quite a bit of alcohol, but not much fruit to give a satisfying flavour and *weight* once in the mouth.

**honey (and flowers)** traditionally evocative tasting note for

Chenin Blanc Loire wines and also for some German Reislings.

**inky** red wine that tastes metallic, acid and often rather thin.

**juicyfruit★** luscious gulpable fruitiness, characteristic of Beaujolais.

**lanolin** rich, almost lemony flavour and texture taken on by good quality Sauternes.

**length** of flavour, a giveaway of quality in a wine. Any well-made wine that has had time to mature should leave a long aftertaste once it's been swallowed or expectorated. Such a wine 'finishes well'.

**light** the opposite of *full bodied* and not a pejorative term for wines that are meant to be delicate, such as many dry whites and some reds destined for youthful consumption. A light wine is also, by EEC definition, what we used to call table wine, i.e. one that has less than 15° alcohol and is meant to be drunk with a meal, as opposed to the *heavy* wines Sherry, Port, Vermouth, etc.

**liquorice** some people smell this in mature Nebbiolo.

**lively** a wine that seems bursting with *fruit* and flavour; often due to a very slight 'prickle' of carbon dioxide in the wine, which may for this reason be left intentionally by its maker.

**long** a wine with good *length*, or a good *finish*, is long.

**macération carbonique** French for *carbonic maceration*.

**maderized** sometimes used instead of *oxidized* for a white wine, especially when it's meant without malice – e.g. for a fortified wine such as Madeira (from which the name derives) or for a very old wine that is still interesting despite slight oxidation.

**maturity** that period in a wine's development after its youth and before it starts to decline. It can be after three years or after three decades, depending on the wine. 'Mature' is a complimentary term, as opposed to 'old' or 'faded', which are criticisms.

**meaty** substantial and *full bodied* in flavour, often just as the tannin is starting to reveal the *fruit*.

**mercaptan** substance formed by hydrogen sulphide ($H_2S$) that smells like rotten eggs. A fault, and one Australians are very keen on.

**minerally★** smell of assorted minerals, one that I find suggests volcanic deposits and associate with the Hunter Valley in New South Wales.

**minty** many people smell this spearmint (not peppermint) flavour in California Cabernets, especially those from the Napa Valley.

**Mosel** German wine in tallish green bottles, produced in the valley of the Mosel (Moselle in France).

**mousey** nasty smell associated with bacteriological fault in wine.

**mulberries★** smell (and colour) I associate with Syrah.

**must** grape pulp mixture that ferments into wine.

**noble** adjective used to describe those grape varieties that are most respected and which can produce wines that mature to magnificence. Cabernet Sauvignon, Merlot, Pinot Noir, Syrah, Nebbiolo, Chardonnay, Riesling and Sémillon are the most obvious candidates, but almost all of the grape varieties mentioned in this book apart from Aramon, Carignan, Laski Riesling and Chasselas have some claim to nobility – and there are bottles that prove that even these have some blue blood.

**noble rot** see *botrytis cinerea*.

**nose** (v.t. and n.) the nose of a wine is its *bouquet* or *aroma*, depending on its state of *maturity*. It's the flavour you can smell. You nose a wine when you consciously smell it.

**oaky** a complimentary term meaning that you can smell some attractive wood-derived flavour in the wine (c.f. *woody*)

**oxidized** wine that has been exposed to air for too long and has become stale and flat. A criticism of any table, sorry *light*, wine.

**peachy\*** self-explanatory smell I associate with Viognier.

**pear drops** rather chemical smell reminiscent of acetate or nail-polish remover, sometimes found in youthful Beaujolais.

**pencil shavings\*** the smell (of the wood not the lead) I find in Cabernet Franc.

**perfumed** wine with lots of smellable flavour, usually of a slightly musky sort. A white wine adjective.

**perlant** very slightly sparkling, even less so than a wine that is *petillant*.

**petillant** slightly sparkling, same as *spritz(ig)*.

**petit château** wine from a single Bordeaux property that is not officially classified, i.e. not a *cru classé*.

**petrol** flavour of mature Riesling, especially German.

**plummy** rich fruitiness particularly associated with mature Merlot.

**pourriture noble** French for *botrytis cinerea*.

**powerful** lots of very easy-to-perceive flavour, plus alcohol.

**pricked** same as *acetic*.

**prickle** slight sparkle, same as *spritz(ig)*.

**racy** lively, used often for white wine, especially Riesling.

**raspberries** characteristic scent of the Pinot Noir. Some find that Zinfandel smells of raspberries too.

**residual sweetness** amount of sweetness left in the wine after fermentation has been completed.

**rich** luscious and *full bodied*, though not necessarily very sweet. A rich red wine may taste slightly sweet (not a word often used to describe reds) but probably because of its alcohol content.

**rotten eggs** smell of *mercaptan* or hydrogen sulphide ($H_2S$).

**short** wine with no *length* of flavour.

**smoky** characteristic of the Chardonnay grape; a broad sort of flavour.

**soft** wine with too little tannin. So applicable to red wine only.

**soupy** wine with no distinct flavour, usually low in *acidity* and quite *full bodied*. Old-style Burgundies shipped to Britain were often soupy.

**sparkling** in Europe, where the lawyers of Champagne have influence, all wine that fizzes, but is not made in the Champagne region, is called sparkling wine.

**spicy** Gewürztraminer has an exotic floral sort of spice, while some red grapes, notably Merlot, have a fruity sort.

**spritz(ig)** wines that are slightly sparkling.

**steely** rather loose term used chiefly for whites such as Sauvignon and very cool-climate Chardonnays, meaning they have lots of *acidity* and a very pure flavour.

**still** not sparkling.

**sulphury** wines that have an excess of the much-used disinfectant sulphur dioxide ($SO_2$) may smell of recently struck matches or coke-fired ovens. The smell can be dissipated by swirling the offending wine around the glass.

**supple** wine without too much tannin and lots of attractive *fruit*, usually used of fairly youthful reds in which one might not expect such a quality, e.g. *Clarets*.

**sweaty saddle** famous Australian tasting term, probably what I call *minerally*.

**sweet** self-explanatory, but rarely used for red wines.

**tannic** wine containing lots of *tannin*

**tannin** preservative that comes from the skins, stalks and pips of grapes (and from wood too) and tastes like cold stewed tea.

**tar** some people smell this on Nebbiolo wines, others on Syrah. Both grapes have a depth of colour that helps the auto-suggestion along.

**tart** wine with too much youthful *acidity*. A pejorative term similar to *green*.

**thin** wine lacking *body*, to the extent of being watery.

**tobacco\*** flavour I associate with Tempranillo (different from cigars and cigar boxes!).

**trigger word** expression used to trigger off a mental impression of a wine. If I smell Tempranillo, for instance, I say 'tobacco' to myself and can therefore identify it as such. Very useful for blind tasting, and for measuring samples against the acceptable norm.

**truffles** some tasters find this elusive scent in the Nebbiolo wines of Piedmont, great white truffle country.

**vanilla** self-explanatory flavour closely associated with American oak, in which almost all red Rioja and many California reds are matured.

**vapour** my term for the collection of *volatiles* a wine gives off to communicate its flavour to your olfactory receptors, and thence to the brain.

**varietal** varietal wine (American term) is named after the predominant grape variety from which it was made. This is in contrast to generic wines, named after a wine region and, supposedly, style. Thus there used to be in Britain, and still are in America and Australia, wines labelled Burgundy, Claret and even Sauterne (no *s* on the end) because they were made dimly in the reflection of the region's style.

**vegetal** wine smelling of assorted vegetative matter. Not quite reminiscent of the hedgerow, as *herbaceous*, but of the vegetable patch. Pinot Noir often has this flavour.

**velvety** description of texture, usually used for wines with lots of glycerine and not much *tannin*.

**vinegary** smelling *acetic*.

**violets** smell some associate with Nebbiolo, others with Pinot Noir.

**viscosity** ('stickiness') golden syrup is very viscous, water not at all. A viscous wine is full bodied and leaves great trails down the side of the glass after it has been swirled about. Viscosity is a sign of *body*.

**vitis vinifera** the family of vines that are specifically designed for bearing wine grapes, as opposed to wild vines.

**volatile** something that's volatile vaporizes easily and gives off lots of volatiles that comprise what I've called a wine's *vapour*, which conveys the flavour of a wine to the olfactory receptors. All wines are volatile to a greater or lesser extent. The warmer they are and the more aromatic the grape varieties from which they were made, the more volatile they will be. A wine is described as volatile if it is in fact too volatile, i.e. it is giving off flavour so readily that it is starting to taste *acetic*.

**volatile acidity** ('VA') acescence, or the quality of being *acetic*.

**weedy\*** a combination of herbaceous and tart.

**weight** all wines have one and, just as for people, it's a measure of how much *body* they have.

**woody** the unacceptable face of oak: a nasty, wet, mouldy sort of flavour that comes (but not often) from a cask in poor condition.

**yeasty** smell of fermenting yeasts.

**yield** the amount of wine produced per area of vines. The French measure it in hectolitres per hectare and call it *rendement*. Thirty is low and one hundred high.

## Acknowledgements

A S ANYONE writing on the subject would, I owe a great deal to Michael Broadbent's *Wine Tasting* (Christie's and Mitchell Beazley); also to all my generous friends in the wine trade; to Edmund Penning-Rowsell and to Dr John Piggott.

# Index

## APOLLO

*Bosnian Chronicle* | Ivo Andrić

*South Wind* | Norman Douglas

*Now in November* | Josephine Johnson

*A Jest of God* | Margaret Laurence

*The Stone Angel* | Margaret Laurence

*The Lost Europeans* | Emanuel Litvinoff

*The Case of Charles Dexter Ward* | H.P. Lovecraft

*Company K* | William March

*The Nebuly Coat* | John Meade Falkner

*The Authentic Death of Hendry Jones* | Charles Neider

*The Hungry Grass* | Richard Power

*The Man on a Donkey* | H.F.M. Prescott

*The History of a Town* | M.E. Saltykov-Shchedrin

*The Day of Judgment* | Salvatore Satta

*The Council of Egypt* | Leonardo Sciascia

*My Son, My Son* | Howard Spring

*The Man Who Loved Children* | Christina Stead

*Delta Wedding* | Eudora Welty

*Heaven's My Destination* | Thornton Wilder

# The Ice Saints

*Frank Tuohy*

APOLLO

Apollo Librarian | Michael Schmidt  || Series Editor | Neil Belton
Text Design | Lindsay Nash || Artwork | Jessie Price

www.apollo-classics.com | www.headofzeus.com

First published in 1964.

This paperback edition published in the United Kingdom in 2017
by Apollo, an imprint of Head of Zeus Ltd

1 3 5 7 9 10 8 6 4 2

A CIP catalogue record for this book is available
from the British Library.

ISBN   (PB) 9781784978235
        (E) 9781784978228

Typeset by Adrian McLaughlin
Printed and bound in Denmark by Nørhaven

Head of Zeus Ltd
First Floor East
5–8 Hardwick Street
London EC1R 4RG

To my mother

## Introduction

> 'Today was one of the chill weeping days in the early part
> of May, the days of the Ice Saints, St Pancras, St Servace
> and St Boniface, whose arrival affords a reminder that all
> is by no means well with the year. If you had confidence in
> the Spring, your trust was misplaced; it will let you down.'

Poland in about 1960, the site of Frank Tuohy's novel,
was precisely a country where green shoots of hope had
been blackened by the unexpected return of frost. In 1956,
after enduring years of Stalinist terror, the Poles – or more
accurately, a rebellious faction within the Communist Party
– had defied a threat of Soviet invasion and thrown off direct
control by Moscow. This 'Polish October' led into a brief,
ecstatic period in which censorship was lifted, the secret
police (or some of them) were disbanded, and travel to and
from the Western world became easier. Left-wingers across
the world hoped that other Communist parties would now
take 'the Polish Road to Socialism', combining an enlightened
Marxism with democratic freedoms.

But 'confidence in the Spring' was misplaced. The late fifties was the time when I first got to know Poland and when Frank Tuohy arrived from Britain as a lecturer at the Jagiellonian University in Kraków. By then, the Ice Saints were hard at work. Censorship had returned, the brilliant liberalizers in the Party had lost their jobs and the secret policemen – once reduced to private-enterprise blackmail in hotel bars for a living – were back with their files and microphones. The Party, under Władysław Gomułka, was firmly in control again.

And yet the afterglow of 'the October' remained. Poles could now talk to Western foreigners without fear of arrest. The arts (film and theatre especially) were still bold and defiant and the press could still be critical of Soviet and Polish policies – up to a point. The Catholic Church was given back its privileges. Some attempt was made to redirect the economy away from heavy industry towards the needs of ordinary people.

All this encouraged a minority to hope, to convince themselves that things really were continuing to get better in spite of the 'Ice Saints' frost, that the best of 'the October' would reassert itself. I was one of those optimists. It took me at least another ten years to accept that Polish Communism was unreformable. Frank Tuohy never had such illusions. He seems to have held no strong political views. But he saw Poland through the eyes of an English liberal intellectual, and what he saw was a crushed society living in squalor and shortages, still traumatized by the wartime nightmares of Nazi and Soviet occupation, blocking off reality with fantasies of national self-pity, conditioned to suspect everyone as a potential informer. The fact that the Poland he encountered remained so much freer and livelier than it had been under the Stalinist tyranny did not impress him. The residue of poverty, humiliation and fear was bad enough.

And yet this novel shows that Tuohy was fascinated by the irrepressible vigour, the terrific cultural bumptiousness of the Polish spirit. He contrasts it here to the English upper class of the 1950s, presented in cruelly observed detail as arrogant, effete and hypocritical. *The Ice Saints* begins in the drawing room of the British Embassy in Warsaw, where two strains of snobbery are competing. The Ambassador's frightful wife ('Nanny's such a fearful fascist reactionary…') is flirting over vodka with Adam Karpinski, a handsome Polish intellectual who at once treasures the privilege of being a regular Embassy guest, and gleefully hoards the absurdities of English behaviour. Adam is himself a stack of ambiguous loyalties. He is well in with the remnants of the aristocracy; he is passionately patriotic and wittily contemptuous of the Communist regime. And yet – as the novel will reveal – he is brutally ambitious, and he is paying for his access to the Embassy in the almost inevitable way: by an arrangement with the secret police.

This is a story about two sets of blighted hope. Rose Nicholson arrives in Poland to stay with her older sister Janet, who married a Polish soldier in wartime and now lives in a grim provincial town with their son Tadeusz. Witek, the husband, comes from a poor background and is desperate to become the head of the English department at the town's university. Suppressing doubts, he has joined the Party in order to further his career. The real purpose of Rose's visit is to break the news that Tadeusz, a teenager, has been left a large sum of money by an aunt in England. Rose has no conception of what impact this may have in Poland. One way of reading this novel is to see it as a tale about the way that a sum of money – not a pile of cash, but a shape-shifting Golem of ever-changing implications – can destroy, confuse and obliterate as often as it enriches. It's an insight which seems to have faded out of British literature towards the end of the twentieth century, as the possession of sudden money came to be associated only, and crudely, with greed and celebrity.

But this was 1950s Poland. The holding of unreported hard currency was a crime. Transferred foreign money would be confiscated by compulsory exchange into useless zloties at an absurdly low rate. Or it could be used at Pewex hard currency shops to buy unobtainable luxuries like Nescafé, Dutch tobacco, American chocolate or the bottle of Paris perfume which could persuade that woman in the housing office to put your name higher on the waiting list for a flat. It could even purchase a small car. On the other hand, sudden wealth could be toxic. Families could turn resentful and grasping; neighbours would grow envious and suspicious. Rose and Janet, the two English sisters, try to keep the news from Witek, but when he finds out he is panic-stricken. The Party will accuse him of illegal currency hoarding; he will lose all hopes of promotion and even his present job:'You ruin my poor life'.

Rose believes that she can rescue her nephew Tadeusz from 'this appalling place', and give him a proper life in England. Witek insists that things are getting better, tries not to see the corruption around him, and trusts that his Party loyalty will be rewarded. Both will be humiliated, as both are brought to admit that their hopes are delusions. Frank Tuohy's novel, first published in 1964, belongs to a grey mood in English fiction, as an 'only connect' literature of optimism about personal relationships darkened to a more 'French' perception: that individuals were impenetrably isolated from one another. On the last page, after the departing Rose has failed to connect with her sister, her nephew, her brother-in-law and a treacherous Polish lover, she leaves 'a whole landscape waiting for explanation'.

And yet *The Ice Saints* does explain Polish landscapes, geographical and personal, with harsh accuracy. Now that Kraków is a sparkling tourist honeypot, it's hard but healthy to remember Tuohy's comfortless, stranded old city where cobwebby princesses clung to ancient snobberies and martyrologies. 'We are just survivors, by mistake. Our neighbours always wanted to destroy us and next time they will do it properly.' But with this self pity went wild high spirits, an underlying resilience. In a wonderful account of intellectuals at a party in Kraków, Tuohy remarks how these elderly figures 'did their best to involve themselves at every opportunity with the arguments of the age ... Because of this, though their lives were extremely hard, they were never bored.'

There has been no shortage of books – memoirs and fiction – about the brutality and unreason of life in Communist Europe. *The Ice Saints*, in contrast, is something different, rare and valuable: an outsider's take on the compromises with power undertaken by decent people – some skilfully managed, some disgraceful or tragic. Current Polish governments affect to believe that Communist Poland was a binary thing: either you were a stainless Catholic patriot or you were a corrupt tool of the 'foreign Bolshevik creed of hate'. Frank Tuohy knew better, which is one reason why this novel has become once more important.

Tuohy spent most of his life abroad, a British Council lecturer in English who lived in Brazil, Finland, Argentina, Portugal and Japan, as well as in Poland. He died in 1999, an aloof man who wrote much less than his admirers hoped for. *The Ice Saints* was not his first fiction. But it produced a critical sensation when it appeared in 1964; Tuohy was briefly 'discovered' as one of the most talented English writers. And yet, although it won the James Tait Black best-novel prize that year, this was the last novel that he completed, and in recent decades it has been almost completely forgotten. In part, this must be because the East European world it describes vanished so rapidly and completely after the democratic upheavals of 1989. But it is also because the way he wrote fell out of fashion.

Tuohy wrote to please himself. He had an extraordinary ear for class-inflected dialogue, a collector's eye for the small details of a person or a place, a rare sense of the music of words. All that can be found in *The Ice Saints*. But he pays little attention to the orthodoxies of a modern creative writing course. When he feels like halting the flow to discuss an ethical dilemma or to categorize somebody's motives, he does so. He changes narrator points of view and pops in and out of characters' heads with abandon. Neither does he tie up all loose ends: for example, a character called 'Mickey' is twice mentioned in this novel but the reader never discovers who he is. This is not poor editing. Tuohy means the reader to be too alert to the story to stop for an answer, to see these little puzzles out of the corner of an eye and follow on.

He elides information which another writer would feel obliged to offer – especially about sex. A reviewer of *The Ice Saints* once complained that a crucial seduction – central to the whole narrative – is simply skipped: we see Rose on the edge of it, and then glowing with love afterwards, but nothing in between. Again, Tuohy knows what he is doing. Admittedly, it's clear from his other fiction that he didn't care to write about sex, perhaps for personal reasons. Instead, he is asking the readers to use imagination, indicating elegantly how they might fill the gap he has left. And it works.

A Cold War novel? *The Ice Saints* is much more than that. It is a severe lesson in empathy, about the impact of well-meaning strangers on the 'unfortunates' they propose to rescue or relieve. Witek looks at Rose's clothes and belongings strewn about his flat, and sees that 'these extensions of Rose into the surrounding area were what made her remarkable. Here nobody's possessions had any personality any more, so that where you lived became no more informative than the mark of your head on the pillow'. *The Ice Saints* shows that Europe in those decades was divided not only by wire and walls but by a historic failure of imagination.

*Neal Ascherson, 2017*

Author's Note
For obvious reasons it is important to state that all the people
and incidents in this novel are imaginary.

*Chapter One*

The drawing-room was entirely English. The Office of Works had provided deep armchairs, a sofa you could have slept on, though of course nobody had ever done so, and a low glass-topped table. The only exotic things lay on this table: a bowl of arctic anemones, and three or four consecutive copies of *The Times* and the *Guardian* for a week in April, 1960. These had recently been torn from their postal wrappers and were still half-unrolled.

Between chintz curtains the windows looked out hopefully, as though on to herbaceous borders planted ready for the spring. But it was like being back-stage, where the scenery comes to an end. There was an iron fence topped with barbed wire, and a wall of yellow, unpointed brickwork, which was beginning to crumble away. The street was paved with stone and opposite stood a ruin, pockmarked by gunfire from long ago. At some distance were large grey buildings and over them a greyer sky.

The sky is enormous in those parts. Its huge arch covers the city and the great river and the flat sandy plain on which pinewoods and heath and infertile fields stretch out as far as the horizon. Patches of exactly the same landscape can be seen at intervals from Aldershot and Camberley, across Belgium and Pomerania and up to the Russian frontier. It is military country, beloved by the organizers of manoeuvres and battles. Its dry gullies are as convenient for firing squads as for lovers; its bracken and heather are more accustomed to mortar fire than to the minor conflagrations caused by picnickers, and its deadly fauna include the adder and the unexploded grenade.

Pine logs from these forests were crackling in the drawing-room fireplace and a young woman was standing in front of it, talking.

This young woman stood on the outsides of her feet with her hands clasped behind her, as though she were still obeying a forgotten governess's injunction to straighten her shoulders. She was ungainly, badly dressed and her voice was shrill and discordant, but she had a perfect skin and a rather beautiful face. She could only have been what she was, a confident member of the British ruling class.

'Thank God you've come, both of you, I must say. Because I'm here all alone until Mark comes back. He'll be late because of this girl, this friend of his sister's we're looking after. Do please sit down, Miss Er – Mark's gone to the airport to pick her up. Does that sound nasty, Adam? You speak English so much better than we all do. Does that sound nasty when I say Mark's gone to the airport to pick her up?'

'Alexandra, it sounds wonderful when you are saying it.'

'Hum!'

She had asked for the clumsy compliment, yet seemed bored by it.

The man who had spoken was over middle size; he had black curly hair, a square face, with a nose which curved up like a saddle. When he smiled he showed a steel tooth, and sometimes his pale eyes gave the false impression that he wore contact lenses.

'Look, do come nearer the fire, Miss Er—'

'Handisyde.'

'What are you going to drink?'

'I'd just love a real Polish Vodka.'

'Adam will have a dry martini because he always does. Adam, give Miss Handisyde a real Polish Vodka, will you?' Alexandra returned to her stance in front of the hearth. 'How have you been getting on, I'm sure Adam has been filling your ears with all sorts of subversion.'

The guest, having got through a smoker's cough, bowed her short-cut, greying head as though she were beginning to recite: 'Well, this has really been a most wonderful experience. I don't think I've ever met people who seem so' – she gestured with rough hands – 'I can't express how much—'

Alexandra looked down at her cheerfully. 'I know. I'm just like that. But I'm sure you'll find it's quite all right the moment you get back home. Look at me. When I'm here I can hardly think of anything to say at all, but the moment we got to London at Christmas the whole thing became absolutely and completely clear to me. I mean, I simply felt I was a one-girl bureau, don't you know, of Iron Curtain affairs. Of course

I do speak the language much better than Mark does, and that does help.'

'For instance, we spent some time this morning with a really interesting man. I'm afraid I don't quite remember his name. Adam darling, what was that man's name again?'

Adam Karpinski was standing between the women, watching them with attention and wonder, as if they had been two fireworks, two set-pieces, which he had managed to set off in conjunction. Neither, he thought as his gaze moved from one to the other, could have fulfilled the exotic roles he had given them with more perfect timing and intonation. Only his glee at this must be always unshared, because there were few people around who spoke and appreciated English as well as he did.

'Which man do you mean, Margaret?'

'The man at that place we went to this morning. With those column things. They weren't columns really,' she said to Alexandra.

'I'm sure they weren't.'

'What was that place called, Adam?'

'Which place, Margaret?'

'Oh, it doesn't matter really. But it was fascinating, I was most impressed. I intend in my report to emphasize most, most – You can't believe it, when you think.'

'Oh, I can.'

A car drew up in the street outside.

'That must be Mark. I wonder if he found Rose. Rose is this girl. Please be nice to her, Adam. There was something quite interesting I wanted to tell you about her, only unfortunately there hasn't been time.'

'I'll be very nice to her, Alexandra.'

'Of course she may be awful.' Alexandra was silent and a lost, crazy look came over her face as though stumbling, hurrying on, she had reached a part of the forest she had never expected to see. 'I've never met her. Of course, she may be quite awful.'

Mark Tatham came in, a little disarranged, pushing a handkerchief up his sleeve.

'Washing her hands. Plane was late.'

He immediately went over to Miss Handisyde, and began the effort of engaging her in conversation.

Bringing him a drink, Alexandra interrupted: 'Does she want to stay the night? Because if so, Simon has been sleeping in the spare bedroom and I'll have to tell Nanny.'

When Tatham looked up, his long white face was lined with strain and tiredness. 'No. She's going to Biala Gora on this evening's plane. Apparently they are expecting her.'

'Poor girl, I must say. Why is she going to Biala Gora?'

'Don't speak against that place, Alexandra. I may be deserting you all to go there one day soon.'

'Oh, Adam, no. What will we all do without you?'

Alexandra stood in her old place on the hearthrug but now with her legs crossed and the outsides of her feet laid together. Her colour was high, her eyes bright and fearsome.

'Have I been there, Adam?' Miss Handisyde asked.

'No, Margaret.'

'I seem to have been just about everywhere. As I say it's been the most fascinating – I must say the spirit of the people, that's what I find amazing. I'm going to put all that in my report when I get back. They may have political problems but they've got spirit.' She stared at her empty glass. 'That sounds rather funny, doesn't it?'

Alexandra snatched the glass from her. Karpinski followed across the room.

'My dear, it's simply all the time,' he whispered. 'We buy only the best Wodka Wyborowa, with real pounds and dollars, at the Grand Hotel kiosk every morning. And furthermore she keeps wanting to S-L-E-E-P with me.'

This joke about the spelling out of simple words he had been amused to adopt from Alexandra herself: she had inherited it from a nurseryful of sisters, the daughters of a pre-war Conservative minister.

'Adam, no! How ghastly.'

'What was it you were going to tell me about this girl?'

'It's just that—' she broke off. 'Here she is.'

*Chapter Two*

'Miss Handisyde, this is Rose Nicholson. Mr Karpinski. This is Elizabeth's friend. Darling, do give Rose
something to drink. Rose, are you quite certain you can't stay,
I mean it's so simple, really, Simon can have Nanny's bedroom, Nanny'll be quite glad to go into the night nursery and
we can move Juliet's cot out into the—'

Alexandra tried to present this girl, who was extremely
pretty, as just somebody else that she and Mark were obliged to
deal with. The girl, however, seemed unwilling to be managed.

'No. I have already booked my place on the aeroplane.'

Alexandra's voice trailed irritably away. There was a small
silence while they all watched Rose. The world outside was
still with her. How long, they were thinking, would she keep
that slightly abstracted look of self-assurance? Miss Handisyde was quite forgotten. Adam Karpinski moved slowly
across the room towards Rose.

'Alexandra tells me that you are travelling to Biala Gora.'

'Yes. My sister is married to someone at the University there.'

Karpinski looked puzzled. 'I have heard that there is an
Englishman. But I did not think he was a married man.'

'But he's a Pole. My brother-in-law is, I mean.'

Karpinski emitted the three humming notes by which his countrymen express dubiety and surprise. 'I see. And she has been there a long time?'

'Ten years. No, twelve. Janet is older than me.'

'Obviously, if I may say so. I wonder, is she happy there?'

'Well, perhaps not at first. But everything is much better now, isn't it?'

'Some people try to think so.'

Rose dismissed any attempt to discourage her. 'I'm looking forward to getting to Biala Gora.'

Alexandra came up and said something like 'Biawa'. 'Did I do it right, Adam?'

'Alexandra's dark "l"s are always very nicely formed.'

Alexandra took Rose's arm and led her into the dining-room.

'Rose, how I wish I was you. She's going off to the real world where we've never even been. We just see all the same people at all the parties here. Rose, I wish I was you, I do really.'

Karpinski said: 'And do you imagine that you could see how people in fact live? The moment you go to their flats they would bring out the food they have bought on the Black Market and the Nescafé from the Komis shop and they are wearing the clothes their cousin sends them from America.'

'Adam, you are so depressing. Why does Adam always have to be so depressing?'

During luncheon Rose was so placed that she could not

help watching the short-haired elderly Englishwoman opposite her. After a few more incoherences, Miss Handisyde
gave up all attempts at conversation; her head bowed, her
hand fell dead-heavy on the table, upsetting her empty glass
which rolled on to its side.

The new-comer had no idea of the importance of all this
to any of the others but soon she noticed signs of a jubilant
conspiracy between Adam Karpinski and Alexandra, who
was blinking and shaking with almost imperceptible giggles.

She turned to Mark. His sister Elizabeth was one of her best
friends but she had not seen him since his marriage; there
was an altered stateliness about his bearing, as though one
might hope for kindness but not humour from him. Now
Mark winked at her gently and after a little he too began to
tremble with laughter. The rest of the meal went as a sort of
wild burlesque in which every conventional remark bubbled
with hysteria. Adam Karpinski kept nudging Rose and mop-
ping his eyes.

Finally Alexandra helped Miss Handisyde out of the room,
and after a moment Karpinski followed them.

Still laughing, Mark said: 'I'm awfully sorry about all this,
Rose.'

'Who on earth is she?'

'I don't know. A progressive journalist. One of these people
who get wished on to one.'

'Is she always like this, I wonder?'

'Perhaps not. Odd things happen to people when they
arrive here. Either they hole up in the Grand or the Bristol,

complaining of tummy-aches and demanding to see the Embassy doctor – who isn't, of course, allowed to see them. Or they find that vodka is the best way out.'

'But why?'

'Shock.'

'I haven't felt any. Ought I to?'

'Delayed. No, honestly I expect you've got enough to occupy your mind as it is.'

The girl looked relieved that the conversation had at length turned to the only thing she could talk about.

'Yes. I still don't know what I'm going to do. There's one or two things I must be sure of.'

'We'll do our best to help. The Embassy lawyer—' He stopped, seeing that Karpinski had returned to the room.

'Mark, I really do apologize most profoundly. I've seen this crisis approaching but the old girl was simply insisting on coming to luncheon here. Keeping in with the jolly old Embassy, you know. It is too very bad that it should happen in your house. Alexandra has most kindly offered to drive us back to the Grand Hotel.'

He picked up his wine glass and drained it off.

'Still, if she passes right out, it at least means I may have a rest this afternoon. And tomorrow morning, thank God, she is off to Prague.' He turned to Rose. 'I was thinking, is your brother-in-law perhaps called Witold Rudowski?'

'Yes, he is.'

'I see. Then perhaps we shall meet again. I am frequently in Biala Gora.'

'Oh good.' She sounded pleased. She liked him. With his vivid smiles and his air of tightly-packed energy, he was quite unlike the glum exiles one saw in South Kensington.

'That's rather strange, isn't it?' Rose asked Mark when the other had gone.

'Everybody knows everybody else in this country. The trouble starts when they don't know what everybody else is up to. Let's have some coffee.'

While Mark fetched a bottle of brandy and a couple of glasses Rose sat staring unhappily in front of her.

'Cheer up. Have some brandy.'

'Thank you. All the same I do hope I'm not going to get drunk or have tummy-aches.'

'Well, if you do, you need only come running back here. Alexandra would love to have you.'

There was a moment's pause between them, sufficiently protracted to throw some doubt on this.

'Thank you,' Rose said again. 'You see the trouble is I'm so frightened of breaking this news to Janet.'

'How long since you've seen her?'

'Two years. Of course none of this was in the air then. Aunt Louise was still alive, though we'd none of us set eyes on her for ages.' Rose cautiously sipped at her brandy. 'Janet came home when my father was dying and we were pretty much taken up with that.'

'Your sister doesn't know anything about it, then?'

'No. She thinks I'm just here for fun. She always spoke about not mentioning important things in letters. This *is* an important thing, isn't it? Somehow, now I'm actually here, it doesn't seem so terribly important after all.'

'You were quite right not to mention it. *They* would think it terribly important.'

'Why?'

'That's what we must ask the lawyer ultimately. Roughly something like this: legally any property, monies (I wonder why one always says monies) et cetera owned by a national abroad must be realized and transferred into local currency. I don't know which exchange rate it'd be at, but there wouldn't be much left.'

'I'm sure we don't want to do that.'

'Then you have to be careful who you talk to. You're breaking the law. Someone may object.'

'Who?'

'What about your sister's husband?'

He spoke with a hint of distaste. The Poles these English women married were always reprehensible, and to be admitted to the discussion as late as possible.

'Witek? Why should he object? I don't know. He came back here after the war when all his friends stayed in England, so we were always frightfully suspicious. And then they sent such cheerful letters, during the Stalin period. I liked him as far as I can remember. I was only a child.'

'He's doubtful, then?'

'I suppose so. Of course he may have changed.'

'You can't tell about people here. They'll protest any amount of pro-Western feeling but you can't expect them to do anything about it. Why should they? Their best hope is to go on with things as they are.'

Rose thought for a moment and said: 'Well, that simply doesn't apply to the Rudowski family any more. Everything is altered. Decisions have to be made. I suppose it's Janet who must make them.'

'Is she expecting this?'

'No, not at all. You see, my great-aunt thought women with money were a prey to fortune-hunters. She was only going to leave her money to men. We knew she meant to leave something to Nicholas. He was my brother. He was killed in the war.'

'So you're the herald angel?'

'I suppose so. I feel scared of the whole thing. The solicitors insisted I should come.'

'There wasn't any other way, Rose. You couldn't write letters. I'm sure you'll find the best solution in the end.'

'It's strange, with a thing like this. You feel grim but happy. Think, after all the Rudowskis have been through, to be saved by a bit of money.'

'How much?'

'The solicitors think it'll be almost fifteen thousand.'

'You don't know for certain?'

'Probate hasn't been given yet. But it'll be a lot to them. It would be to me.'

Mark smiled, hesitated and said: 'Rose, you possibly may find they don't consider it as important as you do. After all, money means such different things in different places.'

Rose remembered that Alexandra was very rich.

'Of course if it were changed into local currency its value would be only a third; £5,000 can't be a lot, even here.'

'You'll have to see.' He stood up. 'Be careful who you tell, that's all. There's Alexandra back. We'd better leave for the airport quite soon.'

Alexandra came in, pulling off a round fur hat.

'We got her up in the lift and I left her being very sick. Adam spoke to the chambermaid and to the old horror in the navy sateen dress who sits at the end of each corridor and spies on you. She must have got a lot on old Handisyde, if all Adam says is true. Oh Rose, poor you, do sit down and tell us all about Elizabeth. How is she? You've been swigging brandy. Without me. Let me get a glass.'

'Rose and I must go to the airport almost at once.'

'Must you?'

'We've been talking about Rose's trip.'

'Have you, it's really too exciting, isn't it?'

'All the same, darling, I don't think anyone else should know about it, except us.'

Alexandra picked a dead flower out of the bowl of blue anemones. 'No, of course not. Though I can't imagine who'd be interested, can you?'

'They might.' Mark looked at his watch. 'Will you be needing the car, darling? Because I'll take Rose to the airport and then go back to the office. If you want it, come with us.'

Alexandra went on pulling out shrivelled flowers. 'The children and Nanny picked these, but they don't last. What's that? No, I don't need the car. Good-bye, Rose.'

## Chapter Three

Out of the small window with its doll's-house curtains, Rose noticed several hares loping away into the spring grass; they looked very large in the evening light, their shadows stretching out towards the runway. Then the aeroplane humped and jolted to a halt. The passengers, who included three priests in raincoats and cloth caps, at once stood up and began pushing towards the door. The smell of winter clothes and tobacco and people, the whole very tough smell of Eastern Europe, blotted out the inward rush of the evening air. However, when Rose stood for a moment at the top of the iron steps, she thought she could hear blackbirds singing.

The bus was already waiting. But first an assortment of objects had to be hauled out of the aeroplane and resettled beside the driver's seat: the usual newspapers and postbags; a keg of acid; a bale of fox skins; bundles of skis; a child's tricycle. When everything was ready they drove off through the ploughed fields towards Biala Gora.

On the pre-1914 maps it is called Weissberg. With some effort you could distinguish a nineteenth-century German city among the factories which were now pumping bland columns of smoke into the sky. You could see, among the new blocks of flats, large houses divided into tenements and falling into ruin; they stood in gardens where the trees had been damaged by shell-fire and the earth had long ago been stamped naked and hard. The old market-place, where the air-port bus stopped, had been blown up by the retreating armies; now, under a maze of scaffolding, it was being restored.

Rose and Tadeusz recognized each other immediately, for photographs had been exchanged at intervals. He was fifteen, with reddish hair and a narrow white face. He kissed her confidently on both cheeks.

'Hadn't we better take a taxi?'

'It is not necessary. I may carry your luggage.'

'I'm afraid it's very heavy.'

'That is nothing.' He gathered breath and said in a rush: 'Only last week, for instance, I was ski-ing in Tatry mountains. We made thirty-one kilometres with packs on our backs. We saw a bear.'

'How exciting.'

'Yes, it was very interesting. Most of the bears live now in Czechoslovakia. Mostly they are coming here only in sum-mertime.'

Rose's suitcases were put on the pavement. They were clean and expensive among the others of bursting cardboard. The boy picked them both up. She could see it was an effort for him but knew it would be no good asking him to give in.

'I expect they come for their holidays, like me.'

'Please?'

'The bears.'

The boy frowned, and before she could explain he had started off through the crowd, as though pulled forward by the momentum of the two swinging cases. Rose followed as best she could. Her shoes, though they had low tapered heels, were not good on the broken pavements. She was wearing a heavy-knit sweater and, since it was a mild evening, she soon began to feel hot, and uneasy at the stares of the people who passed them. She was shocked, too, at their difference from herself. Most were dressed in little more than rags, jumble-sale clothes. There was no effort, such as you might find in a southern country, to present a façade of prosperity to the world. Each seemed to show a face and figure which said: 'Look, this is me, smashed.' And her nephew, with his fierce unhealthy look, fitted easily into this background.

Once he stopped for a moment and jerked his head, without letting go of her cases. 'Over there is the Popular Comedy Theatre. They are playing *A Policeman Calls* by J. B. Priestley.'

'You mean *An Inspector Calls*.'

'Perhaps.'

He scowled and began walking again. After this, she was careful not to correct him about his knowledge of English things.

Near the market-place there had been two or three massive State department stores, and an occasional scribble of neon lighting. Now the city grew darker and dingier. Small shops crouched half-hidden under greyish-black buildings. The buildings which had stucco on them appeared to have been kicked systematically round the base of the walls, where they showed a surface of crumbling brick. Others were built only of brick, cracked and diminished by the weather.

'Look, please let's take a taxi. I've been travelling all day.'

'If you like we may take the tram.'

Thinking that Tadeusz was still worrying about Priestley's play, she dared not object. But even the tram-ride seemed to take longer than was conceivable. Everybody stared at Rose, who stood with her eyes downcast. She felt impossibly far from England, and even from the Tathams' house in the capital. Only to imagine Alexandra here would be absurd, and all Mark's considered advice seemed to refer to nothing at all. Rose's elation at her arrival had gone. Instead she quaked with nerves at the prospect of meeting her sister.

Janet, who was twelve years older than Rose, had trained as a nurse and met Witek in a war hospital. Their son Tadeusz was born in England but the Rudowskis had proudly bestowed on him a name that could not be anglicized. Janet, like many nurses, had always been unquestioningly kind to everyone, and her kindness had led her to this war-pocked city in Eastern Europe.

At thirty-six Janet had the thickened body of a woman in late middle age. She clung to Rose with hands that were like claws. Emotion welled up, originating from the separation, but due as much, in Rose's case, to physical exhaustion.

Very soon after, however, the staff nurse's briskness came out once more and Rose recognized it with affection. 'Witek has the front room all to himself now. His books are there, of course. You and I'll sleep in here.'

The room they were standing in had divans along two of the walls. There was a round table in the middle of the room, some potted plants, dog-eared American magazines; a shelf of Janet's favourite books from her childhood, and copies of Eckersley's *Brighter English,* Allen's *Living English Structure* and Jespersen's *Growth and Structure of the English Language.* The furniture had a poverty-engrained look like the furniture in very cheap lodgings.

'This is where I work, really, so you'll have to move out during the day. But I'm sure Witek won't mind you sitting in his room while he's at the University.'

'Where does Tadeusz go?'

'He's on a camp bed in the kitchen. He's fine there, frightfully tidy. He gets it from me. Well, now you know how we stand. There are some hangers for your clothes in the hallway. And I've cleared you out a couple of drawers. I packed the things into an old trunk, actually. Do you know, I've still got my school trunk, the one I had at Cheltenham. I don't know why I keep it really. It isn't as though I was ever likely to move anywhere any more. Is that all right, then?'

'I'm sorry, darling, I simply must go somewhere.'

'Oh dear, I've got out of the habit of asking. They never ask you here. The aunt is through the kitchen.'

The place was not clean, and squares of newspaper were pushed on to a nail. The printed language looked frightening, so utterly unknown.

Janet took such pride in her arrangements that you had to accept them without question. Rose remembered Mark Tatham's warnings about drink. I'll need about half a bottle, she thought, before I dare tell her that from now on, all this can come to an end.

The moment he had delivered Rose to the flat, Tadeusz stepped backwards and disappeared into the dusk. He and Witek were both absent for supper. Rose thought this was insufferably rude and it was almost too much for her waning self-confidence. While they drank tea and ate cold ham with very good bread and butter, Janet talked on.

'Do they all do their eyes like this now?'

'Like what?'

'You know – mascara. I saw it in those *Vogues* you send me but I thought it was only for models. I mean, I wasn't to know, living here, was I?' She seemed on the defensive as though everything that had happened was her own fault.

Rose noticed that Janet still held her knife like a fountain pen, the way nurses did, and remembered how her father used to tease her about it. Watching her while they ate, she was all at once overwhelmed by pity for Janet. She needed the attentions of their childhood, hot milk and biscuits, an early night. Could you get biscuits here or even milk? From Janet's conversation she gathered that the extent of one's deprivations was so enormous as to be only a subject for jokes. You could only suggest something for her to deny its possibility with a hard laugh. Rose was sure that this bitterness was something new, that it had not been there when Janet last came to England.

'I have to pay twenty zlotys duty on each of them.'

'On what?'

'The *Vogues*. But it's worth it. You see I give them to my dressmaker. She copies the patterns and she alters things or makes them up for me free, from time to time. You've got to be smart about things like that in this place, I can tell you.' She poured out more tea. 'Not much supper tonight, I'm afraid. You see I had my evening lessons earlier, to be free when you came. No time for shopping.'

'The ham was jolly good.'

Rose was miserable. Her father and she had comforted themselves for some years with the idea that Janet's stoical cheeriness made her life here somehow possible. Evidently this was not so. Rose tried to cheer herself by thinking that her own arrival had made Janet homesick – she had always surrendered easily to the simpler emotions – and this had turned her against her surroundings. Whatever was to happen to the Rudowskis now, Janet was too emotional to be permitted to have her own way. She had to be told, but it was Witek and of course Tadeusz who were the ones to decide.

## Chapter Four

When Witold Rudowski finally returned from England in 1948, it was proposed that he would head the new Department of English Philology at Biala Gora University. But the plan came to nothing. Next year two departments of English at other universities were closed and their staffs dismissed. Except in the capital, all teaching of English above the elementary level ceased. Witek instead received the post of arranging and conducting translation classes for the other departments at Biala Gora. His colleagues were mostly elderly ladies in destitution, who had once had English governesses or had been to convents in England. He found himself guiding young historians in translating from English translations of Marx and Lenin or from original texts by Howard Fast and Jack Lindsay.

During these years Janet and he lived by teaching privately and by doing translations for official publications. When more English was permitted in the secondary schools he quickly wrote a textbook which was accepted by the Ministry of Education. It was not a very satisfactory book and he realized its imperfections sooner than anyone. But this led him to a more detailed study of phonetics and intonation and idiomatic expressions. He was a man who, once he took something up, became easily obsessed by it and devoted himself to it to the exclusion of everything else. In spite of having a foreign wife, Rudowski survived the difficult years without danger, and although exhausted from overwork he conducted his course at the University with an efficiency which shone beside the amateurish efforts of his colleagues. He went to the political meetings and seminars which were numerous at that time, feeling that he ought to be interested, and survived them in a state of torpid inattention like a public schoolboy in chapel. As with so many hardworking people, he did not have quite enough time to bother about what was happening to his colleagues who failed to adapt to the régime.

When after 1956 a new proposal was made for a Chair of English at Biala Gora, Witek was the obvious choice of candidate. He alone had continued with English studies all the time. He was supported at the University by several influential people, including Dr Zwiersz, the representative of the Party. And he had good friends in the Ministry of Higher Education whom he was always visiting with plans for student exchanges or for holiday courses to be directed by himself, which they politely pigeon-holed.

Against him, however, was a faction which included Professor Markiewicz, the international lawyer and present Rector of the University, old Professor Barcik, of the Chair of Comparative Philology, and their supporters. Rudowski had done nothing which they considered to be a work of serious scholarship. His doctoral thesis, which he had put together hurriedly after his return to his native land, was an ill-constructed effort entitled 'H. G. Wells: Prophet of Revolution'. It had been accepted at Warsaw University but the professors here did not think much of Warsaw. Above all – this, though not consciously formulated by any of them, was always at the back of their minds – Rudowski had nothing of the *mana* which surrounds a professor.

In a society which now considered itself to be classless but which still paid respect to its intellectuals, this aspect of university life had increased in importance with the years. One elderly man might be surrounded by half a dozen assistants, former pupils, usually women, who typed his manuscripts, brought him mushrooms from the country and tried to keep on good terms with his wife. His influence would also be felt among his male disciples not only in Poland but in the Polish diaspora at universities in North and South America. How could you imagine Rudowski in a position like this? Choosing him for the Chair would in fact diminish themselves, the professors thought.

Witold Rudowski was short and square, and his hair and skin had the same pale almost colourless look. A true Silesian, he came from the border country near Biala Gora where there had always been a strong German influence. But traditional characteristics must have been dormant in him, because already Tadeusz looked like a nineteenth-century patriot on the barricades.

Witek kissed Rose affectionately and asked her about her journey.

'Tadeusz met you all right? He always gets everything wrong.'

'Oh perfectly. And I recognized him at once.'

'Would we have recognized you, I wonder? Your photograph does not do justice to you.'

'I photograph terribly badly.'

'I thought that last one was very good,' Janet said.

'You must excuse my not being present when you arrived. You see, I had a meeting of the lecturers at the University. In any case I thought the two sisters would like to have the evening to themselves.'

'But I expect we'll have lots of time together.'

'Darling, I must tell you I've got lessons nearly all tomorrow. Zosia cooks lunch for us at about two.'

'I'll be all right. Please, you mustn't worry about me.'

'Tomorrow, let me show you the buildings of our university. They are not very beautiful, in a bad German style, I think.'

'I don't know if Rose is interested.'

'Oh, I am. I'd love to see them really. Not just the buildings, but to know about it all.'

'Would you like me to make some more tea, darling?'

'Perhaps Rose would prefer something stronger. I have some *jarzembiak*, a sort of vodka made with some berries. I don't know what the berry is called in English, if indeed it has an equivalent. A dictionary I have consulted on this point suggests "spindleberry" but I believe that is not probable.'

'Whatever it is, I'd love to taste it.'

While Witek went into his own room to fetch the bottle, Janet sat silent and looked offended. Rose had agreed to the last two things suggested by Witek. Was she going to have to accept each of their suggestions alternately, regardless of what she herself wanted, in order to avoid coming down on one side or the other?

Witek poured little glasses full of red liquid, for her and for himself.

'Cheerio.'

The liqueur, after a delicate summer taste, was a slow-spreading warmth.

Witek fixed Rose with a bright interested look.

'You must know that we are very anxious to know of all aspects of English life. Could you not tell us something of your experiences? Anything.' He laughed. 'The first thing that comes into your head.'

He created an atmosphere of sadness and embarrassment.

The girl was determined not to wince but to help him as far as she could: Janet must really learn not to be beastly to him in front of her.

'Witek, you make things much too difficult. What is it you want to know?'

'Everything! Your work, for instance. We know so little of modern English life.'

'But you meet other English people, don't you?'

'Rarely in Biala Gora. There is Mr Loasby, a young English scholar, who was once at our house. And when I am in Warsaw I go to see Mr Pilkington, at the British Council, usually to borrow films and tape recordings. But Mr Pilkington is a very busy man and has not time for many callers.'

'Oh, I thought English people came here quite often.'

'Ah ha!'

All at once he was prancing up and down in front of her, rubbing his hands together. She watched with astonishment, wondering what had happened.

'She says off-ten. She says off-ten. You see, Janet, you and Daniel Jones's dictionary are not always to be relied on.'

Janet was roused by this. 'But, Rose, we all said "orphan" when we were little. Surely you did, too. Can't you remember?'

Rose, who had not appreciated why all the fuss was being made, said: 'I must have picked it up somewhere.'

'Can it be that there has been a change of usage in recent years, since, for instance, we left England? That might bear some looking into. Well, we cannot worry Rose about this. It is our profession and not hers. But what about Rose's profession? What job have you been doing, Rose?'

'Well, after Daddy died you know I went to live with this friend of mine who was at school with me, Elizabeth Tatham. I got a job as a secretary, as I'd already done typing and shorthand. But it was terribly boring. I mean there was no one you could talk to, I mean no one you could really talk to. So I gave that up and got a job with this friend of Elizabeth's. She has a sort of furniture shop and does interior decoration, that sort of thing.'

Rose felt foolish reciting all this to Witek Rudowski, on a spring evening in Biala Gora. Beauchamp Place, Knightsbridge, was at the very opposite end of the world. Witek could not possibly picture anything she was talking about and watching him she could almost see his mind still working away at the problem of 'off-ten' and 'orphan'. She hurried through as fast as she could, chattering merely to convince Janet that she took no sides.

'Well, this friend, my friend's friend I mean, was frightfully nice but she was always going on at me. I mean I tried to stop her but in the end I had to leave. So that was one job.'

Rose laughed a little triumphantly at reaching this conclusion. Witek stood up and poured her another tot of *jarzembiak*.

'What do you mean? Was she unjust to you? Did she restrain your wages?'

'Oh no. Actually, it turned out she was a Lesbian.'

'And what is that?'

Rose was vanquished.

Janet explained briskly.

'I see.' He was genuinely shocked. He gulped and said in a strained voice: 'Thank you. I had always been meaning to look that word up.' Then, more confidently: 'I did not know that that kind of thing still went on.'

Rose felt a sudden wave of fondness for him.

Later, when they were in bed Janet said: 'I wish you hadn't told him you would go to the University tomorrow morning. He'll keep you there for hours, and I'd promised you'd have coffee with my friends.'

'*I've* promised now.'

'Try and get away as soon as you can.'

'Perhaps I won't want to.' Rose tried to find a comfortable position on the divan, which was hard and lumpy. 'Don't think I'm being beastly. I want to find out about things for myself.'

'I'm sorry I'm sure. I thought you came here to see me.'

Rose put her face on her elbow and looked across at the other bed. Janet was staring at the ceiling. They waited for the silence between them to turn into sleep.

## Chapter Five

The next morning Rose was hurried out at half past eight when her sister's first pupil arrived. She found Tadeusz in the kitchen, and hugged him. Afterwards, she was surprised she had done this: the previous evening she had felt he disapproved of her.

'There is tea. Mummy said, will you make eggs if you want them.'

'I don't think I do. Did you sleep well?'

'Yes. I can sleep anywhere. In February when Papa and I went to ski, we slept on the floor of a hut with twenty-six other persons. Twenty-eight of us and the stove. That was all in the hut. We carried our food on our backs.'

'Where was this? At Zakopane?'

'Everybody goes to Zakopane. This was right up in the mountains.'

'Where you saw the bear?'

'No, that was last week, in a different part of Tatry.'

'You seem to spend a lot of time on holidays.'

'Polish people like excursions. They all live too close together so when they can get away, they go. Also there are cheap tickets for students. But now I must not go so much because I am working for *matura* examination. It is very difficult, there are many subjects and I cannot do Russian. Our Russian teacher is no good, she is an old woman who was born in Kiev and looks like a pig. Nobody likes her.'

'Because she is Russian or because she looks like a pig?'

'Both. Only she is not Russian really, but Ukrainian. We do not like Ukrainians, too.'

'Either,' Rose corrected him.

'Please?'

'Either, when there are two things. You meant to say "We do not like Russians and we do not like Ukrainians either." So there are two lots you don't like.'

Tadeusz said: 'More than two. We do not like Czechs, too. And Lithuanians. And Germans. And Jews. Couldn't I say "too"?'

Rose was silenced.

He devoured a large slice of black bread smeared with very pale butter. 'If I pass *matura* examination, I will try to go to the University. Either here or in Warsaw.'

'Are you going to do English?'

'No.' He filled his glass up with tea. 'There is no English department yet at our university. Probably they will begin one soon, with Papa to teach. But what is the use of studying English if we cannot go to England?'

'I suppose not.' She looked away from him, her eyes hot with nervous excitement, and down into her glass of tea. 'What *do* you want to do, Tadeusz?'

'Engineering. Engineers can go everywhere. There is here an engineer who Mummy teaches, who was to China and India and last year he was to Ghana. He builds dams.'

'You'd like that?'

'Only for a time. I would not want to live with niggers. I always want to come back to Poland.'

Tadeusz stood up and washed his plate and glass. He came and stood beside Rose. Wherever he was, his physical presence was turned on to her, like a beam of light. He was hungry-looking. Not perhaps in the immediate physical sense, though he was certainly thin, but because the unfinishedness of adolescence seemed more acute in his case. He was gasping for more of life, as though the atmosphere he breathed lacked some chemical constituent he could barely live any longer without.

Because of his incompleteness, he was always worried about other people.

'How do you think Mummy is looking?'

'She seems quite well, but I think she works too hard.'

'Everyone works too hard. I think she is unhappy. Did she love Grandfather very much?'

Rose was surprised at this. 'Yes, at least, I suppose she loved Daddy. But not specially, if you see what I mean. You see, she was so seldom there. Always at boarding school, or being a nurse. I can't remember her before that.'

The boy frowned and sat down again opposite her.

'Then why has she changed so much since she was in England two years ago?'

'Has she?'

'Do you know, all through the Stalinist time, when they tried to collectivize the farms and there were only potatoes to eat, and we had U.B. – that is Secret Police – watching our house, all that time Mummy was wonderful. She hardly ate. She put a little on her plate and went out to the kitchen to look for something, and when she came back we had nearly finished and she finished too. Papa did not notice, he does not notice things like that, but I notice. You know eight years ago I was going to have a brother but he died because Mummy was working all the time and so weak?'

'Yes, I knew that. Of course I didn't really know until I came here. It is difficult to imagine these things from outside.'

'And now everyone here is getting happier and she is still unhappy.'

'But why, Tadeusz?'

'I think it was because she went to London. It is a very beautiful place?'

'Not really.'

'I know I have been there, when I was three. To the zoo. But I can't remember.'

'Would you like to go again?'

'For a visit. But not before my exams.' He stopped, hot-faced. 'I am sorry. I talk too much. But it is not like you being my aunt.'

'I should hope not. Do you smoke?'

'Not yet.' He walked up and down the kitchen, preparing to say something. 'Since Mummy comes back from England, she does not like being Polish any more. I am very proud of being Polish. Do you know Polish history?'

'Not much, I'm afraid.'

'Later on I will tell you. What time is it?'

'Half past nine.'

'I am to take you to the University for Papa to show you round.'

'Good! Is it far away?'

'Only one kilometre. Less than last night.'

The Rudowskis' flat was on the ground floor of a block forming part of a recent housing development. Other blocks, all exactly the same, blotted out the distances, and the only way you could tell which was which was by a number roughly whitewashed beside the door. Between the blocks there was raw earth and rubble, with cinderpaths leading to an unpaved road.

It was a sunny morning and swarms of small children were playing outside. They were still wrapped up in heavy clothes, some so solidly that their arms and legs were forced to the corners, as though they had recently been blown up with bicycle pumps. They had no toys but were apparently able to cover empty space with self-contained and purposeful activity. Farther on, there was one tricycle, whose owner was riding savagely round in wide circles, isolated already in the loneliness that great possessions bring.

These children looked healthy, far healthier than Tadeusz, whom the bright sky seemed to oppress.

'We were lucky to get a new flat,' he said. 'We had to wait many years on a list.'

Rose had not realized the flat was new. Its plaster was cracked and it had already taken on the drab unpainted look of the city.

They set off away from the road, between broken-down palings and the backs of single cottages. The black earth was mostly bare but there were clumps of yellow coltsfoot. Away from the blocks of tenements, the sky looked enormous and the view to the horizon was interrupted only by the little hill that gives Biala Gora its name in German and Polish.

Rose and Tadeusz arrived at the broad Jan Kochanowski Avenue which almost encircles the town. There were market carts, some lorries and one or two taxis. The University buildings stood opposite and over the main portico was written 'Universytet Biala Gora im. J. Kochanowskiego'.

On the steps, they were stopped by a most extraordinary female. She was all of six feet tall, with a slight stoop, and dressed in a mustard-coloured knitted suit. She had bright, inquisitive eyes and a nose which gave her the look of a fierce lady-eagle.

'Tadeusz! Tadeusz? And Rose! I must call you Rose, I think, because I am already knowing you so well. How pleased our dear Janet must be, isn't Mummy pleased, Tadeusz? How lovely you are, my dear, you cannot know how exciting it is for all of us to have you here. You come to us for coffee this morning—'

'Yes, but—'

'I know, I know, dear Janet has telephoned to me already. What must be, must be. But it is all right, we are doing it then instead this afternoon. Tadeusz will bring you—'

Tadeusz looked uncomfortable. They had not yet enough confidence in each other to unite against this stranger.

'No,' Rose said quickly. 'Give me the address and I'll find it.'

The café turned out to be in the market-square.

'I'll be there,' Rose said. If she did not go, Janet would be angry with her. It was obvious that promises had been made for her, expectations were to be fulfilled.

'My dear, that is wonderful. Only a few of us. Janet's true friends. We are all so excited and we hope you will be so happy here. How long do you stay?'

'My visa's for two months.'

When she had gone, Rose said: 'People think I'm a fool, incapable of moving round by myself.'

'I must study with my colleagues this afternoon.'

'I know. I feel guilty about keeping you from work. Who is that woman, anyway?'

'She is Mrs Kazimierska. Her husband is a doctor here. She is Mummy's greatest friend.'

'You don't like her much?'

'She talks very much. She does not always say good things.'

'What sort of things?'

Tadeusz wriggled uncomfortably. He was really very thin, almost snuffed out by the Marks and Spencer sweater Rose had sent him a few months ago. 'It is still difficult to be a for-eigner here and I do not think Mummy realizes.'

'But what is wrong with this Mrs Mazi-Kazi—?'

'Mrs Kazimierska? Nothing. She is one of the pre-war people. But we'd better go up. Papa will be waiting for you.'

## Chapter Six

Because Witold Rudowski admired Rose and wanted to interest her, he could only imagine doing this by telling her about his work. In fact there was little else he could talk about. He had always been too busy to go anywhere where opinions were exchanged. His only outside experience had been as a soldier in the war.

He had first spoken English with the girls in Manchester dance halls. At the back of his mind, unvoiced because there was absolutely nobody he could share it with, was the memory of those girls with the shoulder-length hair of the war years, the short swinging skirts and the wedge shoes. He had explored their soft bodies through interminable American patriotic films, *This is the Army, Two Girls and a Sailor, Up in Arms* (he remembered the titles because he was improving his English from them). Often he had held a blonde girl called Rose; for the last time, during a film in which the Andrews sisters, singing gamely, went down on a troopship torpedoed in mid-Pacific. He remembered that because the next day he broke his arm falling off a Bren gun carrier, and in hospital he met Janet. Later, when he was already engaged to Janet,

Witek looked up the Manchester Rose again, but by then she was only interested in Americans.

Witek had no idea of the number of girls in England called Rose. It might be as frequent as 'Marysia' here. The little girl he came to know as Janet's sister was called Rosemary; it was only when she left school that she became Rose.

Now, fresh from her walk, she came through the door of his office, ushered in by Tadeusz, who once again made one of his sudden disappearances. Rose and Witek were left facing each other. There was always a lack of ease, something ponderous and embarrassing in his manner, but his face shone with happiness.

'Here is where I work. I am afraid it is not up to the standards of an English Speech Training Department. We have to put up with what quarters we can get.'

Rose did not know what an English Speech Training Department looked like. There were rows of dusty books, mostly in late nineteenth-century bindings: dictionaries of English place names, Anglo-Saxon texts, the works of the English philologists, Skeat, Sweet and Weekley, whose very names screech like chalk on a rough blackboard. A large number of the books were in German.

'Those are from the library of the late Professor Rozwadowski. They are intended to form the nucleus of the English Department's library.'

'They look rather old.'

'Yes, I don't think they will be very much use.'

'Does anyone read them?'

'No. But Mrs Rozwadowski comes in and dusts them from time to time. There is no room for them in her flat.'

'Doesn't anybody else come here?'

'You see we have no English Department in Biala Gora yet. I am teaching students of history who must learn to read books in English. Most of them have no interest but some make good progress. We work together on tape and with gramophone records.'

Two tape recorders stood on a desk, one of the Russian type, in which the spools are one above the other, and an East German 'Smaragd'.

'Please sit down, Rose. Would you like some Nescafé?'

Witek came and sat on the desk opposite Rose. 'You must forgive me but this is rather a hobby-horse of mine. You see, I know we could have a good English Department here, but there are many persons who do not want it. The professors of Russian and French are afraid English will become too popular. The professor of Comparative Philology thinks that no one should learn English without first having mastered Anglo-Saxon. Then they say I haven't the correct qualification, I have only a doctorate. But I have taught English all the time when nobody else did. Rose, you see I came back to Poland to do this. I am sure I could make a good department, perhaps the best one in Poland.'

He was carried away by his enthusiasm; he went over to the kettle and shook it fiercely to make it boil.

'For instance, I am in constant contact with Mr Pilkington of the British Council and Mr Golombek of the American

Embassy. I think none of the English departments at the other universities avail themselves of such opportunities.'

He opened a drawer in his desk and showed Rose a pile of brightly coloured magazines. 'Mr Golombek has sent these to me last week. *Holiday. Harper's Bazaar. Good Housekeeping. Screen World.*' He picked them up one by one and let them fall. 'I cannot lend them to students, of course, because they would sell them on the Black Market. Also I do not think the English style is a good one. Mr Pilkington too has sent me several records by a composer named Vaughan Williams. Unfortunately we have not a suitable gramophone for these. But you see, they are ready to help.'

The kettle boiled and Witek mixed two cups of Nescafé. He stood close to her while she stirred and drank it. When he spoke of his ambitions the expression on his face was lively and attractive, though his breath was very bad.

'The Ministry of Higher Education, too. There my friend Mrs Goldberg is very helpful and has good ideas. The Ministry supports me. It is the University that is against. The Rector wants a man who did philosophy and wrote his doctorial thesis on "Sir Gawain and the Green Knight". He lectures at Warsaw but most of the time he is a journalist. But his uncle is professor at Krakow and has many friends here. The students don't learn anything from him, but these people don't care about the students. The professors come into the room and deliver a lecture and go out again and do not know the name of any students. They leave the assistants to correct the examinations. So the students graduate without speaking the language. I am sure that this should not happen in Biala Gora. Here they must learn by the best modern methods.'

'What do people do who want to learn English now?' Rose asked.

'They must have private lessons. The younger generation – or, as we call it here, the new generation, the young people whose parents were not educated, they are anxious to learn. But now they are following other courses because there is no English course. And it is two years since the Ministry gave permission to start.'

'What will happen, do you think?'

'Nothing, while we have this Rector. He has five months more to serve. Then it will be too late for next year.' Witek stared into Rose's eyes. 'Rose, life has been very difficult for Janet and me. But I am sure if I can get this job everything will be all right.'

Confused by his vehemence, she turned away. 'Look, you haven't finished your coffee.'

'Sorry.'

'Now let me show you some things we have done.'

He opened the East German tape recorder and switched it on. It hummed for a little, then spun to a halt, with the tape flapping frantically like a butterfly between two panes of glass.

'I must fix the correct tape, which will take about three min-utes. Perhaps you would like to give me your opinion on this.'

He handed her a book. *First Moves in English* by Witold Rudowski, Doctor of Warsaw University. State Publishing House.

Rose opened a page at random. It was a reading text.

'In England and America the workers are working for the gain of capitalists or "bosses".[1] Only in the Peoples' Democracies do they get full value[2] for their work and share in all the benefits[3] that it brings.'

After all he had been saying, it was a little shock; almost as if a dirty postcard had been left in the book by mistake.

At the end of the exercise there was a list of questions:

1. What is it only in the Peoples' Democracies the workers get?
2. What is a 'boss'?
3. What has Dickens told us about the position of the English workers?

She closed the book and sat rather hopelessly with it on her lap. It was as though she had suddenly discovered Witek to be wearing a toupee.

'Of course there is a lot of things that may seem strange or perhaps silly to you. But I must put them in, in order for my book to be accepted by the State Publishing House. Otherwise they would have the book done by a Miss Makula, a very nice lady who knows rather little English.'

'I see.'

He turned away, but worry was written all over the back of his threadbare suit. A moment later he faced her again.

'I am sorry, perhaps I give the wrong impression. I know now that it is not a good book. There are several errors in the treatment of the anomalous finites, for instance. But shall we say, it is better than any of the others?'

He turned to the tape recorder and soon had it working again. 'Here we have the student who speaks and the teacher who corrects him.'

A voice said: 'The trees are greener since Easter.'

'The student,' Witek said.

There was more whirring but otherwise silence. Rose was apprehensive, for to her the voice had been unmistakably Witek's.

Half a minute's silence told him something was wrong. He looked worried, then pressed the reverse button, and they started all over again.

This time the confusion was increased. Both voices were male, and Witek could not remember whether the teacher or the student had spoken first. Finally a female student took over. Now it was clear that Witek's was the better pronunciation, though by not very much. He was unusual among his compatriots in not having a musical ear.

Rose listened patiently through a series of exercises, until suddenly a girl's shrill voice broke in, there was an unidentifiable verse of 'Clementine', then a tempest of wild giggles.

Witek pressed the button hastily. 'That is nothing. We were having a little fun.' He quickened the speed and the whole tape ran through until the butterfly sounds started again. 'You can see, in any case, what we are trying to do.'

'It is very interesting.'

The girl's voice on the tape had infected Rose with a violent desire to laugh too, a thing which rarely happened when she was alone.

## Chapter Seven

'Mrs Blaut.'
  'Blaut.'
'Miss Barcik.'
'Barcikowna.'
'There. And this is Miss Rose Nicholson whom we are all feeling we know so well already.'

The three women gleamed at Rose across the corner table in a crowded café. Rose did not like the unmixed company of women and seldom sought it if it could be avoided. She had come here for Janet's sake, as part of the balancing of favours to which the Rudowskis seemed to have committed her.

'Coffee? And cakes?' Mrs Kazimierska asked. She waved for an elderly waiter who shuffled towards them.

'How do you like Poland?' Miss Barcik leaned forward with a helpful smile and a sudden excess of blinking. The negotiation of unfair and leading questions was not a thing Rose was good at. She was about to plunge in, when Mrs Kazimierska came to her aid.

'Come, come, Elzbieta, that is not a thing you must ask her, I know she is much too polite to tell us the truth. First she must try some of our very good cakes and then like silly women we will gossip about clothes and about people. Is that all right?'

Rose was as much put out by this as by the blinking woman's question.

They talked about clothes.

Though it was a weekday afternoon every table at the café was occupied and men with briefcases were waiting in the doorway for somewhere to sit down.

'Of course we are following all the fashions from the magazines you are sending to Janet.'

'And Janet, for you how is she looking?'

'She works too hard.'

Unlike Tadeusz, Mrs Kazimierska was inclined to dismiss this. 'It is not so necessary, all this work. She is bad about asking enough money, our dear Janet. Look, I will tell you. A man goes to her and says: "I must learn English, I am going to Egypt, to Iraq, to Indonesia, please please teach me in three months, but I am so poor", and Janet believes him and takes him for nearly nothing. But we all know that man is an engineer making good money, more than any of us will ever see.'

'But she oughtn't to do that. Why don't you do something about it?'

'What can we do?'

'Can't you tell her who the people are when they come asking for lessons? Can't Witek tell her?'

It was the first time his name had been mentioned. The three round the table stiffened and the cake they were eating stopped dead in their mouths.

'Dr Rudowski would think it beneath his dignity.'

'What do you mean?'

They looked at each other. Mrs Blaut spoke first: 'Here we are all friends of Janet, you see.'

Rose examined her closely for the first time: a solid, handsome woman, by far the best dressed of the three. For her at least all the talk about clothes had not been academic. But, as happens when people speak a language with difficulty, her face was inexpressive.

'Yes?'

Mrs Kazimierska patted Rose's hand. 'Hala means there are no secrets from us. What Janet has not told us we can guess. We all of us know Rudowski.'

From the gleams of accord in the eyes of the other two, you could see that they would not hesitate to go on. They did not know there could be such a thing as reticence. Whatever went wrong with anyone, however private or illicit the distress, they would be snuffling it out with the excited yelps of terriers.

'She hasn't told me anything,' Rose said.

Mrs Kazimierska smiled fondly. 'You are so young, dear, but you can see when people are unhappy?'

'Well, perhaps they are not very happy.' She was going on to say that she could not imagine how anyone could be very happy in Biala Gora. The three women, however, would feel this as somewhat near the bone. People like to tell you their misfortunes; they do not much like you to tell them.

'I've only been here one day. There hasn't been time—'

Talking like this Rose was going along with them in the subject, assuming their possession of superior knowledge, which was flattering to them and also humiliating to her. She was hemmed in by the three intent faces, by Mrs Kazimierska's huge nose, Miss Barcik's ceaseless blinking and Mrs Blaut's solid calm. How well in fact did they know Janet? Were they fishing for more information?

She wished she could turn on them and tell them to shut up. But she was naturally without pugnacity and hated to be rude. Compared with them, too, she was over-armed with peace and security, and therefore crippled.

'And Tadeusz,' Mrs Blaut asked. 'How do you find Tadeusz?'

'Oh really I—'

'He is a nice boy, very good-mannered. Rose – may we call you Rose – we always talk of you as Rose!'

'Oh, do.' She did not ask them their names nor wished to know them. To her they seemed infinitely old.

'I think Tadeusz is a little like you.'

'Oh surely not. I mean, he's so Polish, isn't he?'

'Not to us. To us he is very English.'

Rose felt a spark of excited hope flash through her: If Tadeusz is really English he can be saved from this after all, he can go away from all these people and never come back. 'He is not like Dr Rudowski, I think,' Miss Barcik said.

'You went to the University this morning and he showed you his magnetogram – how it is in English?'

'Tape recorder.'

'I think it is not very interesting. Hala, Krystyna and I,

we are laughing at him for this. He is like a silly man with his little machines.'

'But everyone uses them now. I mean writers, actors, singers, all those…I know it's very boring when people turn them on at parties, and everybody thinks they ought to be funny into them. But if it helps people to learn English, why not have one?'

'It helps people to think Dr Rudowski is important and up to date. We would all like to have magnetograms, it would impress very much our private students. But we cannot have them. But of course it is easy for him. He is on the right side. He has only to ask for things.'

'Elzbieta knows,' Mrs Blaut said. 'She works with him.'

'I am teaching English to economists and it is Dr Rudowski who looks after us poor teachers and tells us what we must do. To mind our p's and q's, is that right?'

'Tell her about the system of marking.'

'Tell her how he changed the results of the examinations.'

'He does many things,' Miss Barcik said. 'But it is all right for him. He is on the right side.'

'What do you mean, he is on the right side?'

'He is Party, *ma chère*,' Mrs Kazimierska said.

'Oh, I see.'

'Of course we must understand that it was difficult for him. Coming back from the West with an English wife. And he wanted so much to be Professor of English.'

'He will be,' Mrs Blaut said. 'He will be. His friends will arrange that.'

Mrs Kazimierska lit a cigarette in a little tube of red glass.

'I do not think so. My great friend, Rektor Markiewicz says not. And Elzbieta's father is against him. There are standards to be kept up, whatever people say. Even Zwiersz agrees with that. Zwiersz is a very intelligent man. Naturally Rudowski thinks that Zwiersz is on his side but really he is not.'

'Who is Zwiersz?'

'He is one of the Deans of the University. He is the Party man and deals with all that in the Dean's office.'

'Zwiersz is a friend of Adam Karpinski,' Miss Barcik said.

'No, I do not think so.'

The names proliferated. Even with regard to Witek Rudowski, their passion for gossip was hardly malice, but an intense curiosity about people and motives, as though these provided some energizing factor, some salt or spice that their usual fare lacked. They rushed to a foreigner like cats to catmint, yet at the same time could easily be distracted into speculations about anyone they knew of. The effect of their gossip was not trivial, but rather strong and stifling.

'If only Adam would come here,' Mrs Kazimierska said. 'He is so very clever. There is somebody for Rose to meet, a true Polish intellectual. His thesis was quite brilliant. They wanted to publish it in America. I read it, it was brilliant.'

'What was it about?'

'Sir Gawain and the Green Knight.'

'He was in Biala Gora last week,' Miss Barcik said. 'I saw him. Of course I did not speak with him. He was married to my cousin,' she told Rose. 'He was very bad to her and so we do not like him in our family.'

'Magdalena is a stupid girl. So, Adam was in town and he did not come to see me! I expect he was making intrigue. He must hurry up with it now. You see he is a great friend of Rektor Markiewicz and when *his* term of office is ended, there are no more chances for poor Adam in Biala Gora. But if he comes here again, Rose must meet him.'

'Do you think it is good?' Miss Barcik asked.

'Oh yes, he will like Rose. Forgive me, dear, but you are very like a Polish girl. You have not seen any of our pretty girls yet. They are lovely. Before 1956 they were not pretty, now they are pretty. In a year's time they will be ugly girls again, who knows?'

Mrs Blaut said: 'No, they are always pretty. In the war, I remember that I say to head of Gestapo in Biala Gora: "No wonder your soldiers are liking so much our Polish girls. Your German men are handsome but your Frauen, so big and fat!" He laughed and agreed with me. He was not so bad, that one.'

'What was his name?' Miss Barcik asked.

'Fleischer.'

'Fleischer, ah, yes. I remember when they take over my father's flat. It was a beautiful flat, by the river – they dynamite it when they leave. My father said, where can we live? And Fleischer said, don't worry, you'll get a good flat. Then they cleared the Ghetto and we got a very good flat.'

Rose glanced quickly at Mrs Kazimierska and Mrs Blaut to see if there was any reaction to this. There was none.

'Rose must also meet her compatriot,' Mrs Blaut said.

'I do not think she will find him interesting.'

'He is learning Polish with me. He is clever, but' – blinking furiously, Miss Barcik seemed about to commit a social indiscretion – 'I think we must take what he is saying with a pinch of salt. Is that correct?'

'Yes – I mean, I don't know. But why?'

'For instance he is saying he was at Cambridge. Evidently he is not *du monde,* indeed his parents are quite poor, he tells me. How can I believe that?'

'Believe what?'

'That he went to Cambridge. Only the well-born can go there, I think.'

Rose said: 'No, that's frightfully out of date. You see nowadays—'

While she spoke their mouths turned down. It appeared that they regarded this opinion as part of Rose's official instructions.

Miss Barcik laughed shortly. 'You see when you meet him. You will agree with me. He is a nice boy, but he is not always telling the truth.'

Rose said suddenly: 'Could I buy a bottle of vodka, do you think?'

'Not today,' Mrs Blaut said.

'Why not?'

'Today is the day of paying wages. The drink shops are closed on such days. It is to prevent drunkenness.'

'One moment,' Mrs Blaut said. 'You have dollars?'

'Pounds. At least, I've got one pound note with me.' Rose looked in her bag. 'Yes, here it is.'

'At Hoffman you can buy.'

'What is that?'

'Hoffman is the hotel. Now it is called "July Manifesto" but before the war it was Mr Hoffman's and we still call it that.'

'Could I go there?'

'Of course,' Mrs Kazimierska said. 'I'll take you, I live near there.'

Rose said good-bye to Miss Barcik and Mrs Blaut without any particular wish to see them again. She greatly preferred Mrs Kazimierska, though she knew now why Tadeusz had been so antagonistic to her. Mrs Kazimierska had a certain detachment: the pleasures of gossip did not absorb her so completely as they did her friends. Rose was pleased that it was she who was walking with her through the twilit streets of Biala Gora.

The little shop windows were already lit, but most of them contained only scarlet and white decorations of crepe paper, and framed portraits of Gomulka and Cyrankiewicz. The windows of meat-shops, however, displayed painted plaster models of legs of pork; inside, people were queueing for lengths of sausage.

Near the Hotel of the July Manifesto Mrs Kazimierska said: 'Three years ago we were all too frightened to come here. It was only for foreigners and we did not want to be seen visiting them. And the staff were all U.B. Perhaps still are but they do not do anything now.'

She strode imperiously into the foyer, which was gloomy and unwelcoming with its heavy red hangings and varnished wood. A magazine stall stood beyond the reception desk, loaded with copies of *L'Humanité,* the *Daily Worker, Rude Pravo, Pravda,* and behind it were two showcases. One was full of folk art, dancing dolls with cretinous expressions and some lumpy embroidery which looked like kettle-holders; in the other there stood a display of bottles of vodka and the various cordials that are made from it. Everything was priced in dollars and cents.

Rose produced her passport, forms were to be signed in triplicate, she was sent twice to the reception desk and back again. She had to buy three half-bottles as they were not permitted to give change for her pound note. In the end, clutching her parcel triumphantly but with the grotesque vision of Miss Handisyde at the back of her mind, Rose said good-bye to Mrs Kazimierska and took a taxi home.

## Chapter Eight

Rose unwrapped the bottles on the kitchen table. In the next room Janet was finishing an English lesson, the last of the day. Her voice sounded hoarse.

Rose looked into some drawers, could not find a corkscrew and pecked at the neck of the bottle with a fork. The little paper-wrapped cork slid out. She got a glass and poured herself a shot. By the time Janet came in, she was half-way through the second.

'Have some of this.'

'Darling, three bottles!'

'I need this, I can tell you. Your friends, I'm sure they're very nice and all that, but they're rather a lot for me to take, just at the beginning. They go on and on.'

'Hala and Elzbieta and Krystyna are the best friends I've got. They've always stood up for me.'

'I'm sure they have. They know far more about you than I do.'

'Rose, we know so little about each other at all.'

'I felt a terrible fool,' Rose said, turning away.

'You're tired, ought you to drink like that?'

'I told you I need it. Janet, I must ask you something. It's about Witek.'

'What about Witek?'

'Your friends talked about him like a sort of monster.' The drink and her impatience made Rose exaggerate and dramatize.

'I see.'

'I like Witek. You didn't tell us much about him when you were in England. Only about Tadeusz.'

'We were taken up with Daddy, weren't we?'

'There was lots of time to talk, those last days. You could have told me about it then. I'd have understood. We'd always suspected, Daddy and I, but we didn't know for sure.'

'What *are* you talking about?'

'About Witek being a Communist.'

'Oh that. That doesn't matter at all.'

Rose was silent for a moment, wondering how to get to the point. 'It seems to matter, to your friends.'

'They're my friends, not his. I can't explain very well. Perhaps we'd better leave it till you know this place better.'

'Perhaps we'd better leave it.' Rose was being soothed down, and objected. 'If it doesn't matter, why won't you speak to him. It isn't very pleasant for me being in the house.'

'There isn't much Witek and I can discuss any more. We've been through it all. We look at things quite differently.'

'What about Tadeusz?'

'Especially Tadeusz.'

'But Tadeusz is all right, surely. So frightfully nice and intelligent. Honestly, I adore Tadeusz.'

'Perhaps you'd better take over from me, you seem to like everybody so much. Except for me. I seem to be the odd man out.'

'That's not fair. I'm trying to be helpful. All this makes it very difficult.'

'You can't help, Rose. You can't really.'

'Oh, I can. That's what you don't know.' Rose clutched Janet's arms excitedly, her eyes full of sparkle and distress. 'Only it's all going to be difficult.' She began talking very fast. 'You know last night I said I wanted to come here because I wanted to know about things here? You were hurt, you said you thought I wanted to visit you.'

'Yes.'

'Janet, I have got some exciting news. If I'd told you before I found this thing about Witek, something might have gone wrong.'

Janet sat down, huddled and tired. 'Tell me.'

'You remember about Aunt Louise?'

'Yes.'

'You know how she only wanted to leave her money to men, and when Nicholas was killed, our side of the family was out?'

'Yes, I know.'

'Well, she changed her mind. At least, she didn't really.'

'You mean, she left something to us?'

'It's a lot more difficult than that. She left it to Tadeusz.'

'Oh, my God. A lot of money?'

'Yes. A lot.'

Tears began streaming down Janet's cheeks, She sobbed and laughed. Rose could do nothing any more. She sat back exhausted on the divan, picking at the rough cloth under her fingers.

'It's all over then.'

'What's over?'

'This.'

Rose felt that for the last moments they had both been shaken, half-laughing and half-crying, on a large slightly out-of-control machine. Now she was worried that the shock might cause Janet to behave foolishly.

'We must be very careful to do the right thing.'

'When did all this happen?'

'She died just after Christmas. You remember, I wrote to you. I didn't say anything about what the solicitors told me. You know you said not to put important things in letters. I decided to give up my job and come here.'

'Otherwise you wouldn't have come?'

'Well, I don't know. Anyway, Mickey was still around then. I told you about him. Actually, there was another thing.'

'Was there?'

'I was afraid to find you were unhappy. And not to be able to do anything about it.'

'Unhappy!' Janet laughed wildly. 'Just look at this flat. It took five years on a list to get it, and it's falling to pieces already. I've worked till I'm dog-tired every day. They're trying to take my own son away from me. You were afraid I might be unhappy.'

Rose was beyond listening to all this. Instead she thought of the complications ahead. Janet's whole life was disorganized by the news. Until some decision had been reached, there was a risk of more misery and even disaster.

'Aunt Louise was an old devil,' Rose said carefully. 'I expect she knew she was making difficulties. You must remember it's Tadeusz's money. What will he think about all this?'

'He's only a child.'

'It's his money. And in some ways it isn't a terrible lot.'

'If for years you've had nothing! Witek and I saved some money once and then they changed the currency and we lost it all. You'll never understand, Rose.'

'I mean, the money is not a lot if it is to help Tadeusz through his life. How's that to be done?'

Janet's silence showed that she had got the point. 'I see. Yes, it's going to be very difficult.'

'The boys are coming back for supper, aren't they? I don't think we should tell them yet.'

Janet nodded.

'It'll be a shock for Witek. I mean, he's after this job at the University, isn't he? And he's in with the Party, so he can't be expected to be pleased at the idea of his only son becoming a Capitalist.'

They both giggled at this. Janet said: 'Of course, it has nothing to do with him at all.'

'He controls Tadeusz's life.'

'I have no intention of telling him about it.'

The two women were a little drunk now, and exhilarated

with dealing with something rather out of their depth. Their voices, chiming to a family tune of the upper middle class, rang out strangely through the dark, cramped flat. For them their grandparents would have expected marriage trusts and portions, but rising prices, the war and their father's career in education had made this impossible. Nevertheless both the sisters still thought and spoke about money in a way which was quite unknown in the city outside, where the native population had had a tradition of proud spend-thriftness, of leaving commerce to the Jews and German merchants. Communism, which makes all financial values completely arbitrary, had only increased this.

What the men of the family would think, therefore, was uncertain. Rose remembered how Mark Tatham had warned her in Warsaw: money means such different things in different places.

Witek and Tadeusz could now be heard coming into the hallway. Flushed, tipsy, the sisters embraced one another and prepared to tell lies.

Witold and Tadeusz were in the middle of an argument which did not break into English until they sat down at table. In this house, their language, with its slithery arcane noises, had become like a secondary sexual characteristic. It emphasized their privacy and separateness as men. You could as easily keep secrets from them as they from you: people can't guess thoughts in a foreign language, however well they speak it. Now, apart from their polite greetings, Tadeusz and Witek were too preoccupied to notice the suppressed excitement of the two women.

Tadeusz turned to Rose: 'It is not right. This teacher is giving us so much work for her class, we have no time for anything else. My colleagues wish to make a protest.'

'She is quite correct,' Witek said. 'It is in the syllabus. She will show you it.'

'Then we shall all fail.'

Witek said to Rose in his educational voice: 'It is difficult for him because many subjects are required. But he must do well. The number of students with secondary education increases every year and there is great competition for university places, especially for the courses he will follow.'

Rose tried to listen but she was watching her sister. There was a strange expression on Janet's face: she looked as if she was about to call Tadeusz back from somewhere he was going, but did not have the courage to raise her voice.

Tadeusz as usual ate ravenously, refused a second glass of tea and asked if he could leave.

When he had gone, Janet said: 'It's his health I worry about, with all this cramming and homework. A few years ago he had a spot on one lung. I sent him to the mountains at once, and it cleared up. But with this continual strain and being forced to keep up with others at all costs, you never know. There's a bad family history too, unfortunately.'

She fired a glance of hatred across the table and Rose saw Witek flinch from it.

Rose felt sad for him. He was not much as a man, but he had

everything to lose, and he was going to lose it. After the giggling excitement of half an hour ago, Rose protested inwardly against these wrecking tactics, longing to blurt out the truth if only it would take away the stricken look from Witek's face. For the first time, Rose feared that Janet was a little crazy. She would use this good fortune, not for the calm and absence of desperation which a bank account was supposed to give you, but for revenge, to smash and destroy and create an unhappiness as fierce and broken as her own had been.

*Chapter Nine*

After three days Rose began to move more easily in and out of the three rooms of the flat and the triangle of Rudowskis. There was still the discomfort of being accommodating instead of helpful, the slight ache of always feeling one is in the wrong chair, the hurry of shifting from room to room with the risk of leaving a pair of nylons, a half-finished detective story or a packet of cigarettes stranded, while the money-making activities of the house went on. The Rudowskis were furtive about these in a way strange to Rose, who had earned her own living since she was eighteen.

For the time being everything went on as usual. Neither of the sisters made any move towards confiding in Witold. Instead they bickered indecisively between themselves.

'I told the solicitors I'd find out what would be best for Tadeusz.'

'But it's so clear, isn't it?'

'Is it?'

'Rose, there are hundreds of people in Biala Gora who'd give their right hands to escape to the West. They are too proud to admit it to you. But I'll admit it because I happen to be one of them. Do you imagine I'd have come back in 1957 if it hadn't been for Tadeusz?'

'Why don't they go then?'

'Because they can't get passports. And *they* haven't any money.'

'That's older people. They want to be comfortable and there certainly isn't much of that here. But what about the young? I wouldn't want Tadeusz to end up like Mickey.'

'That's quite different,' Janet said impatiently.

'Mickey's Irish. They're supposed to be like the Poles. We must try and find out what's right. Not make him unhappy, too.'

'He's too young to know what he wants.'

'And Witek, too.'

'Him!'

On the fourth afternoon, Rose was cornered in the kitchen without cigarettes.

'Derek Loasby is on the telephone.'

'Who's he?'

'The Englishman at the University.'

'I remember. Your friend, the one who blinks, told me about him.'

She went into the other room and picked up the telephone. Janet's student, an elderly surgeon, was sitting on the divan breathing heavily just behind her.

'Yes?'

A hearty English voice went into some complex apologies

and emerged with: 'I just wondered if you'd like to come out sometime and have a cup of coffee or something.'

'When, exactly?'

'Well, now.'

Rose glanced round her. The surgeon was staring politely ahead of him. The alternative to Loasby's invitation was the afternoon in exile, isolated in the kitchen. On the other hand the coat and skirt she would have to wear lay in the divan drawer underneath the surgeon. Already she seemed to feel his measured breath on her calves, urging her to decision.

'All right.'

'Shall I come and call for you?'

Janet and the surgeon were as motionless as waxworks.

'I'll find the place. Where is it?'

'The Kaprys. You were there with Miss Barcik.'

'I'll be about half an hour.'

Without looking round again, Rose snatched a packet of cigarettes from the table (these in fact belonged to the surgeon) and returned to the kitchen. Some time later she heard the surgeon leave. She went through to retrieve her coat and skirt before Janet's next pupil arrived.

'I must say I haven't found that young man very friendly considering we were the only two English here. I could have given him a lot of tips. But he goes off on his own and nobody seems quite to know what he gets up to.'

'Perhaps I'll find out.'

'Did you remember your key? I've got my class at the Engineering Institute this evening.'

## Chapter Ten

In the café where Rose had sat with Janet's friends, the first room was quite full and there was no sign of anyone who looked English. She headed through the tobacco-smoke and smell of old clothes into a larger room beyond. Here faces were thrust forward at each other over the wet-ringed tables, tongues loosened not by drink but the urgency of getting their say. On a yellow brown dais ornamented with plywood cut-outs of lyres, a violinist and a pianist were performing. Above them hung a sort of mosaic relief, representing a huge-footed woman carrying sheaves of wheat.

The girl saw a hand shoot up, followed by a young man in a tweed coat.

'I daren't leave here, someone will grab the table,' he shouted to her, and indeed at his first movement two stout surly men carrying plastic briefcases pushed Rose aside and made towards it. One of them seized hold of the chair Derek Loasby was keeping for Rose. Loasby got it away from him by force.

'Sit down on it quickly.'

She did so, feeling herself used as a weapon in their conflict. The men moved off, scowling, between the tables.

'They're so predictable, the Poles. Hospitality at home and awful manners in public.'

Rose looked doubtful at this generalization, which was perhaps only occasioned by the pomposity of nervousness. She hated the starts of conversation, 'drawing people out' as though they were to be extracted from holes: they had far better stay where they were.

As soon as she could, she took a careful look at Derek Loasby. His hair was dark red, his nose another shade of red and some pimples along his neck, made by a dull razorblade, were nearly purple. A fall of dandruff lay on the rough tweed of his collar.

'Coffee? It's not bad here, compared with the other places.'

He would keep shifting around, in his seat. These movements, which were constant with him, did not indicate any particular excitement, nor were the questions he now fired at the girl evidence of any real curiosity. He was too full to the brim with himself for that.

In the end he got hold of a waiter, a surviving pachyderm from the days before the war, whose mournful appearance was enough to make even Loasby reject the pretence, often helpful with girls, that he was a *habitué* of the place. Instead he quite competently ordered two large coffees.

'It's jolly nice seeing someone English again. I love it here, of course. But you can't go around saying that to people. They don't even like you to, for one thing.'

'Surely some people like to hear nice things?'

'Party people. They've no time for us, we're the decadent Westerners. Jolly good fun, too. Some people say to me, why didn't you go to Warsaw or Krakow, more going on. I like it here. Do you know, I've been the only English person here this winter.'

'There was my sister.'

'British wives don't really count do they? Sorry, is that rude?'

'I suppose so. I don't know really.' Rose was not really attending to what he was saying, being put off by the pugnacity of his approach. He was half-way over the little table; he had adopted from the natives the tactic of close breathing, even the direct stare into the shrinking pupils. He only drew back when the waiter placed two glasses of muddy-looking coffee between them.

'Put the sugar in and then the saucer on top. The theory is the grounds go down.'

They emptied the little bowls of grey sugar on to the bubbling surface of the coffee. Rose burnt her fingers trying to get at the saucer under the scalding glass.

'Here, take my hanky.' He produced something stuck together and sooty.

'No, thank you.'

At this rate it would take half an hour to drink the coffee and he was pushing nearer.

'I wanted to ask you. We meet up, me and my friends, every Saturday. We dance at the Students' Club. How about it?'

Rose did not bother to hide the effort of reaching a decision on this. She did not even pretend that she had not understood, as one often did on receiving an invitation that might be unattractive.

Though callow, Loasby was not stupid. A moment of pure misery made him tremble: he had overshot the mark with someone who was really worthwhile.

'All right,' Rose said.

A smile of relief shone all over his face. It would not stop, it went on and on.

Rose smiled back.

'Jolly good. I'm sure you'll like this place we go to. They've got a very good jazz group. There's a lot of good things about this country when you know your way around. And, with parcels, there's very little you can't get.'

'What parcels?'

'You have them sent from England. Nescafé, aspirin, things like that. Ball-point pens. You haven't any ball-point pens, have you?'

'I've got one but I use it.'

Now he had started to press his foot against hers. The girl retreated. She hit an unexpected leg of the modernistic table, and their coffee slopped over.

'That's a pity.' He was still talking of the ball-point pens. 'You could have some sent, couldn't you? Though through the post you might have to pay duty. Nescafé is better. I've got friends who'll take anything like that off me. I sold some clothes before I went to Vienna at Christmas and stocked up again there.'

'How did you get the money out?'

'Easy. I took a Russian camera and sold it.'

He had got carried away again. He shot a panicky trapped

look at the surrounding tables. There was no sign that anyone had understood a word he was saying, but should there have been? He gulped, turned pinker, and was silent for a moment. Miss Barcik had hinted that Loasby told lies; in fact his stumbling candour was so obvious that it was quite unrecognizable to anyone not accustomed to the English.

'I – I must say I've met an awfully nice lot of people. There's this girl, perhaps I oughtn't to mention her name just now' – he gave another glance at the grey men surrounding them – 'You'll meet her on Saturday. And the others, too. Everyone here is really sociable.'

'It's surprising, isn't it, when they all live so close together.'

'Perhaps that's just it. If you've never been lonely you never want to be alone.'

'What happens if you can't stand the people you live with?'

'That's too bad.' His face drew nearer again. 'In London if you're young and poor you can have a horrible time. They said: "Join the Young Conservatives". Well I did and all the girls were plain and the lads just as desperate as me. No help at all. Coming here was a revelation, I can tell you.'

There was a sort of wet film on his eyes; pity for himself.

Somewhat repelled, she said: 'But you only have a nice time because you're English. What if you were a Pole?'

He leaned back in his chair and put his thumbs in the armholes of his pullover. 'I'm sure I'd have an even nicer time.'

'This is a wonderful country,' he added in a loud voice, looking furtively round him.

This seemed to leave them much where they were before.

## Chapter Eleven

While Rose had coffee with Loasby, Witold Rudowski was sitting at home with a pile of language tests in front of him. Outside the walls and windows of the opposite block shone with the melancholy light of a late spring evening; inside the flat, it was already dark.

Witek was unable to work. Two or three times his impatience at himself brought him to the window: the mere sight of other people, the representatives of mass society, might remind him of his duties towards them.

The janitor's children were playing in the dust under the walnut tree. Three young men who had acquired shares in a motor-cycle were engaged in roaring the engine up and down. And now the lame ex-soldier had gone to let out his tumbler pigeons. Five of these flew up on to the roof opposite, where they fussed and shimmered in a black and white group. Then, when the soldier called them, they fluttered down one by one, performing on the way a complete back-somersault in the air, and alighted inside the walnut tree, which was still leafless. The pigeons stayed there, dark fruit-shaped objects against the bright sky.

Motor-cycles and pigeons were cures for the depression and anxiety caused by the blunt resistance of the physical world. This seemed not to obey his compatriots as it did the Germans and the British. Witek's cure was ski-ing, in which nothing whatever got in his way. But now the hills nearest Biala Gora were bare except for little corners of old snow among the spruce trees. You had to go to the Tatry, a hundred and fifty miles away, for good ski-ing at this time of the year.

Dreaming of mountains, Witek went back to the language tests.

Each period of his life had presented him with immediate problems which must be solved before he could move on. Like most conformists, he had no resonance. He bored others because of his lack of feeling for the past; he never joined in those impassioned conversations by which Poles recapitulate their country's history and increase the unease of their destiny. Up till now his hopes had been limited and precise.

The shock had come the moment he saw Rose's luggage: two suitcases of brown pigskin, the smaller one having zip-fasteners. She had bought them for this visit and because she had travelled by air they were still unbattered. They smelt new.

As such things will, however much we tell ourselves they are evidence of no importance, the suitcases represented all the difference between his life and the life of somebody who might have a chance of possessing Rose. You couldn't get anything so completely achieved as those suitcases here. Not a pair of scissors nor a vacuum cleaner nor a decent meal: they all had something wrong about them, some immediate defect or built-in drawback. Increased prosperity would never change this. Officially he considered it unfortunate that people here attended church so assiduously, but the churches were the last places where, among properly made things, actions were properly performed.

And so even in Rose's absence, Witek was disturbed, steeling himself not to look at the frail tangle of her nylons across a chair, her underclothes innocently hanging up to dry in the kitchen. These extensions of Rose into the surrounding area were what made her remarkable. Here nobody's possessions had any personality any more, so that where you lived became no more informative than the mark of your head on the pillow. Rose's irritating untidiness made her always present.

He could escape to the University; there his tape recorder was waiting to be played with, papers were ready to sign and useful little conversations happened in corridors. But this afternoon by chance he was alone at home. Tadeusz was at a school meeting: he was his class representative on the committee dealing with summer excursions. Janet at the Engineering Institute was giving one of her evening classes.

Giving up the attempt to work, Witek lay on the trestle bed which stood among his bookshelves. He yawned and stretched in the way people have whose fantasies are too much for them. Then he dozed off.

He awoke to hear someone coming into the flat.

'Tadeusz?'

Rose stood in the doorway.

'You've been asleep,' she said.

He sat up, confused. 'Impossible to work. A slight headache.'

'Shall I make tea or something?'

Waking reality descended on him like a cloak of lead. His tongue fumbled with the stiffness of the English language, which so often seemed to paralyse a small section of his brain. He could never manage to say quite what he meant but always something ponderous and banal. He had hardly realized this before and it would not have mattered with anyone else but Rose.

'I help you,' he said, 'Rose.'

They stood on either side of the kitchen table. Against the drumming of tap-water in the kettle, Rose said: 'I've been meeting the local Englishman.'

'I hear he is very nice.' In fact, he had heard of nothing but suspicions and pertinent questions.

'No, not really. Rather stupid.'

Witek laughed nervously, a little appalled that she should criticize one of her countrymen to him so brusquely. Giving opinions about other people was betraying them a little: it was not to be done without a painful sense of duty.

Rose lit the gas. 'I want to find out things and he obviously doesn't know the right answers.'

'Please? To find out things?'

'Yes. Witek, what do *you* think is going to happen here?'

'Please?'

'Is life going to get any better?'

'But life is getting so much better every day. Sometimes we must be wondering, can it be true?'

'I suppose so. Are you happy? I know it's an awful thing to ask.'

'We have our work. Janet has her work. I have my work.' It sounded like an exercise in the Simple Present Tense. 'This is not perhaps interesting for you. But – I feel I am doing good.'

'I'm sure you are,' Rose said, slightly repelled. 'But what about Tadeusz?'

'He is an ambitious boy.'

'Can he do any good here? Would he be better off in England?'

'I cannot tell. Remember, he is a Pole – I do not hear very good accounts of Polish people in England.'

How impossible it was! All that one might offer Tadeusz, perhaps holidays abroad, perhaps an English University, the freedom to go anywhere he liked for a few years, would mean nothing at all to Witek.

'But wouldn't you like him to travel abroad?'

'Here we cannot get money for foreign travels. Only for scientific workers. There is not foreign currency.'

'They use that as an excuse. In the West, even the poorest students go. They just go. Why can't Tadeusz?'

Witek looked pained. She was attacking him. What good would it do him to agree with her, merely to join in her mood?

'He would waste a lot of time from his studies and the others would be in front of him.'

She turned away, defeated. Witek watched her, with hurt love in his gaze. Any relationship with someone who disapproved of him as much as Rose did could only be painful.

Mentally he tried saying good-bye to her, in the same way that Janet was always saying good-bye to Tadeusz: they existed in another world, into which they could not be followed. But, like Janet, he could not quite give up hope.

When Rose faced him again, she was fierce.

'If you could leave Poland, would you?'

'No,' he shouted back. 'Of course not.'

After this, they both faltered.

'Do forgive me asking, Witek. You know, with Janet and everything, I can't help thinking about it.'

'I understand.' He frowned. 'I cannot know what Janet tells you. I know she is not happy.'

'Well, I—'

'I know,' he said, more loudly. 'But perhaps we are not all to blame. This is new, since she was in England. Before that, life was very hard for us and then she was wonderful.'

'She thinks Tadeusz is missing something.'

'I understand. You think so, too.'

'I don't know. But I must find out.'

'Why must you find out?'

Rose made the tea with a good deal of fuss and then said: 'Because I'm fond of you all and at the moment I don't have anyone else I much care for, that's all.'

It was enough for him. He was perplexed by their whole conversation: half-scared and half-flattered, like a hired guide to whom lady tourists suddenly ask a lot of personal questions.

Rose poured two glasses of tea. 'Here you are.'

'There isn't lemon, I am sorry.'

'Do you have lemons here?'

'There were some about three weeks ago. I could get two for Janet. She was keeping them for something and they went bad.'

'Poor Witek.'

He frowned, stirred his tea and handed her back the spoon.

Then he looked quickly down into his glass. The warmth in his eyes was not only from the tea. Again he had noticed her nightdress hanging on the line behind her. It was all frills and ridiculousness and it made him want to cry. With anguish he imagined Rose's flat in Kensington, a place where she was not merely represented by a nightdress or a crumpled stocking, but extended to pictures and furniture and a bed. A bed which was not folded up before breakfast, but existed in all its flagrancy throughout the day. He had covertly examined the pictures of such beds in the magazines which Rose sent to Janet.

'You asked me if I leave Poland. I did not say clearly what I mean. Later, if I get the post of head of the English department, I wish very much to re-visit England. In one year, perhaps.'

'That would be lovely.'

He stared across, deep into her eyes, then looked away. 'You will be in London?'

'I don't know. Probably. What about Tadeusz?'

'Tadeusz?' He was puzzled.

'Witek, why don't you let Tadeusz come to England for a little while. I'd pay his fare and put him up and I know some children of his own age who'd love to show him round.'

'Tadeusz?'

'Yes. I want him to come – on a visit.'

'But why?'

'Just so that he can see England.'

'That is not possible.'

'Why not? It'd be such fun.'

'It is not possible.'

'I don't see why. I mean, if he can get a passport and everything.'

'It would disturb him in his school work.'

'All right, for a short time only. In the holidays.'

'No. I can't allow it.'

Suddenly she was sick of him. She moved off to the sink, showing an impatient back.

He watched her for a moment and then realized that she was not going to speak to him again. She was sulking, as Janet did. Neither of them wanted anything to do with him, only with Tadeusz. He put down his glass, began to say something but the numb feeling of speaking English lay over his brain again.

Yet he could not leave her thinking ill of him. 'Rose.'

'No, it's no good. You've told me it's no good.'

'It is not me but—'

'It is you. Other people go.'

'No, you do not understand. Things are not so easy for me. In any case, it is too late to apply for a passport. That takes four or five months.'

Rose counted quickly on her fingers. 'July, August – say the end of August. There'd be time.'

'Perhaps.'

'Witek, do let him come. He'll love it.'

'You have not spoken with him about this?'

'No, but I will. He'll persuade you, I'm sure.'

'Please not. Do not speak. It will disturb his work. Although he complains of his courses he is a very diligent boy.'

'He can't apply for a passport without knowing it, can he?'

'I will see first what may be done.'

'You'll let him apply. Oh, Witek, thank you.'

'No. Well, perhaps.'

He had never seen her look so happy before. Since her arrival she had been cast down, not only by the way in which she found them living but by the muted sadness which lay over everything in Biala Gora.

'Yes?'

'I promise nothing. But there is a chance.'

He shivered, feeling he had bartered something away for nothing, or for nothing more substantial than a frilled night-dress on a hanger. Later, when he was alone, he would run his face across it.

## Chapter Twelve

Rose was delighted at what she had gained. Once she had got his confidence, she thought, Witek would accept her judgement on a good deal more. And that night, before they went to bed, she told Janet.

'He said Tadeusz could come to England this summer.'

'Oh, darling.'

'All very secret, of course. He doesn't want me even to tell Tadeusz yet.'

'Then I'll tell him.'

'Please don't. You'll make my position very difficult. I'll have to make all sorts of promises, of course, about looking after him and sending him back in time for the school year.'

'Of course.'

'But it's what we want, isn't it? We want Tadeusz to be able to choose his life.'

That night Rose's elation was so great that she did not notice that Janet was scarcely enthusiastic. But by the following morning Janet had evidently changed her mind. With the replete looks and shared glances of those who are keeping secrets, the sisters watched Tadeusz eat his breakfast.

It was as much as they could do to stop touching him the whole time.

As he devoured his scrambled eggs Tadeusz was conscious of something going on behind his shoulders. He judged it to be one of those female mysteries which adolescence had made him confident to dismiss. He smiled tolerantly to them both, swallowed a second cup of coffee and prepared to leave. They kissed him, seeing him off out of their immediate love with a sense of relief.

Janet had only three pupils on Saturday and the rest of the day she wandered round absent-mindedly attending to the flat, humming bits of dance-tunes that dated from the war years. She was much nicer to Rose, who began to regret Derek Loasby's invitation and the prospect of a student's Saturday evening.

While Rose was changing to go out, Krystyna Kazimierska arrived. Janet went to make tea, and Rose, too, was retreating into the kitchen. The other stopped her, and sat admiring her clothes while she changed. She made little appreciative noises at Rose's underwear.

'How is Janet?'

'Much more cheerful,' Rose said, without equivocation.

'I am so happy. It is a wonderful thing to have you here. But Rose, when are you starting to see the rest of our country? My sister has written from Krakow saying you may go there whenever you like. She has the room empty because her daughter is abroad.'

In the stress and complications among the Rudowskis, Rose had forgotten she was here disguised as a tourist;

everyone expected her to go away from Biala Gora at some time or other.

'I'd love that.'

'She has many friends who would take you around Krakow. Here there is nothing for tourists to see.'

'I suppose not.'

'She doesn't speak English. But you can speak French with her.'

Janet, humming 'You are my sunshine', came back with tea. Mrs Kazimierska watched the two sisters intensely. She caught Rose's eye and seemed to be signalling indecipherable messages, perhaps about Janet. Rose was being asked to take part in one of those Slav bouts of feeling, so strange to the Anglo-Saxon, in which sympathy goes mounting up to the point of explosion, after which any indifference looks like betrayal.

There was no doubt, however, about the change in Janet.

She swirled airily between them and when the bell rang she ran to it with a stagey lightness.


'Oh, do come in. You are a stranger. It's really quite an honour for us isn't it? I'm sure you're so busy.'

At the doorway, Derek Loasby eyed Mrs Rudowski with distrust. Though he still shifted from one foot to the other with his usual suppressed excitement, he was still constrained and embarrassed when he greeted the other two.

'Now do tell us what you've been doing,' Janet went on. 'We're fascinated to know, simply fascinated.'

He blushed. What was the hag up to? His confidence waned; he suspected he was being teased. He muttered something about learning the language.

'Try some out on Mrs Kazimierska and me. Oh, please do!' She clasped her hands to her breast, pleading.

Loasby looked at Rose but she was offering no help. He toyed with the idea of an obscenity he had just learned, but was scared of the formidable Mrs Kazimierska.

She rescued him. 'Elzbieta Barcik says he is very good. But he speaks Russian, I think.'

'Yes, I learned it at the University.'

'Oxford or Cambridge?' Janet asked.

'London, actually.'

'Oh, I see.' She looked at Rose with a twinkle.

Loasby stood frowning, unable to understand what was going on. Perhaps Mrs Rudowski had heard some scandal about him and he was unwelcome. With an effort he tried being less self-conscious, and decided that she might be drunk.

Rose said: 'We ought to be going.'

'Yes, they'll be waiting for us.'

In the hallway, surrounded by bicycles and packing cases and skis, he helped her on with her overcoat.

'Just a moment. I'd better take my key.'

Rose, too, was surprised and worried by Janet's behaviour. Perhaps this was how middle-class women had spoken in the thirties; how their mother, as housemaster's wife, had dealt with the parents of boys she considered common.

Or perhaps Janet had learned it at a military hospital, from some snobbish matron roaring through the menopause. It was a folk memory preserved through years of Communist exile, a faded wreath from the bourgeois world.

Loasby heard Rose's voice raised in anger. Her sister answered: 'Why should he get away with it, a little oik like that?'

Rose came back. She did not speak but pushed her chin right down into her coat collar. She took his arm as they walked to the tram stop.

When they were in the tram she said: 'I'm sorry about that.'

'Don't give it a thought.'

'No, I must. I think living here turns some people mad.'

'What's an oik, anyway?'

'It's – it's a slang expression. From the war, I think.' She stared out at the dark blocks of buildings and the empty streets.

'You have to be tough living here, that's all.'

'Why should anyone *have* to be tough,' she complained. 'It's awful isn't it?'

Loasby was silent: the Spartan atmosphere was one of the things that attracted him, though it would be impossible to explain it to her.

They had forgotten to pay their fares. The conductress now stood between them, in a coat of rough sheepskin and with a face of Mongolian impassivity.

'She's tough all right.' He handed over two coins. '"What breath blew out the light within that brain?"'

'What's that?'

'From a poem. I can't remember which,' he added awkwardly, though he could.

'Oh.'

'Some people have still got the lights in their brains all right, I can tell you. You just follow me.'

## Chapter Thirteen

The whole centre of Biala Gora, including the medieval market-place and the Town Hall, was destroyed by the Germans during their retreat in 1945: a centre of Germanic culture could not be allowed to fall into the hands of Slav barbarians. The Polish authorities, when they re-occupied the city, were in some doubt about restoring it in a style which had never been Polish. But evidently these conflicts of opinion had now been overcome. The gables of merchants' houses were beginning to take shape behind a maze of scaffolding. The Gothic Town Hall was already completed and its cellar had been handed over to the Students' Union. Soon the market-place of Biala Gora would be a place for tourists to visit. Its years as a mass of rubble would scarcely be referred to: it would be first new, then old, all over again.

Derek Loasby led Rose Nicholson across the cobbles to the portico of the Town Hall. While they waited to be let in, music and light were welling up out of a grating at their feet.

A small plump girl with crew-cut hair was the first to greet them. Derek biffed her confidently on the behind. 'This is Wanda. She doesn't speak any English, in fact we don't let her. Her job is to help me with my Polish. I wonder what's happened to old Mirek. *Gdzie jest Mirek?*'

The girl shrugged her shoulders and continued to stare blankly at Rose. Three other girls left their friends and gathered to inspect Rose. Loasby greeted them all. This, then, was the explanation of his bouncy happiness: here he crowed and strutted in triumph. He had found a place where neither his spectacles nor his manner nor the recrudescent boil-crop on the nape of his neck made any difference; a place where, as now, some incomprehensible mistake in his use of the language roused a conjoint peal of laughter; where he could be a joker without ever making a joke.

Half-hidden by the massive pillars that supported the vaults, five young men sat on a platform playing jazz. Abstract paintings hung on the whitewashed walls, amateurish and probably self-mocking, as though whoever painted them had not considered them anything more than a necessary gesture for the place and the time. Everything here was a gesture, the jazz, the pictures, the Western clothes and hairstyles. In recent years such things had become officially tolerated but somehow unrenewable. The students, however, were always being renewed and nearly a whole University generation had passed since the October revolt. Some of the faces in the cellar had the candour of those to whom everything here was still exciting. They had the rare charm of the young who do not pretend they have seen and done all this before, and their liveliness made you happy to look at them.

Derek gave Rose a glass of Jugoslav wine. 'I can't think what's happened to old Mirek.'

In the presence of his friends, he backed away from her a little and she was left isolated with the glass of wine, trying to make it last, while the girls waited for her to manifest herself in some typical way or other. The blank-faced Wanda even came up and fingered the woollen dress Rose was wearing, at which the small group was rocked by giggles. But no conversation ensued.

After another conference with Wanda, whom Rose was beginning to regard with some antipathy, Derek asked Rose to dance. On the little dance-floor their progress was halting, because the jazzmen's intense attitude to their task led them into self-intoxicated 'breaks' of great complexity. Everyone stood still and listened. During one of these interludes a tall man, with short blond hair brushed forward, came and stood beside them. He placed a large hand on Derek's shoulder. Derek flushed with pleasure. His face always transmitted everything he was thinking.

'Miroslaw Sypniewski.'

The young man bowed and brought his heels together. He kissed Rose's hand.

'This is Mirek. He speaks perfect English. Our worries are over. Let's all go and have a drink.'

The three of them sat at a small table to drink more of the mouth-drying red wine.

'This character here, honestly, I can tell you it was quite something to discover him in a town like this. He's the perfect introduction to life here. If you want to know absolutely anything, Mirek's your man. Yes, sir. He's a real fixer. Correct?'

The newcomer did not answer. He flicked sly, rather small green eyes from one to the other, while his meaty hands were crumpled in front of his face and his body was shaken by the unvoiced giggles and breathy grunting noises which Poles emit at times of surprise and amusement.

'But you're a student, aren't you?' Rose did not want either of the young men too sure of themselves.

'Yes, I study Sanskrit.'

'Oh.'

'One must continue to be a student, it is much the best way to live. The Sanskrit course is rather a long one. Perhaps also I am often failing in the exams.'

'He thinks they'll take his scholarship away,' Derek said helpfully.

'At present that does not much matter if I may stay at the University. You see, I earn by giving lessons in English. Perhaps my English is not good enough but I must work.'

He presented this as his fate: he did not think he should. With his height and looks, there was about him certainly a sort of damaged authority, as though fallen from antediluvian glory; this separated him from the others in the place who were dressed, like him, in dirty black sweaters and tubular trousers.

Derek, who was staring at them both with the pleasure of the successful go-between, now became conscious of the girl Wanda standing at about three yards distance. He shifted around undecidedly, then left them.

For a while Mirek was silent, with a stillness not of timidity but of speculation. He did not look at Rose; he was absorbing her presence by a kind of mental deep-breathing.

When at last he spoke, he was still formal. 'I am told this is like a *cave* in Paris. You think so?'

'Oh no.'

'The students will be disappointed to hear that.'

'The faces are quite different here. More hopeful.'

'Is that so? I wonder why?' He looked behind him at the dancing couples as though he expected to see something different. 'They must be very stupid then. What can they be hopeful about?'

'Perhaps they are glad to be students. Perhaps they wouldn't have been students before the war.'

'And now they are students what can they hope for? What can I hope for? Please tell me.'

She laughed. 'You tell me. I've only been here a week.'

'I can tell you. I hope for nothing at all.'

Against the blank stare with which he said this, she was silent, but since Mirek belonged to a class or a way of life which might sooner or later include Tadeusz, she felt concerned and interested.

The music stopped. Derek relinquished his partner, and came back to the table:

'Why aren't you dancing? Slackers!'

'Would you like to dance?'

'Not really,' Rose said. 'Please go on about the students.'

'What's all this about the students? I think they're terrific.'

Mirek looked at Derek with tolerance. 'For Mr Loasby it is very good here because of the vodka and the nice Polish girls. But Polish people are always taking this for granted even in the worst times. Not like England where you have Puritanism and are against pleasure.'

Derek nodded vigorously but Rose said: 'That's not really true, you know.'

'I think so. My uncle was there in the war.'

'Things have changed.'

'Perhaps.' Rose had got to know that this word expressed strong disbelief. 'But in Poland we have drink and making love all the time. We are always looking for something which our history will not give us. We will never get it and so I think the students are stupid to look hopeful.'

'Would you leave here if you could?'

Derek looked embarrassed at this: His eyes fled from one to the other. Mirek blew out smoke and said: 'I cannot ever leave Poland.'

'Why not?'

'Because I was in prison.'

Rose blushed. For her the word connected still with guilt. 'I'm sorry.'

'Don't mention it.' He smiled crookedly. 'That is why I am older than the other students. I did not really fail some examinations.'

'Oh, good.'

She wondered what it was correct to think, and what Derek thought. If Mirek was really his friend, he must condemn this iniquity in a place he so much approved of. But perhaps the lurid fact of gaol gave Mirek an added attraction.

'You see why it is better for me to live here than Warsaw. In winter I am giving English lessons to my colleagues and in summer I am taking foreign visitors round factories. I am a very good guide. I have all of statistics at the tip of my tongue. I know where the canteen will be built and the washroom and the flats of workers. I know the production figures for next year—'

'But not last year?'

'Next year is so very much better. I tell the visitors all that and they are much interested. They return to their countries pleased and frightened a little, which is a nice feeling to have.'

'Why can't you tell them the truth? They'd be just as interested.'

'This is my job. I do not wish to go back where I came from just because I tell two Dutch journalists or an English Trades Unionist something they are incapable to understand. However they try, if they try till they explode, they will never understand what it was like living under Hitler and Stalin and what it is going to be like again. This is like talking through a wall of glass. Even if our factories will work just as well as yours, do you think the wall of glass will go away?'

'I suppose not,' Rose said. 'All the same, if you won't tell the truth to Dutch journalists, how do we know you tell it to us?'

Derek squirmed again at this, but almost at once, another of the girls appeared beside him. Mirek watched them go, laughed to himself, and then turned again his look of absorptive charm.

She was not going to be put off. 'Well, suppose you do tell us the truth, why?'

'Derek is my friend. He must learn.'

'And me?'

'You are involved a little, I think. You have relatives here. You are not dangerous.'

Rose finished her glass of wine. 'Life here doesn't look the same to everyone, you know.'

'I know, I know.' It was something he had heard too often before. He held up a large hand, placatory but at the same time repressive. 'People forget. Or they are too young, they have nothing to compare. I am old enough. I remember how we found one day that the whole world had turned grey, grey streets, grey houses, grey faces, grey girls. The war didn't do that and statistics will not change it. Stalin did it. It was like a bomb. It was his fall-out. We are trying to tidy up but the greyness has got into everything. I will fetch another drink.'

She watched Mirek return with two brimming glasses. In front of him the crowd separated without being asked to: you realized that in the most democratic society people must be born knowing where to put their hands and feet, possessing grace, this word for a physical thing which has always the shadow of a religious meaning.

Rose's brother Nicholas had possessed it, and now perhaps Tadeusz. But the ambitious ones are people like Witek Rudowski who have always to struggle to make the events of a year or a moment turn out correctly.

Arguing from Witek's side, Rose said: 'My nephew is going to be an engineer. Surely he won't see everything grey?'

'Don't you know what a dictatorship means?'

'You think nobody can be happy. But I think he can be.'

'Who?'

'My Polish nephew,' she said patiently. She wanted him to agree with her about something, it did not matter what. His reckless way of talking had been intended to attract her, and perhaps had done this, but it really was not worth his while to put himself into danger.

'I think he can be happy,' she said again.

'In the mountains. The first time he has a woman. When he gets really drunk at somebody's name-day party. Is that enough? Perhaps for the English. We had better ask Mr Derek.'

Loasby was jigging past them with a third girl. His forelock was flapping up and down and his face was radiant. It was difficult not to take him as an example of someone falling into exactly the place intended.

Rose agreed with Mirek: she wanted more than that for Tadeusz. For the last moments she had been thinking of Tadeusz here in three years' time as one of these students, even as Mirek perhaps. But, with Tadeusz's chances of escape, would anyone here have chosen this? Almost certainly not. But would they have been right?

Mirek watched her perplexed face. 'Well?'

'I think you're very depressing.' The inadequacy of this remark emerged charming and shrill. He accepted it with glee.

Rose's attempt at optimism had been exactly what he

wanted. She realized this now. The sort of things you could say, the sort of answers it was incumbent on you to make, were drastically limited. In the end from courtesy and kindness you were the sort of person they wanted you to be. You kept their argument going by always losing it.

'Let's go away from here,' he said. 'Let's go for a walk.'

'All right.'

They left. They did not say good-bye to Derek.

## Chapter Fourteen

The nights are quiet in Biala Gora, which then enters the pre-industrial age. Even on Saturday nights the drunks, though ragged and fierce, are quiet as they stumble along in their happiness. A faint light hangs over the factories and occasionally blue flashes from the tram wires illuminate the lower sky, but otherwise it is very dark. When a horse and cart go by the hoofbeats echo into completely empty streets. Few people hear them. In grim last-century houses the inhabitants lie packed together in exhausted sleep, three and four to a room.

Rose and Mirek walked away from the Town Hall, rather separated and pacing rhythmically as people do who do not yet know where they are going. The night was warm with spring, but Rose shrugged her coat round her neck. Large and placid, Mirek still walked apart.

On the embankment of the river street-lamps shone through the branches of trees, and along the twigs leaf-buds were beginning to show like knots. They stopped walking. He stood, a tall shadow in a dirty raincoat, and gave off melancholy in waves. How sad that the race should still produce people like him, when what was needed was someone more compact, as it were more resilient to atmospheric pressure.

'Let's look at the river.'

It flowed in a gulf in front of them, black and greasy. Unhindered by buildings the wind brought a wild stench, like a blow on the face. It caught at their throats, roughened by the wine they had drunk in the Students' Club. The girl bent her head and choked. He came towards her.

'God, what is that?'

'It is from the cellulose factory outside the town. By night you can smell it a long way.'

She hurried across the bridge and he followed with long strides.

'It's terrible. How can people live here?'

'They are accustomed. I think it is much worse in the factory but that is one of the problems of reconstruction.'

'What do you mean?'

'It affects their brains and they become mad. This is an important industry and we make cellulose very cheaply. We cannot afford safety devices. And you see in this country people work where they are told. The workers are in power. They cannot strike against themselves, can they? That would be ridiculous.'

He spoke with polite ferocity, as though making a quick winning move in some competitive game.

'Has this been going on long?'

'Some years. But you see the river is quite poisoned.'

'Polluted. It's awful.'

The dead stream would always be flowing through Biala Gora. Rose knew the obsession which Mirek was trying to make her share: that nothing would ever go right here, whatever they said, for hundreds of years.

'I don't believe it.'

'What?'

'About the factory.'

'It is what people say. I do not take visitors over this factory so I cannot know.'

'Can nobody find out for certain?'

'If they did? We may not write it in a newspaper. If it is not written about, how can people feel anything about it? With a censorship like ours we are not permitted a sense of injustice.'

'Someone must know the truth.'

'Why? Truth is for Western journalists and they do very well without it. We don't want it. We want fantasies.'

They arrived at the housing estate on the edge of the town, and the cinderpath leading to the Rudowskis' flat.

She turned towards him with a helpless gesture.

'Don't worry. You do not have to stay here. And perhaps we have got used to it.'

'Will it ever stop?'

'Nothing ever stops.'

'Damn.' She was wrestling ineffectively with the key, which fitted badly into the lock. She wanted him to go away; in spite of his healthy appearance, he was ill with unhappiness.

'Let me help.'

The lock yielded to him in one turn. He was very strong, breathing heavily there beside her in the dark. He put one hand on the corner of her shoulder.

'No,' she said. 'Sorry. Good night.'

## Chapter Fifteen

In the club, Derek Loasby was still dancing with Wanda. He pulled his arm tightly round her and looked down at her round head, which she had just had cropped short like a boy's.

She and some of her friends had copied this hairstyle from an American actress in a French film. This morning at his Polish lesson, Miss Barcik had told him it reminded her of the Camps, this new generation, she wailed, was repudiating absolutely everything about their parents, the suffering as much as the ideals. Derek thought about this for a little without agreeing and without being able to make up his mind. Then he wondered where Miss Barcik had seen him and Wanda together. It was not important but it gave him the feeling of being watched.

He himself rather disliked Wanda's hair. It increased her disconcerting air of detachment, and so did her sudden blank stares and the little yawns she gave, as unrepented as a cat's. True he had possessed her (on a Sunday afternoon in the Students' Hostel, her room-mates being at the cinema) but she still seemed only to possess herself.

Suddenly he noticed that Rose and Mirek had gone.

Derek felt deserted. All at once he was sure that he had greatly overestimated the charm and interest of the young people who surrounded him. You had to take their goodwill on trust, for all the time there were muffled giggles, comments you didn't quite catch, and the sense that their very enthusiasm was isolating you. He held tightly on to Wanda while once again they circled the floor in and out of the stone pillars and past the squealing jazz group. He tried to think about tonight.

On his arrival at Biala Gora, he had been given a room at the Students' Hostel. After two weeks of discomfort and good intentions, he had deserted it. Now he lodged with a lawyer, his wife, their daughters and a cousin or two: the Tulewicz family had contracted, like a crab fitting all its legs into a rock-cleft, in order to make room for Mr Derek Loasby, and he was never sure how many of them slept in the room next to his. Whenever he entered it, it was perfectly tidy, with heavily-fringed table cloths and potted plants and the usual row of divans round the walls.

Tonight he knew the flat would be empty and the stack of skis gone from the hallway, for the Tulewiczes were away in the mountains for the last of the snow. But while he was shepherding Wanda through the door he felt a qualm. It was like a blasphemy, this rape of the Catholic family atmosphere. And supposing one of the cousins should choose to return earlier? It would not seriously matter for himself but for Wanda it might.

In his room he switched on the bedside lamp. They undressed in the shadows. He lowered himself beside her, aching for the warmth of their complete embrace. Smiling he ran his hand over the blunt, cropped head. It was jerked away. Wanda burst into tears.

'What is it?'

He really wished to know, though he hoped the reason was flattering to himself.

He held her in his arms and her whole body was tense and shaking. She went on crying and he felt himself beginning to get quite wet. Then she began to whisper to him – all those repeated 'cz's' and 'sz's' reverberating in his ear, like the inside of a sea-shell. When she stopped he had understood nothing much, except that she had said he would not understand.

Derek was in despair. He wanted above all to comfort her, but the only obvious way seemed uncouth and insensitive. Sometimes he wished it had all begun like that, coarsely, paying her off each time with a pair of nylon stockings. With Wanda, he was afraid this might have worked.

He shifted the lampshade so that the light fell across her body. She was staring past him with empty eyes; for her, he was not there. The building was silent around them. There was no sound from outside except for the lonely howl of an east-bound train being driven towards the steppes.

'Why did you weep?'

She did not reply. He began to touch her again but she held his hands away.

'It wouldn't be any good now,' he said, looking down his stomach. He lit a cigarette and offered it to her, but she refused it. She leaned over and pulled up the sheet.

'I will have to stay here till morning,' she said, bleakly. 'Because of the concierge.'

'The Tulewiczes are coming back in the morning.'

She fell asleep. He embraced her and held her, managing to salvage something out of this defeat, and she did not wake.

Later he watched the dawn whitening the opposite wall. He was calmer now, but the bed was too narrow for them both to sleep. His thoughts wandered off. On the wall there hung pictures, nineteenth-century landscapes the Tulewiczes had brought from Wilno with the rest of their furniture, after the German invasion of Russia. How had they managed it? You thought of the war here as being all massacre and chaos, yet there had been areas of normality, more then than afterwards, and to hear of them could still surprise you. All the same Derek, watching for the onset of morning, felt a muddled antagonism at the fact that the Tulewiczes had moved their furniture. His was a reaction fairly usual among foreigners; if anything at all went right here, you accused the inhabitants of being far better off than they said they were.

Derek's thoughts went back again and again to the girls he had danced with the previous evening, and how they spoke about him among themselves. Wherever he went, he walked into sudden silences, phrases were bitten back or breathed off in whispers he could not possibly understand. Sometimes he was almost proud of this, the free man in the Communist world, like a Sheriff striding the empty street at high noon with everyone watching him, but after such fantasies he quailed because he knew, compared with Mirek even, he was not free at all. He lived only on the information provided him, and if something was inexplicable like Wanda's tears he was utterly lost.

He fell asleep and when he awoke it was bright sunshine and after eight o'clock. Wanda was still beside him, awake and affectionate. But he was unmanned with apprehension, for the Tulewiczes would be returning at any minute. He got her out of bed but she took a particularly long time to dress, while he sat on the bed and bit his nails. After that she disappeared to the bathroom for about half an hour. Derek heard every banged door and scamper of feet announce the return of the Tulewicz children.

Finally she was gone. He stretched out, exhausted, and slept till noon.

## Chapter Sixteen

Janet made a startled movement as if to protect some papers which were lying on the table in front of her.

'What are those?'

'The forms.'

'What forms?'

'For Tadeusz. For his passport.'

'Oh.'

Rose sat down opposite Janet and took one of her Bulgarian cigarettes. The sight of the papers, a step taken, disturbed
her. Of course, Witek's promise had been given. Perhaps it
was a mistake to have wheedled it out of him, to have bitched
him into giving it, as she had done, for since then the poor
man had gone round with a countenance of fixed glumness
and an unkempt look. Still, a promise was a promise.

In Janet's elation there was something even more wrong.
She kept on singing those wartime dance-tunes and rem-
iniscing about her experiences at military hospitals with
staff nurses, army doctors and even a 'very nice Cana-
dian major who wanted to marry me, only he was killed at
Dieppe.' Rose had never heard of this character before; he

was a ghost summoned up to dance at the defeat of Witold Rudowski.

In one way Rose understood her sister better now than she had previously done. Since talking to Mirek Sypniewski, she was prey to the same sense of anguish about Tadeusz. His fate was in the air in a quite especial way; they all seemed to carry it around here, their past and their future, like an aureole or a spotlight following them, but Tadeusz alone might be given the right to choose.

'There's tea in the kitchen.'

When Rose came back with a glass of tea, she said: 'We oughtn't to push this too much, ought we? Not if it's going to mean a fuss.'

'If it's going to mean a fuss, that can't be helped. He has to sign.'

'He'll have to have photographs too, won't he? I mean, I don't see all this business about not telling him. It's treating him like a child and after all he is fifteen. I know we were treated like that but nowadays in England—'

'I mean Witek has to sign.'

'Oh, I see. Well, he promised.'

'I bet you he tries to wriggle out of it.'

If he does, Rose thought, it is your fault. She said: 'We'll have to persuade him again.'

'You persuade him. Your idea in the first place.'

'All right. But we could put it off, couldn't we?'

'No, we couldn't. He promised, you told me he promised. I won't have Tadeusz disappointed.'

'But Tadeusz doesn't even know about this.'

'He must go. I've set my heart on it. Don't you want him to go?'

'Yes, I do,' Rose said. 'For three weeks or so, anyway. Poor little beast, he deserves a good time.'

'I want him to learn what it is like to be English. Then he can choose. That's what the solicitors suggested, isn't it?'

'I suppose it is. I don't think they'd any idea how silly it sounds.'

Janet sulked at this and no further discussion took place until Witek returned from the University. He looked strained and haggard. There was a piece of his hair that would not stick down. He saw the papers lying on the table and at once guessed what they were.

He sat down and said: 'Rose.'

She was torn with pity to look at him. 'Yes.'

'I think perhaps this is not possible. So sorry.'

'I do not understand, Witek.'

He was trembling and on the other side of the table Janet was trembling too. Rose loved them both, and was sorry for them, and she dared not speak.

'Better not, this year,' Witek said.

'Rose has invited him. She has been kind enough—'

But he could not look at Janet. 'Rose?'

'I told you I wanted to and I thought you said "yes" but if—'

He stood up and put his arm round her shoulders, leaning on her; breathing close, touching her more heavily than he had ever done before. One of his hands was tight on her upper arm, the thumb pressing in where the muscle slipped on the bone.

'Rose.'

'Yes?' She was frightened, feeling crushed against him.

'May I speak with you alone, please?'

Rose looked despairingly at Janet, who turned away.

When they had gone, Janet unfolded the papers again, put on her spectacles and began to fill in the blank spaces.

Rudowski, Tadeusz, born Glasgow, Scotland, 19 January 1944. Father: Rudowski, Witold Wlodzimierz, born Katowice, 2 May 1916. Mother: Nicholson, Janet Elizabeth, born Barnham, Surrey, England, 3 August 1922. Social Class: Working intelligentsia.

She completed the whole questionnaire three times and then sat back and lit a cigarette. Her hands were shaking. Twenty minutes had gone past.

She heard somebody stumbling over the bicycles in the corridor. It was Rose, returning alone.

'Well?'

'Damn that bicycle. Yes, all right.'

Janet was silent and Rose saw that she had been crying.

Rose put her arm round her sister. 'Cheer up, it's all right, I tell you.' But by now she herself felt badly in need of convincing and so, as she usually did, she went on talking. 'Poor Witek, can you believe what he thought I was up to? He thought I was going to kidnap Tadeusz and take him to England and never let him come back. Honestly. I mean, I suppose everyone suspects everyone here, but really that does seem a bit much.'

Rose was talking against a gulf of anxiety. Things were far worse than she had imagined and she was deeply sorry for him.

'What did you tell him?'

'Oh, I gave him absolutely every guarantee under the sun. Return ticket, to begin with. I said we'd only ask for a six weeks' visa and I swore I'd see he got back when it was finished. There was a bit of trouble because we couldn't find anything I thought sacred enough to swear by. To Witek I'm really a terrible pagan, aren't I? I mean, he's always believed in something, hasn't he? But in the end we made it. I told him I'm sure Tadeusz will be longing to get back. After all, he's a tremendous patriot, isn't he?'

Janet did not speak.

'Actually I'm scared Tadeusz will be disappointed with England.'

'He's too young to be disappointed, except in people. He'll be thrilled.'

'I wonder. Well, there we are.'

'Thank you, darling.' At last Janet smiled.

'Anything to oblige. Now I've got to break the dreadful news to Tadeusz. Witek said I could.'

## Chapter Seventeen

The tram crossed a bridge over the polluted river and ran far out along the edge of the pine forest. At the last stop Tadeusz helped Rose to get down. They watched the tram grind round in a large circle and set off back to Biala Gora. Beside them a sandy track led away into the forest.

'Don't go out of sight. If you disappear I'll never find the way back.'

The boy did not react; he thought she was trying to make him feel important. Although this walk was one which they had promised each other since Rose's first day at Biala Gora, he did not appear to be particularly cheerful about it. There was a mulish look about him. He picked up a stick and began slashing away at things.

The forest was composed of pine trees. Paths and fire-breaks ran through it, and occasionally there were black bubbling pools, round which the new sedge sprouted a brilliant green. From one of these came a riotous sound, honking and cackling.

'What on earth's that?'

'Frogs.' He threw his stick and the cackling stopped.

'You've frightened them. It was a lovely noise. They don't do that in England.' She walked towards the pool but the ground was marshy and she soon returned.

'In autumn we are coming here for mushrooms.'

'It's lovely. Thank you for bringing me. Look, there's a lizard. If you don't move they can't see you.'

Tadeusz immediately moved and the lizard ran away.

Rose watched him for a moment, surprised and a little put out by this lack of sympathy. He did not look at her. He picked up another stick and went on slashing the green plants.

'I'm sorry. Aren't you enjoying this?'

He did not answer for a moment. Then he said: 'I think English persons like going for walks.'

'Yes. Don't you?'

'Not just walks. We like to go to see something or to do something.'

'We've seen a lizard.'

He did not reply and they went on walking down one of the wide fire-breaks.

Suddenly he said: 'Mother says you have invited me to England.'

'Yes.' Rose drooped a little with disappointment. 'I did think she was going to let me break the dreadful news. Why didn't you tell me you knew? Oh, Tadeusz, you are pleased, aren't you?'

'Of course,' he said politely.

After a while he said: 'I want very much to go to England.'

'Then what the hell's wrong?'

When he sulked, he looked like his mother. He had retreated into one of those difficult corners where one holds out, at all costs, against showing gratitude.

Though they had been walking for only twenty minutes, they were now deep into the forest. There seemed no point in being where they were. Pinewoods are too dry and aseptic to be attractive in any way. They had nothing to do but talk to each other, but this was proving increasingly difficult. Rose was asking too much of him, trying to force out understanding and love. But there seemed to be nothing between them now, only this haze of polite English – it was Witek's English really, not Janet's at all – through which Tadeusz spoke to her.

'I know I shall think of Poland all of the time. Comparing things and – and arguing with myself. But it is not to be helped.'

'Try not to worry too much. You're young.'

'But I must learn about this.'

'There's nothing much you can do about it, is there?'

For Tadeusz this remark was worse than nothing. Of course you had to tackle everything while you still believed you could. Rose knew this but she was still annoyed and offended with him. She had made what was really an offer of love and he was too young for it. He had no idea yet that his indifference had any power to hurt.

'In any case,' he said gloomily, 'there is still the visa. Perhaps I cannot get it.'

'I'm going to Warsaw the day after tomorrow. I'll get the forms from the Embassy.'

'Going to Warsaw – then you are leaving?'

He was worried now, she noticed with a little stab of happiness. 'No, I'm coming back. I'm going to Krakow for a few days to stay with Mrs Kazi – Kazi – thing's sister.'

Tadeusz thought about this. 'Krakow is a beautiful place. I was there with an excursion.'

'Yes, I'm sure it is.' She did not want to be put off now. 'I'll post the visa forms and you can have them ready before I come back.'

'I must have people to sign.'

'You can do that, too.'

'Even then perhaps I will not get the visa.'

'It oughtn't to be difficult. You're a student.'

'There is one girl I know that was refused.'

'Oh?'

'She was an orphan. They don't want orphans.'

'Well, you're not an orphan.'

He appeared not to be listening, but went on in a wondering voice: 'It is strange about England, they take in niggers but not Poles.'

She was appalled by this and wondered where he had learned it. 'You mustn't talk like that.'

'Why not?'

'Because – because people – my friends – won't like you. They'll think you are uneducated.'

This sounded inadequate but she thought it would do for him. He accepted it without comment. The essential thing was not to blame him, to go on talking as though nothing had happened; for the first time, however, she realized something of Janet's urgency to get him away from all this. He was damaged, but in a way that was unexpected; with his intelligence he could catch you off your guard.

Rose went on talking. She chattered to him about London, describing her flat where, now that her girl-friend had moved out, Tadeusz would be able to have a bedroom to himself for the first time in his life. She told him about the places they would visit together and the people she wanted him to meet.

Tadeusz walked quietly and intently, his face inexpressive. Rose could not tell if he was listening or not. The forest began to get thinner around them and now they were following a sort of sandy ravine which led on to a main road.

Tadeusz stopped.

'Tired already?'

He did not answer. His silence was heavy, meaningful.

Beside the track stood a large block of concrete with a plaque made of bronze let into the front of it. On the plaque there was a date, some writing in Polish, then the hoops and gallows of a Hebrew inscription.

'What's that?'

But she knew at once what it was. Two bunches of coltsfoot lay on top of the block; a bumble-bee tussled at one of the yellow flowers.

All afternoon the boy had been leading Rose through the pinewoods towards this place. For this reason he had suggested the walk, had taken the tram, and to counteract her natural cheerfulness had slashed sullenly at the vegetation and listened unmoved to all her chatter about London. This, with an intensity of adolescence almost like malice, he had been planning for her. Now he watched her. He wanted to know whether he had succeeded or not.

He translated the plaque. 'There were fifty-eight shot here. The others in Biala Gora were taken to the Camps.' He was out of breath and his cheeks were flushed. He had failed absolutely, for Rose was only trying to imagine what it was like being Tadeusz.

Her second thought was that he could not possibly understand this himself or feel anything genuine about the skeletons in the sandy soil. It had happened in the year he was born, and he had been born in Scotland. 'This is what the Germans did here.' Yes, it was true but he had been told to say it. You shouldn't have to make propaganda, even true propaganda, to near relatives. They had damaged him, all right, even when they made him tell the truth. He was corrupted by the truth and this was what in the future it would be almost impossible to explain to him.

She gave him a look of deep pity and love. Now he, too, knew he had failed. He had meant her to assent and be in some way broken, but she only sympathized.

A few yards farther on they emerged to the main road, which was lined with poplar trees.

'So this walk wasn't just a walk, after all.'

Tadeusz laughed. 'A Polish walk. Not an English one.'

He was relieved to have got his task over. He had given

up sulking and was as confident and attractive as he had ever been.

Where the forest ended, huge fields stretched out, divided into a mosaic of little strips. Some women were thrusting seed potatoes into the thin soil.

'Tadeusz, do let's stop trying to prove things to each other. Come to England just for a holiday. No one's going to make anyone believe anything by pushing it down the other's throats.'

She was the one who failed now; he merely waved her away. He talked without stopping all the way back in the tram and they arrived home cheerful, confident and hungry, and friends for the first time.

## Chapter Eighteen

Tadeusz and Rose were walking down a long slope of grass towards the water. He had changed his mind now and was quite used to coming for walks for the mere pleasure of a beautiful day. Behind them somewhere Janet and Witek were following. Some sort of break-through had taken place; everything was going all right with them and from now on it always would. They were perfectly happy, as happy as one was in the summers of childhood. Boats were gliding up and down the lake – of course, it was the Serpentine! – and between the trees you could see the flash of the new glass buildings of Knightsbridge. To the right, though, over beyond the Barracks, stood a tall chimney which Rose did not remember having seen before. She had heard they were knocking down the Imperial Institute and this must be some part of the reconstruction plan. All the same, the black chimney looked out of place in the sky over South Kensington.

'That's the Imperial Institute, isn't it?' she asked Mirek Sypniewski.

He flinched at the word 'Imperial'.

'No, it's a factory,' he said.

'But it doesn't smell.'

'Nothing smells in dreams.'

Witek was gently shaking her shoulder. 'Five o'clock.'

She gasped with anguish, unable to remember where she was. The room was dark and Janet still slept.

Rose sat on the edge of the bed shivering. It was her first experience of the great Iron Curtain dream which, under the fences and naked sand of the frontiers, links up a world of sleepers with its vision of the summers which have for long been left out of the calendar.

In the kitchen Rose and Witek drank tea and chewed at pieces of bread. Tadeusz's bed was beside them; he lay in an almost frighteningly deep sleep, twisted as though he had been thrown down from a great height.

They took a workers' tram to the railway station. She had wanted to travel by air but Witek paid only half fare on the trains. Witek had insisted on accompanying her, in order to surround her with attention: he felt that if she could see how smoothly it was possible to manage things, she would approve more both of the country and himself.

When they arrived at the station the platforms were almost empty, brightly lit and raked by a cold wind. The waiting-room, however, was crowded with people, soldiers, peasant women with bursting bundles, old men in suits of dark corduroy, children and young girls, who seemed to have been there all night at least, waiting for the train. There was nowhere else to go and nothing Witek could do to alleviate the impact which he imagined this must be having on Rose; but if he could have arranged the train an hour earlier, or hurried the sun into the sky, he would have done so.

When finally the train was shunted in, he was among the first to stampede the still-moving carriages. He secured a corner seat for her but in the ensuing struggle was forced out of his own place by a woman with a baby. Rose was left isolated, speechless, while Witek retreated to the corridor. Their journey was to take five hours.

The train did not move off for another hour.

The lamps paled along the platform, where soldiers and militiamen were pacing up and down to keep warm. There was no real dawn; everything became dully visible, the darkness going away like a strain from the eyes. The train shuddered and began to move. Factories slid away; there was a long view of fields, and from time to time a river, a battered village or an old woman watching a cow.

Witek threw anxious looks in Rose's direction. He was ashamed of the rough appearance of the peasants in the carriage. He had no sense of common identity with them but only of impatience that they existed, in such large numbers and so obviously not up to standard. After about twenty minutes he leaned across to ask Rose if she was comfortable.

She was not, but nothing was to be gained by saying so.

Now that her suspected foreignness was confirmed, the other passengers reacted to it in different ways. Two or three turned their heads away and did not look at her for the remainder of the journey. The woman next to her, however, gave a little fluttering smile. Rose made gestures of admiration at the baby; it was a sturdy child with a large nose and a positive attitude.

The train moved slowly across a plain which seemed designed for a battlefield and had often been exactly this. The landscape was uninteresting but there were always people in sight, for all grazing animals must be watched and discouraged from wandering. Goose girls drove their flocks over the shorn grass and little boys threw stones at horses to keep them off the railway line.

A boy came swaying down the corridor expertly carrying a tray with glasses of boiling tea. Most of the passengers took one. Rose burnt her hands. The woman next to her blew on the tea for a moment, then gave a sip of it to the baby. The baby fixed Rose with a solemn and perplexed stare, and was suddenly very sick.

Rose at once put her tea on the floor, stood up and took a box of English Kleenex from her night-case. Together, she and the woman cleaned up the baby and threw the balls of soiled paper out of the window. Rose gave the rest of the Kleenex to the woman. The blue and white box excited comment and admiration and was handed all round the compartment. After this, she decided to give up her seat so that the baby, which was far too large for the woman's lap, could lie down and sleep.

She joined Witek in the corridor. He gazed at her with affection, he was delighted to be travelling with her, but because the peasants were disappointing and the baby had been sick (though very obviously it had been a well-fed baby) he felt he had to keep apologizing.

Rose managed to quieten him down. She asked him what he was going to do in Warsaw. He produced a slip of paper on which he had planned out his day. Rose's time-table was consigned to the margin of this. At the centre was his appointment with Mrs Goldberg at the Ministry of Higher Education: 'I am confident that she will have some good news today about our English philology department.' He would also be visiting the bureau of the State Publishing House which dealt with textbooks. 'They wish to reprint my book – with some important revisions, of course. And then—'

Rose interrupted him. 'What about Tadeusz's passport? You said you'd do something about that.'

'Yes. I have an acquaintance at the Foreign Ministry. I shall telephone.'

'Good.'

Somewhat ruffled, he went back to his list, from which this item had been omitted. Rose would be visiting her friends Mr and Mrs Tatham. Was the pronunciation correct? He would not call for her there but would look for her, during the afternoon, at the British Institute. 'You will have an opportunity to meet with Mr Pilkington. He has been very helpful to me.' From there they would go to take a small cup of coffee, prior to Rose's departure on the afternoon plane.

'You will be staying long in Krakow?' he asked her. This had been discussed several times in his presence. But Janet and he each possessed the faculty of becoming deaf when the other was addressed.

'Four days.'

'And then?'

'Back to Biala Gora.'

'I wonder if you will be pleased with Krakow.'

'They say it is very beautiful.'

'I wonder if you will be pleased with the people.'

'Why?'

'Other Polish people do not like them. They say they did not have the war there. Only one house was bombed.'

'You mean the other people wanted it all to be bombed?'

'They say Krakow people did not suffer so much.'

'Then they only like people when they have suffered?'

It might be true. If you had not suffered, you had less reality for them and they could not concentrate on you for very long. Whenever she was with Witek, she felt he liked her as a person but also considered her as a symbol of something which was not very praiseworthy; like the inhabitants of Krakow, she was classified, dismissed.

You could not judge him harshly, however, when you considered what he had to put up with in the normal run of events. He was returning to Biala Gora tonight, by the train which arrived at four in the morning. He had early classes tomorrow. This was the sort of procedure he was used to, travelling underfed on dawdling trains, waiting in anterooms, suing for power and action at the Ministry. Only with so few other pleasures available, it was perhaps easier for him to sacrifice himself to useful ambition.

## Chapter Nineteen

'Oh, Rose, you must tell us what it was like, was it simply ghastly, we're longing to know. What are you going to drink, I expect you need one, I know I do. Mark will be back fairly soon. You don't mind the children coming in for a bit, do you? They've just been on one of Nanny's smashing walks and I always feel they need reindoctrinating a bit after that, don't you know. Nanny's such a fearful fascist reactionary, it simply isn't true.'

During the ten days since Rose had seen her, Alexandra gave the impression of having increased in bulk and resplendency. In black stockings and a scarlet wool dress designed to celebrate rather than camouflage her pregnancy, she stood wide-legged with her behind to a blazing fire. Her fair skin, her shining teeth and eyes were almost cruelly healthy after the deadened complexions and steel-rimmed mouths of Biala Gora.

Rose drank whisky and retreated into the depths of her armchair. Alexandra did not ask her any more questions. Three small children in gaiters were shepherded in by the nanny. For a few minutes the room was full of their shrill voices in counterpoint to a complicated story which the nanny was telling; a toy had been left behind on the grass and an elderly lady – 'she was ever so heavily made up but her English was quite good' – had picked it up, brought it to them, and then wanted to buy it. 'Of course, it was Simon's own tedda so I couldn't really offer to do anything to oblige her, could I? There'd have been ructions.'

To Rose watching, this scene was like a pastoral entertainment at a considerable move from reality. So Tadeusz and Mirek and such people must have observed her, and felt that the things she told them of London were played out on an apron stage with a set of conventions as remote and arbitrary as a court masque. Only the elderly lady in the nanny's story could be recognized : she gave one the feeling of where one was.

After lunch Mark offered to drive Rose to the British Institute.

'Don't bother yet, please. My brother-in-law won't be there till three-thirty.'

'Come on. I'll show you some of the city.'

She watched him as he drove, liking him more but still a little frightened of him. He was conventional and even pompous, but he was also really interested in what happened. His pompousness was mitigated by the fact that when some situation appeared comic (he did not like wit) he could be seen unexpectedly shaking and weeping with silent diaphragm-heaving giggles.

'This is Lazienki Park. Like to have a look?'

'All right.'

A group of people watched them get out of the foreign car with CD plates. Farther down the path some children were feeding a red squirrel. It jerked to and fro like a clockwork toy, and scrambled all the way up a man's arm. It had thin fur and a degenerate-looking face.

The park stretched out in limpid sunlight, with some of the trees still showing the amputations of shell fire. Ornamental water wandered in and out, and there were swans, a rustic bridge, a Greek theatre. Yellow scaffolding criss-crossed the little Lazienki palace, which was then being restored. The whole place was beautiful but had a strange, vaguely unhappy look, as though it were being called back unwillingly from the past; Rose thought suddenly of those two English ladies at Versailles.

In the middle of the park they sat down on a bench.

'How is your sister? Really, I mean.'

She glanced at Mark, unwilling to offer evidence of unhappiness to anybody so detached and so successful. He was gazing across the water at the Greek Theatre. He sat with his long legs crossed, the right foot twisted back under the left ankle. She had never liked men who were able to do this or who kept their handkerchiefs up their sleeve. His sister Elizabeth, however, had always told her that Mark was good, using the word with an odd precision, like a technical term.

'Is she happy?'

'No, not at all.'

'I see.'

'Mark, it's been awful—' and now she had started, she told

him all about Janet and Witek and their competition over Tadeusz.

'Poor Rose.'

'I'm the last to be pitied. I feel after this none of us, you, me, anyone in England, ought to pity ourselves ever again.'

He was silent at this, and threw away his cigarette.

'I was afraid it might be like that. I didn't tell you this, until you'd seen for yourself. I've met your sister.'

'No? When? She didn't tell me.'

'No, I suppose not. She turned up at the Embassy. I happened to be around, I can't remember how it was now. She was pushed on to me. The Consul usually looks after these things.'

'When was this?'

'Last autumn. Soon after I got here.'

'It was probably my fault then. You see, I wrote that you were being sent here. She met Elizabeth when she was in England.'

'Oh, so that was it.' He sounded irritated.

'What did she want?'

He gave a sort of incredulous snort. 'She asked if I could arrange for her to go to England.'

'Oh, God!' Rose was silenced by this for a moment. 'What did you say?'

'Your sister knew the position really. She has dual nationality. She can get a British passport whenever she wants. But if she did that I don't know that the Poles would let her come back. The real trouble always is the children. They are Poles and we can't help them.'

'Did she mention Tadeusz?'

'No, I don't think so.'

'Perhaps she thought he could be included in her passport.'

'She couldn't do that. He's Polish.'

'He was born in England. Scotland, actually. Glasgow.'

'They won't recognize that here, I'm afraid.'

'No. And last autumn, of course, nobody knew about my aunt's money.'

Mark said: 'When I explained to your sister about the passports, she went away and I thought perhaps she might have settled down again. On the whole it's the intelligent ones who've managed to stick it. The Scottish mill girls and people like that have all gone home.'

'I suppose so.' Rose wondered if Janet was intelligent.

'I thought I'd better tell you that she'd been to see us before she knew anything about this money. Incidentally, who *does* know about it?'

'She does.'

'Nobody else?'

'My brother-in-law doesn't know. He is just getting a new job, and, of course, he's in with the Party.'

'You'll have to tell him sometime. It'll be a bit of a test for him: expediency or belief.'

'Oh, he believes in it all right. If you have anything to do with education, you might. But if you worked in a shoe factory you probably wouldn't.'

Mark laughed at this. 'So you can't tell him yet?'

'No. And so we can't tell Tadeusz.'

'What are you going to do, then?'

'I—' She stopped. At this moment she couldn't tell him about inviting Tadeusz to England. It would appear devious, and was not. Mark might be unconvinced of this, however, and she suspected he could arrange to stop the visa. Rose was learning suspicion easily.

'Oughtn't I to wait, Mark? I want to invest the money and the income and hold on. This can't go on for ever. Tadeusz'll be grown up and able to make up his own mind. Besides, things may get better.'

'Perhaps. Perhaps not. The other thing is they could apply for an emigration visa. Sometimes whole families get these.'

'No good, I'm afraid. Witek certainly doesn't want to leave, nor does Tadeusz.'

Mark laughed shortly. He stood up and then looked at his watch. These difficulties had made him lose interest. 'Then I suppose your idea is best. Waiting, I mean.'

'I suppose so. If only everyone *can* wait.'

They walked slowly up the hill to the car.

While he was unlocking the doors he said: 'By the way, it is better not to discuss these things in the car.'

This remark took away any easiness that was left from the spring afternoon. They had sat and talked in the park only because there were no microphones there.

Later Mark tried to make some amends: 'I don't know how long your visa's for, but I do wish you'd come and stay with us for a few days. Alexandra would love to have you.'

'Thank you, Mark. The only thing is, while I've got time, I feel I should go back to my sister.'

'Of course.'

'But a day or two would be lovely.'

'Let us know, will you?' He stopped the car. 'This is the place. No, I'll come up, too. There's a book they were meant to be keeping for me.'

The stairway of the British Institute was lined with travel posters, Woburn Abbey, the Giants' Causeway, the Trooping of the Colour. In the reading-room some battered-looking old ladies, reading *Vogue* and the *Illustrated London News*, eyed the newcomers furtively: perhaps it was one of these who had offered to buy Simon Tatham's teddy bear. There was no sign of Witek Rudowski.

In the Library Rose and Mark were confronted by a small scarlet-faced man. He was dressed in violently checked tweeds of a type usually only worn by peers or bookies, and then only in the immediate proximity of a horse.

'Hullo, hullo, Mark old boy, how very nice to see you! How is Alexandra? And the children? Alexandra's ragtime band! Ha! ha! I won't forget that in a hurry.'

Mark did not flinch.

'Rose, this is George Pilkington. Rose Nicholson.'

Mr Pilkington eyed Rose, found her pretty and hurriedly looked away. 'Over here on a visit? Weather's turned out well for you, hasn't it? Looks like we'll be getting a game of tennis again, Mark, before we know where we are.'

After the quietness, the grey subdued confidences on the verge of despair to which Rose had been subjected in the last few days, this man's voice, like Alexandra's, was strangely discomfiting.

She moved away as soon as she conveniently could, while the two men went on talking. With nothing better to do she took a book from the shelves at random: it was a large expensive-looking volume on soil erosion. The date of cataloguing was June 1946, the year of publication, a year in which soil conservation still provided another of the fairly easy answers. Here in the British Institute this book had survived Mikolajczyk, Bierut, Stalin and Rokossowski. Rose turned back to the fly-leaf: it was virgin. Nobody had ever taken the book out of the library.

'See if we can't get our revenge on H.E. in this year's doubles, what?'

A timid secretary approached. 'Dr Rudowski is here, Mr Pilkington.'

As soon as the girl was out of earshot, Pilkington rolled his eyes and bit his lips with histrionic rage. 'These people, they're incredible! I ask you, this one seems to think I've got nothing better to do than sit around all day listening to his views on teaching English. I tell him again and again that's quite outside my scope, but does it make a ha'porth of difference? Oh dear me no. As far as I'm concerned, he's the biggest clot on this or any other side of the Iron Curtain.'

Rose pushed the book on soil erosion back into the shelf. 'Excuse me, I think he's looking for me.'

'Who is?'

'Dr Rudowski.'

Pilkington stared at her with popping eyes. 'You don't know him, do you?'

'Yes. He's my brother-in-law.'

Beside them, Mark Tatham was shuddering convulsively. He was like an asthmatic, or someone stopped during the parturition of an overwhelming sneeze. His face darkened and tears of laughter broke from his eyes and trickled down his cheeks.

## Chapter Twenty

'I am sorry we could not have some conversation with Mr Pilkington. He is a very interesting man.'

'Oh, Witek, no, he's terrible.'

He accepted it now as a good joke, her condemnation of everyone he recommended and he smiled warmly to show that he appreciated it. They were sitting in a café near the air terminal, where they had left Rose's suitcase. They had glasses of weak coffee in front of them.

'Perhaps you should not take so much coffee. It may make you nervous.'

Kind, weary and ponderous, a supporter of the Established Order, there was after all nothing in Witek which could appeal to the English. Rose held on to her right to defend him to the utmost; she tried to avoid thinking that, whatever happened to Aunt Louise's money, it was he who finally must be deceived and defeated.

'It's all right.' She was already trembling a little. '*Reisefieber*, you know, before the aeroplane. Tell me, have you had a good day?'

'I have excellent news for you, excellent.'

'About Tadeusz's passport? Is it going to be all right?'

He stopped, checked in his course. 'No, not that. That is –
we must wait.'

'Oh, I see. Well, go on.'

'It is about our department of English Philology. We are
to have examinations this summer and twelve students are
to be admitted.'

'Witek, that's wonderful. And you'll be in charge.'

'Unfortunately, not yet. At the moment we are obliged to
have Professor Mikulski, the professor of Russian, to super-
vise. But he is a good man and very conscientious. And I will
set the entrance examinations.'

'I see.' She wondered if this professor was a good man in
the way Elizabeth had said Mark Tatham was, and what it
meant.

'I'm very happy for you, Witek.'

'And now I must work on my thesis for becoming Docent.
Without this I cannot be Head of our department. I am afraid,
even before that, they may choose another man.'

'But can they do that now?'

'Unfortunately yes. There is one of the lecturers of Warsaw
University. Some persons think he is a good scholar but I
do not think his methods are modern ones. His thesis was
"The Versification of Sir Gawain and the Green Knight".'

Rose fidgeted with her coffee glass. 'I realize now I've met
him.'

'Yes?'

'On my first day here. He was at lunch.'

Witek could not resist the temptation to hear Rose, in her brusque way, condemn somebody else.

'Did you think well of him?'

'Yes. He's very nice and intelligent.' She saw his disappointment and added: 'Of course he's a fearful reactionary.'

Her hand jerked nervously and coffee spilt in the saucer. She was furious with herself, not so much for betraying Adam Karpinski, whom she scarcely knew, but for reducing everything to the level of Alexandra and Nanny: for not taking seriously lives which were fought out in an atmosphere of risk and apprehension.

Since her conversation with Mark Tatham in Lazienki Park, this atmosphere was a sick feeling in the air; everything, sky, street and buildings had grown a little darker. Once you began to think about it, suspicion was everywhere. Did Witek know of Janet's visit to the British Embassy last autumn? Did he think Rose's appearance here this spring was something to do with that, and not entirely to the pleasures his country offered? Everyone here had secrets, the truths you could utter at any moment and must keep simmering in your head behind your tongue. In this atmosphere a betrayal must be like a move towards liberation, the relief from a whispering insistent pressure.

Only Witek was out of this, worrying about his own career. 'And that man is Docent, from Warsaw University. He had many friends among the older professors.'

'But you have friends, too, surely.'

'Not so many. Mrs Goldberg at our ministry. Dr Zwiersz

in our University Council, Professor Mikulski, one or two more. They understand that it is important, what we want to do.'

'I see.'

'The old methods are no longer suiting the students of the new generation. We cannot have professors who are interested only in one or two students who can become scholars or assistants. Everyone has to work, everybody must be useful.'

'Of course. It's obvious, isn't it?' She looked at her watch; there were another ten minutes until the bus left.

'To them, not.'

'But, Witek, it's you who are starting the department. You'll be able to show them what to do.'

'You are very kind to me, Rose.' He shifted his chair a little nearer; once again there was the problem of his breath. 'Rose, I know I am not the best, I know my English is not perfect but I learn only late in life, in England. When I married I spoke only a little – you can still remember?' Rose nodded. He was enjoying humiliating himself rather too much.

'I was frightened of your mother. She was the sort of lady who never realized that some others could not speak English.'

'Oh, Witek, you shouldn't have worried. She never listened to what other people said. It made no difference.'

He smiled. 'Yes, I think sometimes after I married she wondered who I was. She had been told but she was not listening.'

'She was glad you were a Catholic, though.'

Witek went into a sort of mumbling silence.

'I'm sorry – I didn't mean—'

'No, the Catholic church has done much good for our country in the past.'

'Probably. I couldn't take the Convent though – that was my trouble.' She looked at her watch again. 'We must go, mustn't we?'

They stood together in front of the airport bus.

'Witek, I *am* pleased, really. I mean, everybody in authority thinks you are absolutely all right. So there's no need for you to worry about Tadeusz going to England any more, is there?'

'No – yes.' He smiled. 'Please, though, remember that I want him back.'

As she kissed him, she said in a childish voice: 'Of course. How many more times do I have to promise?'

Witek watched her get on to the bus with a pang of loss. He would miss her. It was true that she did not know what all this meant to him, but she was the only one who knew at what cost, against what an emptiness and absence of private affections, he had attained this point in his career. Standing outside the bus in the warm spring evening, he offered his success to Rose, with love.

## Chapter Twenty-one

From the window of Adam Karpinski's flat, in a new block near the intersection of two avenues, Marszalkowska and Jerosolimskie, you look down on to the Polonia Hotel. This is practically the only substantial building to survive the destruction of the city, and now its ugly elaborate façade is like a face which appears in a dream in a wrong country and a wrong era. Adam could remember staying there in 1938, while visiting the capital with his parents. The city he had seen with the sharp eyes of a fourteen year old possessed a sort of Platonic reality for him: it subsisted somewhere else and even today, in certain dream states induced by vodka or love or tiredness, the grey Stalin-period buildings would dissolve like so many screens and that *Ur*-city reassemble its fragments, the Ghetto and the Royal Palace arise from nothing again and even the main railway station, where the family arrived and departed for the country, would manage to disinter itself from under the colossal weight of the Palace of Culture.

This afternoon, however, the sun shone and everything was real. Shelves of books, in various languages, still gathered the dust which the new building exhaled from its brittle plaster. There was no room for pictures and the few he possessed Adam had let his divorced wife take with her. They had waited years on a list for this new flat; he was glad to leave the old one which had witnessed terrible events, but he had left his wife behind on the way. Because he was a writer he was permitted two rooms, one to work in. He had no need of taste – there was nothing much to have taste about – and the apartment was a machine for his various activities and from the window he could watch the new Warsaw rise, which was something with which he was painfully involved.

He packed a suitcase, switched off the refrigerator, and locked the door. He left behind a chess-board, set out with a game in progress by telephone with one of his University colleagues (the friend was already defeated; Adam would win in three moves) and a bunch of red roses, ribbon and asparagus fern, presented by his seminar students on his birthday.

Adam walked down Marszalkowska towards the air terminal, past flowerstalls and wooden palings which were pasted with fresh witty posters for ancient Westerns. At one of the kiosks he bought an armful of literary weeklies, their yellow pages closely printed and stuffed out with the reviews and commentaries and bloc-notes of an always articulate intelligentsia. At least two contained articles by himself. He was the first to take a seat in the airport bus.

He watched Rose approach across the pavement with Witold Rudowski and swore gently. One of those mildly ridiculous swear-words: it meant 'dog's blood'. He had not at first recognized her; the context was so completely different from luncheon at the Tathams'. Then he remembered that the girl was in fact related to Rudowski. All the same, he protested that a peasant like that should be with a girl who, apart from being pretty and well-dressed, was also a friend of the Tathams.

One might accept Rudowski as a scientist or a politician; indeed, one accepted him or, rather, different versions of him, every day. But beside the late Professor Dybowski or beside the late Professor Stankiewicz, and all those high-domed philologists of the past generation – who had trained at German universities and, in several cases, afterwards died in German camps – Rudowski was a figure of farce, a mere puppet dangling on the strings of a few bargain-basement ideas. On closer inspection, even this English girl Rose, this English Rose, appeared to be addressing him with a patronizing air.

Rose climbed in and sat near the front of the bus. She waved through the door at Rudowski, and his decent peasant face beamed back at her. The bus began to move away.

Adam put his face near the window, so that he caught the full afterglow of Rudowski's farewell to Rose. The eyes of the two men stabbed at each other through the glass. Rudowski flinched. His smile disintegrated into abject worry. Adam grinned fiendishly.

The bus gathered speed, carrying Adam and Rose off together. He settled back in his seat and went on watching Rose. There was a new warmth in having her there, about five yards distant, while worried Rudowski stumped off round Warsaw on his clumsy intrigues.

Rose had a bright clearness which was not really connected with any colour in her head or clothing. He was appreciating this, and the line of hair, cheek and arm, so that it came as a shock to perceive that, like Rudowski, she was undergoing a temporary illness of worry. Her shoulders shifted under its burden and her hand kept going to her face. Believing herself unobserved, she could allow herself to look desperate. As he watched, he became so much absorbed in this that he was quite unconscious of the rows of seats which lay between them. He was with her, hearing the inaudible noises of her distress, amused and at the same time liking her because she was not indifferent, as one had so often heard the English to be.

To the others in the bus she was a foreigner and therefore happy. But Adam was not so stupid as to believe material comforts made life less 'real' or their possessors insensible to emotion. Still, she was young and smart, and anguish came more surprisingly from her.

He kept her in sight at the airport, following her across the tarmac to the little Ilyushin aeroplane. When the passengers stood in a group listening for their names to be called, he lost her, but there she was again in the aeroplane, only a few seats ahead of him, huddled against the window. When the stewardess stopped beside her with a tray of boiled sweets, Rose took one with a sort of blind, pawing movement.

The aeroplane taxied slowly across the field, swung round

and stopped. Seagulls fleered up and resettled, farther away. A few spots of water struck the thick glass of the windows.

'Miss Rose Nicholson. May I sit here, please?'

The surprise took her far more violently than he expected. She coloured fiercely, had a moment's difficulty with the sweet in her mouth, stammered something. Then the twin engines roared up. Outside, the seagulls, fields and low sheds began racing backwards.

It was quieter in the air and he heard her say: 'You shouldn't move while the plane is taking off.'

Used to jet planes, however, Rose herself had forgotten that this provincial veteran would be circling sharply. When it lurched sidewards she fell towards him. He felt her bones against him, she smelt as exotic as the Western world, while beyond her small face the wing-tip dropped like a stone, and below them stood the Palace of Culture, an axle with the whole grey city gyrating around it.

'I didn't hear your name called out,' she said.

'You remember my name?'

'Of course.'

The engines roared up. 'Someone else's ticket.'

'What?'

'Perhaps I'm using someone else's ticket.'

'In England you can't do that.'

He grinned. 'No, in England you can't do that.'

'What happens if we all get killed? Nobody will know who you are.'

He grinned. 'Nobody. It will be most confusing.'

She looked out of the window. Webs of cloud were floating past, and the flat country lay far below. On her other side, Adam Karpinski filled up the whole of the view.

'Do you mind if I smoke my pipe?'

'No, please do.'

When he produced it, however, Rose eyed it doubtfully, as though it was an assertion of Englishness she could not quite approve of.

'Have you seen anything of the Tathams?'

'I had lunch there today.'

He got the pipe going and said: 'I'm very fond of them both – Alexandra is a terrific girl.'

Rose noticed that certain expressions brought, like this one, a cawing note into his voice, as though he were mimicking the traditional conception of an English 'toff'.

'I don't know her well,' Rose said. 'She scares me a bit.'

'There used to be girls like that here, before the war. Now they are too expensive for our Socialist economy.'

'Well, Alexandra's got money of her own.'

'Are the Bermondseys rich?'

'I suppose they are.'

She resisted what might be a foreigner's clamorous interest in the English upper classes, and was silent.

He watched her for a little, then said: 'Why are you going to Krakow, if I may ask?'

'To see it.'

She hated having to explain herself, and in any case the

whole operation seemed more and more of a mistake to her. She was not here to look at places, but to look after people. It was not her fault that the people, with the exception of Tadeusz, had proved so unsatisfactory.

'I was told I had to see Krakow.'

'Of course. We Poles are always informing foreigners that we have lost everything. But we must also show them what we have lost.' He pulled at his pipe. 'That is, if they are at all interested.'

'I *am* interested,' Rose said plaintively.

'Or very polite.'

'No. One gets tired of being polite.'

'Nobody can talk politely about what has happened to us,' Adam said.

'But it has happened everywhere, surely. Not just in Krakow.'

'It means more in Krakow. After all it was the old capital, it was one of the outposts of the West against barbarism and it held out against everyone from the Tartars onwards. And in 1848 it rebelled against three empires at once, can you imagine that? But in 1944 your two English-speaking empires handed us over to the barbarians. So it is a sad place now. You will see.'

'Why sadder than anywhere else?'

'You will see. Perhaps it was better that nothing was left of Warsaw. In Krakow you can still see the signs and relics and memorials of what we once were. Everywhere else it has all gone.'

'Surely not.'

'Yes, it has all gone. We are just survivors, by mistake. Our neighbours always wanted to destroy us and next time they will do it properly.'

As she had with Mirek Sypniewski, Rose found that this sort of conversation dragged one deep into the speaker's orbit. She could barely hear what Adam was saying, being deafened both by the engines and by the physical impact of his presence. She was afraid that it was his vehemence that gave him all his attraction and if he stopped addressing her he might somehow deflate and become another of the pudding-featured passengers who filled the rest of the seats of the aeroplane. But while he talked, he was wonderful. The Rudowskis were forgotten. She had left their world of domestic irritation and entered one of tragedy and glory.

The plane began to wheel and descend into the darker evening. They felt a jolt of warm air over the iron foundries of Nowa Huta.

There was a bus beside the hangar. Rose and Adam sat waiting for it to leave. He had given her his vision; he looked tired.

'You are staying at Francuski?'

'No, what is that?'

'The Hotel.'

'No. With friends.'

He speculated a little about this. 'Seeing how the poor live?'

'But why are they so poor in Krakow?' she asked. 'You said they had no war damage.'

'And they didn't have the money which rebuilt the other towns. In any case, everybody is poor. Terribly poor. *You* cannot imagine.'

'I try. I've been staying with my sister.'

'They are rich. They both can work.'

'They seem poor to me.'

'To you, of course. You're Fanny—' he raised a placatory hand – 'No, don't get worried, please. You – are – like – Fanny Price: "Though Mansfield Park might have some pains, Portsmouth could have no pleasures." Poland can have no pleasures.'

Though she already felt she knew him extremely well, she puzzled over this as she had over his pipe. *Mansfield Park*, however, was an aspect of his profession. Perhaps his knowledge of English slang also was.

'I'm not looking for pleasures. You think because you've all suffered so much here, other people are indifferent. But we do try to feel. At least I do. I must. And I think there are good things, as well as bad.'

'Wait till you have seen Krakow, seen how some of the old people live, people like Magda Wahorska, the Palewska girls and their mother, the old Princess. They had everything, remember, and they lost it all.'

She was happy and excited by the antagonism between them. But she did not react to the name of Mrs Wahorska, the sister of Mrs Kazimierska. She was getting used to such conversations full of little gulps of silence, of things you preferred not to say.

## Chapter Twenty-two

The two women rose early and were out to Mass in the Old City. On their return Antosia, the maid, folded away the blankets from the pair of hard *chaises longues* they slept on, and went into the corridor to light the gas. Her mistress moved towards the door of the second room and put her ear to it, listening for the sounds of the girl sleeping. After a few moments she tapped and opened the door.

Rose had been awake for some time, had heard them go out and stayed wondering what to do and not wishing to be in the way. It was indeed difficult to move around, the rooms being so much cluttered with furniture that if you were to shift one object it would appear to blaze a trail of prying curiosity. So she stood still, looking out at the roofs and bell-towers of the city, and thinking about Adam and about Tadeusz.

At the sight of Rose, standing in the sunlight, wrapped in a silk dressing-gown and brushing her hair, the two women made noises of admiration. Antosia hurried off to the kettle which was drumming and blowing in the corridor. She returned with tea and bread and butter.

'It is excellent tea,' Mrs Wahorska said. 'We have already, I am afraid, been tasting a little.'

'But it is for you. Please do not waste it on me, I can have it any time.'

The old woman's eyebrows were raised at this and she observed Rose without friendliness; evidently, she had not forgiven the awkwardness of the previous evening.

The difficulty had begun at the bus stop. Adam had said good-bye abruptly; it seemed he was certain of seeing her again, though she had no idea when or where this might be. She was alone and therefore herself unmistakable when the two shabbily-dressed females approached her. Remembering Kazimierska's great height Rose headed for Antosia, who was large and square, but a brisk angry little woman interposed herself. She was furious and there was to be no laughing it off. While they walked across the public gardens, one difference indeed became clear. The former Countess Wahorska had still a long young stride, like an English girl brought up in the country, while the servant took the waddling steps of the bundle-carrying peasant woman. But a greyness of poverty had taken away all other distinctions; Adam was right: this was worse than either Biala Gora or Warsaw.

Later, unpacking her suitcase, Rose said: 'I have brought you a present of tea.'

Her hostess examined the packet with suspicion. '*C'est du thé, ou du Lipton?*'

'*Thé*,' said Rose, who had been unaware of this distinction. '*Chinois.*'

'You do not take our tea? You wish to drink only this?'

'No, it is for you. I brought it from England.'

'I find that curious, since you did not then know that we should meet.'

This morning nothing had changed: Rose was meant to ask questions and do as she was told. Besides, Mrs Wahorska spoke French, that domineering language, far better than she did.

'This room belongs to my daughter. Up to now, I am allowed to keep it. But perhaps someone who does not like me will say something, and I shall have strangers put here.'

'Strangers? '

'Perhaps a whole family. One cannot know.'

'But won't your daughter come back?'

Antosia brought another glass and a saucer with rounds of lemon.

'Look, Antosia has found a lemon for us. She has a cousin at a State Grocer's Shop.' Rose's question remained to be answered. 'My daughter has been in Paris for three years. She intends to prolong her scholarship.'

'I see. What does she do?'

'Art history, naturally. My niece Halina who comes this afternoon, also. Halina works in the museum this morning and so you must put up with me. I have my lessons in the afternoon and evening. That photograph is of my son. It is not a good one but we never thought, in 1939, that there would be no opportunity of taking others.'

While she was talking a succession of bangs and clattering sounds echoed from the house beneath them.

'Those are the workmen.' The old woman suddenly acquired an air of extreme constraint and embarrassment. 'I regret I must tell you, they use our lavatory in the corridor, it is rather disagreeable. If you would prefer Antosia can bring—'

'No, of course not,' Rose said quickly. 'What are they doing?'

'They are transforming our house into a museum for the Workers' Party.' The first warmth came into the old lady's face. 'Imagine, my dear, this was my father's house. My great-grandfather built it. But, you know there is a point where one cannot complain any more but only laugh. So I had my friends' – a string of names followed, including the ones Adam had mentioned the evening before – 'for my name-day and I made the announcement that they are transforming the house into a Museum for the Workers' Party and we all laugh. We cannot help it, we cannot stop laughing. Staszek Kopczinski, he is my nephew and a very brilliant man, said: "They put all our things in museums and everybody goes to admire them, but all they will have for their own place will be a few photographs and some old pamphlets which everyone laughs at because they are in such bad Polish!"'

The old woman sat back and wiped weak sardonic tears from her eyes.

'When you are ready we may go out. Later Antosia will prepare dinner for us.'

'I want to invite you. I was told the hotel restaurant is good.'

The other looked as if she were being offered charity, which was unwelcome.

'Please come. If it's true about it being good, I mean.'

'That, I cannot tell you. For many years none of us could afford it, and we did not like to be seen there with foreigners. Now perhaps it does not matter for what more can they do to us?'

After Rose had dressed, her hostess reappeared in a coat and hat, both trimmed with fur which seemed not merely old but to have come from sick animals in the first place. However, heavily powdered and rouged as she was, the old lady managed to look both fierce and spritely.

'Today we will use the grand staircase, where the men are working.'

'Won't they mind?'

The old lady snorted.

They went through a doorway and down some stairs which gave on to the mezzanine floor. The house dated from the late eighteenth century, and marble columns rose on each side of the grand staircase. Across the wall at the head of the stairs, there had already been set up a sepia 'photomural' of Lenin, flourishing his fist over a sea of cloth caps.

Mrs Wahorska took Rose's arm and they slowly descended the grand staircase, which was still protected by sacking. At the bottom, in the places formerly occupied perhaps by flunkeys, five workmen were watching. One of them wore a paper hat like the Carpenter in 'Alice' and the others had embroidered skull caps. A sort of bloom of dust and whitewash lay over their hair and eyelashes and blond skin. They leaned back against the marble balustrade and watched step by step the descent of the girl in her smart foreign clothes and the bent, shabby figure beside her. As they got nearer, Rose expected the workmen to smile or say good morning. They were as silent, however, as their prototypes in the photomural up above. It was certain they knew who the old lady was but it was of no importance to them, and the indifference, which had been handed out in this house through the generations, was being given back again with a long stare of their little pale eyes.

## Chapter Twenty-three

'Today there is fish, that is because it is not Friday. No fish is allowed to be served in restaurants on Friday. You see, they are rather childish sometimes, the people who look after us.'

After this disquisition, the old lady went back to reading the menu, while Rose watched the surrounding tables. Next to them a delegation of Chinese, dressed like members of the Salvation Army, sat completely silent while a woman guide addressed them in squeaky English on the subject of industrial development. On the other side some shabby men in grey sweaters with zip-fasteners were talking German; beyond them was a group who looked like Arabs. There were little silk flags on the tables, unrecognizable, of recent countries. One table had no flag and there Adam Karpinski was sitting with two people. He gave no indication of having seen Rose.

Mrs Wahorska began discussing the menu with Rose, who, agitated and hardly concentrating, found herself committed to herring in sour cream, beetroot soup, and chicken *à la polonaise*. After the fatigue of a morning of museums they came to an even quicker agreement that they should drink vodka.

Rose still wondered whether he had seen her or not. Among the confusion of languages in the restaurant, his presence there tingled and throbbed like some sound just above the range of the human ear.

Her back was turned to him, but he surely must have noticed her when Mrs Wahorska and she first arrived. If he had, there might be some reason that had prevented him from attracting her attention. The woman with him was smart and not bad looking, the man squat and unattractive. Were they married? Intellectuals here got the prettiest women, one had been told. Perhaps, however, they were foreigners like herself, even though there was no flag on their table.

The herring arrived, masked in its sauce of cream and chopped onion, and with it the little carafe of vodka. They drank to each other, and the old woman tasted the herring appreciatively.

'That is good. You understand, we do not eat so well on what we make by giving lessons and doing translations. Also, every week I give something to the little nuns at the convent.'

By the time cups of dark red soup were brought, the old lady beamed and glistened: the luncheon was being a success. As they drank another vodka, Rose heard Adam's voice invade a moment of silence: he was speaking in Polish, but for nearly a minute she could hear nothing of what Mrs Wahorska was saying.

'Afterwards my niece Halina will come here. She will take you to see some more churches. The museums will be closed, I think. Halina knows a great deal about our churches, more than I. She is a nice girl but much too serious, I am afraid. Not like my daughter, who is always cheerful. But then, evidently I shall never see my daughter again.' She blinked away a wave of unguarded emotion, took up her glass again and fixed her gaze on Rose.

'And you, you are Catholic? That is strange for the English, I think.'

Rose was puzzled at this. This morning she had crossed herself going into the Cathedral by the Wawel palace; the sharp-eyed old woman had noticed it. Now Rose went rather pink, as she used to when explaining about this.

'My mother was a convert. When I was a child she sent me to a Convent school. It was during the war.'

'And you?' The improbable painted eyebrows were raised.

'My father wanted us to be free to choose.'

'And what have you chosen?'

'Nothing.'

Disapproval is middle class; the upper classes prefer to employ a sudden and complete loss of interest. Mrs Wahorska began to attack the small chicken-half on her plate and the bowl of fresh cucumber beside it. Rose thought that she was about to speak again but when nothing came of these pre-paratory mumbles, which were due to nothing more than the violent tussle with fragile bones, she herself said: 'Of course, it is different here, I expect.'

'You are correct.' The old woman wiped her mouth and said fiercely: 'In Poland if we had lost our religion, we would have disappeared, we too. It defined us. Now they are taking it away from our children and they know what they are doing. We will disappear, we will become a part of Russia or perhaps a part of nowhere. Here we are not free to choose. We cannot choose a nothing.'

'I suppose not.' There were many objections to this totalitarian attitude but Rose was not in a position to make them. The lunch continued, with Rose no longer a person of much importance; she was rapidly demoralized by the sceptical smiles with which the old lady greeted her further attempts at conversation.

When Adam came out of the restaurant, Rose was sitting alone in the foyer of the hotel while Mrs Wahorska telephoned her niece.

'You see, we must always meet. Krakow is like that.' He made a gesture of holding a clutch of eggs or a bird's nest. 'Are you having a nice time with that old thing?'

'No. Awful,' she said vehemently, and then felt guilty.

She hoped he would stay but already he was moving off.

'Don't let her bore you too much, will you?'

With this unhelpful remark, he left her; his two companions were already waiting in the car outside. Rose saw him go with a pang of loss. There was no prospect of escape from Mrs Wahorska for another three days.

Rose was incredibly far from home, and now remorseful at leaving the Rudowskis and at launching out into an indefinite world of strangers. She should not have deserted them in the short time they would have of her in the whole of their lives, with so much that still needed straightening out.

With all this in mind, she forced a bright smile at Mrs Wah-orska when she returned.

The other rejected this as the silliness of a person who lacked any interest to catch the attention. 'Halina will be here directly.'

They took up each other's company like a burden that had to be toted around for some reason forgotten to both of them.

## Chapter Twenty-four

'Et ce Monsieur Armstrong-Jones?'
    'Well, I don't—'
'Marysia Strelicka is now not minding so much her daughter marrying a man of no family. If the sister of the Queen of England may do it, you understand—'

Halina, the art-historian niece, had brought her guest to somebody's name-day party. It took place in a couple of tiny rooms, near some marshalling yards at the farthest edge of the city. The two rooms were crowded with elderly people, whose whitish distinguished look, as though already partly of commemorative stone, made them seem remote from everything else. In fact, whether traditional academics or survivors of the pre-war aristocracy, they did their best to involve themselves at every opportunity with the arguments of the age: they wanted to feel that they were endangered and possibly dangerous. Because of this, though their lives were extremely hard, they were never bored.

Their hostess found no satisfaction in Rose's answers about the Royal Family and turned away. She was glad to have captured other visitors from outside the circle of a provincial town; the writer Bogdan Malczarek, recently returned from the West with his wife, who was rather less interesting; and Adam Karpinski from Warsaw, with flushed face and jabbing forefinger, holding forth to a group and expressing the exact mixture of knowledge and alarm, the painful bite down on to the rotten tooth of fact, which they all appreciated so much.

Though the writer's wife was not as pretty as she had appeared to be at the hotel, her smart clothes and brightened skin and eyes distinguished her from the other guests. This glitter of distinction, however, was a surface result of Western productivity, for she turned out to be the saddest and least convinced of any of them. She had the cold whining voice sometimes found in conjunction with the East European intonation of English, and the moment she found herself with a foreigner she began to chant forth her litany of complaints. England came late on her list, when the little glasses had been refilled.

'You must forgive me but I did not like your country.'

'Oh, yes.'

'I was so unhappy there that I had to say to my husband, take me away or I shall probably be ill.' She had the exile's voice of talking endlessly about happiness, which she referred to as though it was her right, and everything had happened in conspiracy to keep her from it; they had not been received in English society, her husband had quarrelled with his fellow exiles over some political magazine or other. They had been obliged to work – she offered this bitterly to Rose, as something Rose herself would not dream of. But it had been impossible for her husband, who was a Doctor of Law, to find work and he disapproved of the job she was taking.

'In a bakery, imagine, with all sorts of low people. I had enough of England, I can tell you. I never see such ugly people, with such funny clothes like old peasant women. Whatever you can say, Krakow is better than Ealing.'

'Ealing?'

'We lived in Ealing, of course.' The woman stared out on to wild spaces of mania. They were left alone. Her troubles were too subjective to command any sympathy and the other guests avoided her. For many of them, she had been given the opportunity of freedom and failed and she was therefore uninteresting and even a little repulsive.

'Then we went to America. America is terrible. I was shocked, so shocked. We have lived there for twelve years but we do not like the people at all. And now my husband earns some money here with his books, so we are back here again.'

'And here?'

The woman lowered her voice. 'It is terrible, I cried my eyes out. But my husband wishes to stay.'

The long discussion on the other side of the room had been vehement but good natured. Everyone kept a respectful distance from the fierce conclusions such arguments seemed to hunt out: they were recognized and let go, and the participants returned to more tolerable themes. At length Adam was able to join Rose. He lowered himself heavily on to the divan beside her, a little glorified by drink and flushed with the excitement of the hunt.

'What was all that about?'

'You know what it was all about. Miss Rose – may I please call you Rose? You know now, don't you?' Tears came into his eyes. 'You can tell them about what has happened to us, the terrible things that have been done to us.'

She watched him as though about to pick lint off his coat, and was fascinated again at the curious combination of melancholy and extreme high spirits.

While they were walking home, Halina said: 'She is exactly like the Ancient Mariner. She must tell her story to everybody that she meets. It is the tragedy about our people who are scattered. We feel that it is too late now, and we can have no more contact with them, which is very sad because they are our own people.'

'Perhaps those two will stay here. She told me her husband wanted to.'

'They will go, I think. They both have American passports still, you see, and they can travel whenever they like. That is the worst thing for us – we have to stay here. We would like to travel but it is not possible. We may only travel when the Government says so. If they would allow us that, it would still be bad, but not so bad. How long are you in Krakow?'

'Well, I—'

'My husband and I would like you to come to our flat—'

'They – the writer and his wife invited me to go to the mountains, you see.'

The big iron gate of the Wahorska town house loomed up

in front of them. Rain had fallen and the trees in the ruined garden were dripping heavily. Beyond, everything was silent, the city plunged early into medieval sleep. The old lady had lent Rose a key to the inner door, and now they went up the back stairs, with the Museum of the Workers' Party silent and shuttered below them.

The old lady had been working on a translation. Her eyes were dark rimmed and her skin white, almost transparent-looking.

'They are very small people, from near Lwow, I think,' she said, when she was told about the Malczareks.

'They invited me to go with them in their car, to the mountains.'

'My dear, you have escaped well. They probably wish to make use of you in some way or other. She is a very tedious woman and I believe partly Jewish.'

Because the niece did not speak French, the conversation was triangular and awkward. Now Rose had to appeal to her for help.

'Of course you must go. You must see as much as you can of our country.'

A long interchange ensued between Mrs Wahorska and Halina. The news that the English girl really wanted to go with the Malczareks, small people as they were, came as a personal affront; the old lady felt she was being abandoned, her hospitality rejected. This feeling she must have acquired and enjoyed for its own sake, since she showed no violent affection for her guest. Rose wondered whether Halina was embroidering the situation with any other reasons. She listened hard for Adam's name or some word that might mean he was being brought into the conversation. But her effort was unrewarded.

The women turned to her. Their faces were businesslike and unsmiling.

'It is settled then. When do they leave?'

'Tomorrow morning.'

At this the old lady appeared to be offended further. Rose was sorry for her, not liking her much but as usual disarmed by the perpetual defeat. Perhaps that miasma hung thicker over Krakow than either Warsaw or Biala Gora. Escape in a fast car into the emptiness of woods and fields would be the only way to restore anyone's spirits.

## Chapter Twenty-five

Flying back to Biala Gora, Rose stopped for only two hours and spent them walking up and down in Warsaw Airport, happy with her thoughts and only mildly disconsolate at having finished her last detective story. Again the aeroplane wheeled up out of the drab city, the Palace of Culture spun round half-obscured by flocculent cloud, but now the feelings she had towards all of this were changed. Everything had meaning, each sight was a word in a great poetical tragedy and once you had learned this you could not cease from gazing with devouring eyes.

Tadeusz was waiting for her, in exactly the same place that he had waited on her first evening in Poland, which was now so long ago. The sight of him once more, all that youth and intensity, was almost insupportable, and her eyes filled with tears.

'You have a good trip?'

'I've had a wonderful time. Everybody has been wonderful.'

Of course there was nothing at all she could tell him and instead she turned on him a face of such radiance that he shivered, excited already. He wondered, too, why she was crying.

'I love your country, you know, Tadeusz. I really do.'

If Mark Tatham had told her that at that moment she was echoing the drunken Miss Handisyde, who had been at lunch on the first day, she would have denied it with violence. She was not drunk but in love. The world spun round, then settled.

'You saw Wawel? And Zakopane?'

'Everything.' Already Tadeusz had picked up her suitcases. 'No. This time we are taking a taxi. I simply insist.'

'All right. I catch one.'

He ran off. Rose was alone. It was growing dark and for a moment the meaning fled out of everything. The street and buildings assumed a matt, dead look, like an old photograph.

When he returned in the taxi, Rose at last remembered to ask: 'How are Mummy and Papa?'

'All right.' He frowned. 'I will tell you.'

As the taxi drove off, he said quickly, 'I think they are worried because two men were coming to our house asking about the Englishman.'

'What Englishman?'

'The one you know.'

'You mean Der—'

He clapped a hand on her mouth, nodding his head towards the taxi driver's shoulders.

'Who came?'

'You know who I mean.'

The walls and bare trees fled back. By now Rose and Tadeusz had become excited and conspiratorial, in an easy and unavoidable way. He smirked for a moment and then said in a high voice: 'I think taxi drivers are very nice people.'

No tremor to indicate understanding came from the shoulders in front.

'They sometimes do understand, you know. It is because they were in England in the war.'

Silence, while they thought about that distant, empty time, and what it had done to their lives.

'Go on about these men.'

'It was the Police. At least not the Police – you know who.' He made two letters with his fingers.

'But why?' She was startled and drawn-looking.

'Papa thinks he was selling things on the Black Market. Do you think so?'

'Perhaps. He isn't very intelligent.'

'Mummy said he was an oik.'

Rose turned away. 'Oh God. Really!'

A little later the taxi driver suddenly spoke. She jumped with fright and Tadeusz grinned; they had already voted the driver incapable of speech and this was as miraculous as if part of the engine had given tongue. But when it turned out to be Polish, her excitement dwindled down to mere apprehension. Tadeusz, however, carried on an intent conversation which lasted until they had drawn up outside the block of flats.

'I told him you were English. He thought you might be German. He has an uncle in Chicago. So now I knew he did not understand anything we were talking about.'

'Just what were we talking about? Who was it who came?'

'The U.B. The Secret Police.'

'About Derek Loasby?'

'Yes.'

Overhead a flock of pigeons was wheeling round in the last sunlight that could seep through the industrial haze. In Krakow the past continued into the present, but living here in Biala Gora was like recolonizing a dead planet, fearfully camping out in an unfinished world. She followed Tadeusz up the cinderpath.

It was all very like her first evening in Poland except that Janet and Witek both greeted her. They trusted her now.

Rose, although now quite untrustworthy, was no longer a wincing stranger. She found them happier than she had feared. Of course it is when you concentrate on people that their difficulties appear insoluble. Now she could only give them a part of her attention. Work-worn, small, greyish and smiling, the Rudowskis appeared to belong together.

They were disunited, however, over the problem of Derek Loasby.

'Elzbieta Barcik gives him Polish lessons, and he told her they wanted to see him. She thought it was because of Black Marketing. He goes round with all sorts of students and perhaps they've got him into trouble.'

'But they like him. He's lots of friends.'

'The students get all sorts of pressures on them. Ask Witek.'

Witek listened in silence, to indicate that the problem was purely an English one. 'They are young and some of them have not good backgrounds. I am surprised that the Englishman should do this. We are told always that they have high social morality.'

'They do,' Janet said. 'In England.'

Rose was more doubtful. 'He's very unsure of himself and he might easily do something silly, if the others asked him to.'

'Please, silly?'

'Something about money.'

'Speculation is a grave social problem.'

The sisters tried to ignore him.

'What did They come here for?'

'Who told you?' Janet asked.

'Tadeusz, of course.'

Witek shifted about and then said: 'I am sorry that Tadeusz has told you of this. There are still some aspects which a foreigner may find that it is difficult—'

'Oh, Witek. Please! I *am* grown up.'

This was the first time she had lost patience with him and her voice sounded exactly like Janet's. The small movements of his body checked and became total stillness. The hurt sliced through his eyes, leaving them wounded and terrible, and then he got up very slowly and walked out of the room.

'I – I'm sorry about that.'

'It doesn't matter,' Janet said fumbling for a cigarette.

'How are things?'

'We have our ups and downs, but things are going better on the whole. Luckily he wasn't here when they came round. They wanted to know how we met Loasby. I said he had only been here twice. Hala brought him when he first arrived. Then you. You know I didn't like him.'

'Yes. You told me.'

'It was a shock when they came. Like going back to Stalin's time. You see, nowadays we can live from day to day without knowing about all this.' The match flame quivered in Janet's hand. She shook it out. 'I was terribly worried about the passport.'

'Janet, what do you really want to do?'

'I want to get Tadeusz away from all this. For ever.'

'But you?'

'I don't matter, my life's finished.' She blew out smoke and watched Rose. 'Tadeusz must go.'

Rose's face was screwed up with anxiety. 'I'm sure you're wrong. I've travelled about now and I've come to my own conclusions. However bad it may seem, and is, there are so many things to be done here and people to fight for them. A man has to decide this.'

'You can't ask Witek to decide—'

'I meant Tadeusz—' Before she could continue, the telephone started ringing.

'He wants to speak to you. Be careful what you say.'

'Who?' Rose rushed and grabbed the receiver. But it was only Derek Loasby.

## Chapter Twenty-six

Because of the rain, every table in the café was filled. Derek stood outside and was dripped on, and had the usual feeling that rain fell, not alike on the just and unjust, but only on the incompetent. After five minutes the rain was just another aspect of his preoccupation, his sense of the extremeness of life, which kept him bouncing from foot to foot and whistling between his teeth. He was doing exactly this when Rose found him.

'Derek. Hullo.'

He rushed at her as though he had loved her for years, brought himself up short, slipped and almost fell on his thick rubber soles, still holding her hand. She smiled, blinking the rain away.

'Let's find somewhere to sit,' Rose said, 'And then you can tell me all about it.'

'Then you know?'

She looked past him into the crowded café. 'There doesn't seem to be any room.'

He muttered something and steered her out through the rain and into another doorway.

'What did you say?'

'Any port in a storm.' He sounded desperate.

'Yes. I suppose so.'

The place they had now entered had the willed squalor of Slav drink shops. They stopped, feeling already half-smothered by the odours of sour beer and rank bodies. The rain, however, still fell in a solid cascade behind them. Everyone was staring at them and so they sat down, both nervous, at a small table in the middle of the room. At first they did not look at each other; their eyes wandered but soon returned. This squalor seemed exhibitionistic, a denial of anything but the bed-rock upon which life scrabbled to survive.

Even before a youth had put two glass-stoppered bottles and two smeared tumblers before them the effect of all this went a little to their heads; they were young and it gave them so strong a feeling of pioneering, of being where nobody had been before. She smiled at him quite gaily and he was ready to forget everything they were here for.

'Well?'

After this bleak word, he was careful. 'What have they been saying about me?'

'It's that Miss Thing – the one who blinks and teaches you Polish – she said something to Janet. And Janet—'

He gave a patient sigh which suggested that he was more important than all this. 'I haven't told *her* anything.'

Rose was beginning again, when he drank some beer and spluttered. He really was in a violently nervous state, like somebody who has taken Benzedrine.

'I'm sorry about dragging you into this. But there wasn't anybody else to tell. I heard you were away so I waited till you came back.'

Rose realized from this that, rather humbly, he respected her judgement. 'Don't worry about me. Anyway, I—'

'I don't feel I can trust anybody.'

'Derek, what is this all about?'

'They've asked me to stay on, you see.' His fingers drummed up and down on the table. His smile was triumphant, and crafty.

'Is it something about your scholarship?'

'No, no.' He shook his head until his cheeks clicked. 'To come over, to work here – like those Missing Diplomats and people. They offered me a job. Not much money, but their standards are different. Girls, too.'

'What girls?'

'They said there were a lot of nice girls here. I said I knew.'

They were off on the wrong subject again. They guessed that both had felt the sexual touch of the place but the evidence was inadmissible to this conversation.

She tapped at her cigarette thoughtfully. 'Janet and Witek thought the trouble was that you were selling things.'

'That's what I thought.'

'You mean you were?'

'Of course. I told you, you remember. Everyone does here, they keep asking you. Then I found I was being watched.' His face warmed through like an electric fire. 'This bit makes me look rather foolish. You remember that girl Wanda, I think you met her? Well, I left her in my room while I went to get cigarettes and half-way down the stairs I found I'd forgotten my money so I went back and when I opened the door I saw she was going through my letters.'

'But Derek, people often do that.'

'Jotting things down. On a little pad.'

Rose half-closed her eyes and giggled. 'Just trying to improve her English.'

'Wanda doesn't know any English,' he wailed. 'She's always said so.'

'What did you do?' Rose was still laughing.

'Nothing.'

That this was untrue was obvious to both of them. He would have had to do something. But he disliked being teased and at present it muddled him. He stared down at the dirt-engrained table between the beer glasses and his mind flicked over a succession of sore but not entirely disagreeable points, which were the recollection of what in fact had taken place, and he felt again the shock of Wanda standing there by the desk, reading a letter from his mother.

He had retreated quickly, slammed the front door so that the chain rattled, and returned to the room to find her lying, unsmiling but self-consciously posed across the folk-weave cover of his bed. Syntax deserted him, and he could only remember the single word 'money'. '*Pieniądze*' he blurted out, rummaged for his wallet and fled. In the race to the kiosk and back up the dingy staircase he had thought of nothing at all. But when he saw her again Wanda had become a thing.

He could not bring himself to speak to her. She did not drink in the daytime, she had already heard all his gramophone records, and soon she finished her cigarette and still lay there...
This memory he carried around with him like a somewhat grubby handkerchief. Her treachery might have made him incapable but at that point it had excited him extremely.

'I didn't do anything,' he lied. 'I want them to learn to trust me.'

'But you don't trust them.'

'I suppose I don't.' His attention wandered. It was impossible to tell what he was after, beyond convincing himself of his own importance.

'Does Mirek know about this?'

'Who?'

'Mirek Sypniewski. Your friend. Haven't I got his name right?'

'Oh, yes, Mirek.' Loasby fiddled with the ash-tray and said: 'No, I don't trust Mirek at all.'

'Really, I think you must have persecution mania or something. He was frightfully outspoken against anything like that. And, after his experience, he must know all about it.'

'That's the trouble, isn't it? They've got something on him. In any case he is always coming into contact with foreigners. No, I don't trust old Mirek any farther than I can throw him.'

She felt obscurely wounded by this. Mirek Sypniewski had been the first person here really to catch her sympathy. She remembered him standing in the dark, heavy with sadness. To distrust him would be cruel, and yet it might be more cruel to expect too much. He was not after all a noble survivor from the past, like Adam Karpinski, but a product of this generation.

Rose stood up.

'Let's go. This beer's horrid and I think it's stopped raining.'

A few slow sun-refracting drops were falling but there was a lifted clearness in the air. At four o'clock the streets were crowded with workers going home to dinner. The shop windows were filled with the usual unrealities, plaster models of legs of pork and salami and photographs of Gomulka for May Day, surrounded with whirls of scarlet and crêpe paper, and in reaction to this, though most people were wrapped up in sick-smelling plastic against the weather, they had armed themselves with something real to carry home: a loaf of bread, shiny with freshness, or a spray of pussy-willow or apple blossom or a bunch of marsh marigolds.

In this crowd Derek and Rose were soon embarrassed by each other. Each of them wanting to get back to their own Poles and if they spent too much time together they felt diminished and anxious.

Because of this they walked in silence, both listening to the relentless squeals of Derek's new Polish shoes, until Rose said:

'What I was trying to tell you was, that two men came to the flat and asked about you.'

'What did they look like?'

'It was while I was away. The Rudowskis were worried because Tadeusz is trying to get a passport.'

Her Poles, however, did not bother him. 'What did the men say?'

'They asked about you. Janet didn't know too much.'

'Probably they were the same ones. They really are interested in me. They know there are certain things I approve of a lot.'

'Like being spied on.'

'No. Not that.'

Yet he went around administering approval, and was snubbed for it, though less often than he should have been. Only yesterday he had complimented somebody on the cleanness of the streets; 'Yes, we Poles have so little we can afford to throw away.' Today he noticed for the first time the new municipal wastepaper baskets, which took the impractical form of penguins with gaping beaks. 'Just look at those.'

'They're hideous, aren't they?'

He was hurt: if an effort was being made, Rose ought not to be beastly about it.

'At least they're *doing* something,' he said.

At the tram stop, he told her that his new friends had asked to see him again.

'Will you go?'

'What do you think?'

'I think it would be rather stupid. What good can it do you? Or them, for that matter. Besides, I think you ought to tell somebody. Other English students'll be coming here, won't they?'

He shrugged his shoulders. 'Who'll I tell?'

'Our Embassy.'

He sniffed. 'A lot of snobs. What do they know about real conditions here? They live apart, cut off.'

'You could tell them, then.'

'I could write a report, I suppose. For the Ambassador.'

'You don't need to do that,' Rose said, feeling tired by now. 'One of them is coming down next week. I'll put him on to you.'

'Oh, all right.' Derek looked gloomy. His glory was being dissipated all too rapidly.

Rose was sorry for him: 'Look, why don't you come out to supper tonight?'

After listening to him for over an hour, it was really almost too much for her patience to watch him weigh up this invitation against his other opportunities for this evening.

'All right,' he said. Then the tram she was waiting for came swinging round the loop in front of them.

Rather later Derek turned up at the Rudowskis' flat, where he drank too much of Witold's *jarzembiak* and gave a curiously confused account of the possibilities of English life.

'Unless you're in with the Establishment,' he kept repeating, 'You haven't really got a chance.'

After he had gone, Tadeusz asked Rose: 'Is it true what he said?'

'Of course it's not true,' Janet told him. 'He's one of those people who like to blame others for their own failure.'

'I found his point of view most interesting,' Witold said.

*Chapter Twenty-seven*

The following day Rose received the telephone call she was expecting.

'My darling Miss Rose, may we meet very soon?'

'All right.'

'Now?'

A pause. Adam sensed people standing round her and even pictured the stupid Rudowski breathing on her neck.

'All right, yes.'

Adam replaced the telephone and went back to his table.

He had spent the morning at the University, in conversation with a few of the old professors who still retained the glamour which attached to learning in this country. Most of these were survivors from Lwow and Wilno, the lost universities in the East. A good deal of their glory had departed, nowadays they were bald, their features were adorned with every type of wrinkle and protuberance, they were dressed often in garments of what looked like old furnishing material; they remained however both happy and civil. They still had the relish of their obscure knowledge (one of them, Professor Doctor Boczok, spoke all the Melanesian languages but had never left Europe).

Regularly they published the results of their research. They had discovered that even in the worst times only one paragraph of a learned article need to be devoted to the ritual *Ave Caesar;* if the article were to be published in the United States, this paragraph could be excised.

But these graceful and antiquated professors could seldom be got at by themselves. A henchman was always present, an assistant of either sex, bloodless and bespectacled, whose sense of reality was so feeble that it could be satisfied by the latest efforts to make Marxism fit the facts. These poor specimens considered themselves Adam Karpinski's enemies: they were supporters of Witold Rudowski.

Adam did not let them worry him. It was pleasanter to think about Rose, who now came into the café. She was wearing a simple charcoal-coloured dress and had her hair done up in a sort of bun. He kissed her hand, then her face.

She settled beside him. In both of them the insistent machinery of strain was suddenly switched off; everything was calm now and there was nothing to worry about any more. While Adam ordered coffee, her eyes began to absorb him again. Dirt ringed his shirt collar. He smelt quite different from in the mountains. He looked so smashed, she ached with love for him.

From the five days they had already spent together, she had learned the course of the syndrome. First there had been the wild elation, the race in the growling Mercedes towards the snowfields. Adam sat half-turned in the seat beside Bogdan Malczarek, who was driving, and talked continuously.

At such times Adam dominated everything; merely by being there he ridiculed the querulous plainsong of Mrs Malczarek, who once they were out of Krakow became calm and cheerful. Beyond the car windows the sloping landscapes were an unending celebration. The river glittered between new-budded trees, wooden houses were being built, fields were being ploughed. Then the mountains closed in, and in the villages the foreign car was stared at by strange men who wore white felt trousers, elaborately embroidered, and girl-guide hats ringed with cowrie shells.

At Adam's instigation, the writer threw the long black car like a racing toboggan down the thawed roads. Towards evening they came to the rest house where they were to stay. It was sparsely furnished and decorated only with such battered hunting trophies from the past as a stuffed lynx and a frieze of roebuck antlers, or perhaps chamois horns, like little coat-hooks all the way up the stairs. '*Vous voyez*,' Adam said at the sight of these, '*On a été diablement cocu ici*. What's that in English?'

'Cuckolded, I suppose…'

And now, back in Biala Gora, Rose laughed.

'Why are you laughing?'

'I was remembering the little horns.'

He sighed, swinging her hand in his. 'If one could always live in the mountains, one's life might be bearable.'

'Please don't.'

He shook his head. 'You will go away and why should I wish to survive? I don't really want to survive as far as tomorrow, when Mr Mark and Mrs Alexandra will arrive. She is a bitch and a cow, Alexandra, and a terrible liar. I adore her. Tell me what on earth can the Tathams think about us?'

'Us?'

'Poles.'

'Oh.'

From the depressive phase of the syndrome, women and outsiders were excluded.

In the mountains, this phase had followed on the third or fourth day. Rose had sat with him all one afternoon by a stream, burning-cold from the glaciers, while he talked about the trains beyond the Urals, the camp and the Kolkhoz, and his wanderings after the amnesty. Tears scorched her eyes, though it was all long ago and those never released must be dead by now. Bones in the permafrost.

The phase returned now. 'We are infected with unhappiness. Our position is an impossible one. It would be much better if we had been all exterminated. It was a good idea last time but it did not quite succeed. The next time, which will be quite soon now, they will be successful and we Poles will not trouble the rest of the world any more.'

She tried to ride this one out but could not. 'Oh, please. Stop. Stop.'

'What difference does it make to you, Rose? Already you say to me you are leaving—'

'Stop, please,' she sobbed.

He stopped, but only to plunge into a malodorous silence like a sick animal.

After about five minutes of this, she asked plaintively: 'Can't we go and have lunch somewhere? I'm so hungry.'

They went to the restaurant of the Hotel Hoffman, a huge room with galleries and a round glass roof, built in a kind of Baltic baroque style which was now coated all over with sour-cream paint. 'There is nowhere else to eat in this dreadful town,' Adam said. They sat at a square table with a dirty white cloth and two bottles of mineral water.

On reading the menu, however, he became livelier.

'Wonderful! They have *pstrag*.'

'What on earth's that?'

'In English, I forget. A fish.'

'It's usually carp.'

'No, no. *Forelle*.'

He began to sing in a cheerful baritone and when he had stopped they ordered the cold trout and some fillet of beef *en croûte*. This last too was only to be found by occasional good fortune, since in a people's democracy all parts of the animal appear to carry much the same value. Their order was discussed at some length with the waiter and when he had gone Rose asked: 'Do you always call waiters "darling"?'

'Warsaw people do.' He looked around him appraisingly. 'Perhaps it is not so bad here: I am glad because I shall be coming here quite often.'

It was bleakly tactless of him to speak of a time when she would have gone. 'Why?'

'When I have my job at the University.'

'But I thought Witek—'

Adam hunched forward. He was intent, not with personal affection, but with the effort of proving his arguments. His grey eyes looked deep into her eyes and walked about on the bottom of her soul.

'Now, darling,' he said, 'he is quite impossible, isn't he?'

'No! No! Please don't say that. I *have* to believe in my own people.'

'Poor Rose.' He curled his hands with pity.

'What has happened? He seemed to think it was so certain.'

Adam's breath brushed over her face. 'You know that I have had some political difficulties in the past. But this morning I learn that our Party is in a liberal mood just now. So I think I shall be accepted after all.'

'You don't even live here!'

'I shall come down once a fortnight to give my lectures.'

'You couldn't do that in England.'

'No, you couldn't do that in England. Tell me, does your dear brother-in-law actually know anything? I have never been able to find out.'

'Poor Witek. He'll lose everything.'

'Everything?'

'Yes.' She stared away in whirling misery for some minutes. Then she swallowed some vodka. 'Well, let's try and be happy and not worry about my family.'

'Darling, you should be like me and have no family. It is very fashionable here since the war. Even my wife has stopped writing to me.'

The waiter served them with trout in aspic from a long

metal dish. Adam picked up two forks and stared at his plate for a few minutes. Then he looked up, as though he had just thought of something.

'Rose, why do you stay here? Why don't you come to Warsaw? You have three weeks left.'

'Have I?' she asked with surprise.

'Yes.' He removed a bone from his mouth and put it on the side of his plate. 'I saw your weezer.'

'My *what?*'

'Your weezer. On your passport.'

'My visa!'

It was the first proper mistake in English she had heard him make, and she giggled a touch hysterically, even though she saw it annoyed him. 'When?'

'What do you mean when?'

'When did you look at my visa?'

'When you gave them your passport at the rest house, of course.' He tapped the table impatiently. 'Will you come to Warsaw?'

'It's all so difficult.'

'What do you mean, it's so difficult? You can do what you want.'

'Darling, how can I possibly know what I want? I simply can't let them down.'

'Of course you can, you simply do not care. You are cold and trivial like all the English.'

'You know that is not true.'

'Then after this I shall never see you again?'

She looked away. Perhaps she could not imagine this yet and thus could stand it.

'You'll come to luncheon tomorrow with Alexandra and Mark? Please. It will be insupportable without you.'

'It's getting difficult to explain at home.'

'Stop talking about those ridiculous people!' he shouted at her.

They finished their trout in a reverberating silence. While the plates were being changed, she picked up her vodka glass and said nervously: '*Na zdrowie!*'

'And, darling, do stop trying to cheer me up! Polish women let their men be gloomy.'

'Sorry.'

'Never mind.'

He smiled wanly. At that moment he looked so smashed that it was difficult to believe that, in Warsaw, he was a successful man who held down three jobs.

When they left the restaurant he said: 'Now we take a tram.'

The tram wound through the grey streets and went clear of the town. It was the same one that Rose had taken with Tadeusz but today she had forgotten this, being involved in a haze of sunlight and vodka and unhappy love.

'This,' Adam said, 'is the true contemporary problem. Nowhere to make love, except the middle of the forest.'

## Chapter Twenty-eight

'I'm going to be out again, tonight.'

Janet was correcting a translation. She looked much older when she wore her spectacles. 'I thought you would be.'

'What do you mean?'

'Rose, it's difficult to keep secrets here. Mrs Wahorska wrote from Krakow at once to Krystyna Kazimierska.'

'Those old bitches. They've always got their knife into somebody.'

'You're quite wrong, darling. In fact, entirely the opposite. They derive a tremendous kick out of the whole thing. Besides, Krystyna adores him, she can never stop talking about him and old "Sir Gawain and the Green Knight".'

Janet crossed out a word, consulted a technical dictionary on the table beside her, and wrote in another word. 'I'm getting to be such an expert on steel-processing, you can't imagine.' She chewed her pencil a moment. 'The only mistake you can make is to marry them. Then you lose caste absolutely.'

'He's married already.'

'Separated.'

'Catholic,' Rose said.

'I suppose so. You've got something stuck in your hair.'

Rose put up her hand. 'A pine-needle.' She giggled. 'He might have told me. Oh dear, it's all so wonderful.'

'Are you going to tell that to the lawyers?'

'No. I suppose not.'

'What are you going to tell them? You haven't got so long, you know.'

'I know. But I can't think now. I must change. He's waiting for me outside. I couldn't bring him in in case Witek was here. By the way, does Witek know about this?'

'I shouldn't think so. He has no one to tell him. You would be in hot water, then.'

'All these lies. But we've always told lies in our family, haven't we?'

Janet flinched: truth such as this one, certainly, had been avoided at Barnham.

Adam was standing at the nearest tram stop. He still wore his raincoat, although the evening was fine and the wide sky over the plain was pale and translucent, with two storks flying across it.

The rain had held off during the past week now, horses and carts came in from the country covered with dust, and the ground underfoot was beginning to turn into dust. But near the beer kiosk, all the beer that had tilted out of glasses held by contented peasants and soldiers formed into a fine sour mud, which squelched gently under their unsteady feet.

'At last! What a horrible place to live!'

'It isn't so bad.'

By now her eye had grown selective and, from the dull background of apartment buildings and *terrains vagues*, picked out the lame soldier summoning his tumbler pigeons out of the walnut-tree, the young couples in bright cotton sitting among the clumps of weeds. This evening the three boys who shared a motor-bicycle had taken it completely to pieces, and stood round marvelling at the pleasure of something entirely their own.

'For me, it is terrible! Such people!' Adam said. 'They're perfectly ordinary people.'

'Perfectly ordinary! Warsaw people don't have such faces!'

She looked to see the joke and saw he was entirely serious.

That evening, they wandered round the town. They had an unsuccessful meal at the railway station. After sunset, rather late, they ended up at the Students' Cellar.

At first there was nobody Rose recognized: of the feral young men with bad teeth and dirty sweaters, anyone might have been Mirek Sypniewski but none was. Among the girls, though, she noticed Loasby's friend Wanda, standing alone. The girl was wearing a pink sack dress, fierce against her raw complexion. The misfortune in her appearance somehow made it certain that Derek was not far away.

And indeed, while Adam was fetching glasses of wine, he came sidling up.

'I haven't seen Them again,' he said. 'But I've learned a lot since I saw you.'

'Ought you to talk about it here?'

He darkened – the spectral light in the cellar made his

blushes grey – and lowered his voice. 'That girl – you remember I told you?'

'She's just over there, Derek.'

'I know.'

While Derek continued talking, Rose watched the girl who leaned against the opposite wall of the cellar. Quite evidently she was in a depressed state: whenever anybody spoke to her, she did not answer but jerked away as if she had physically been bumped into.

'I chucked her, you won't be surprised to hear. I mean, it was impossible after that business of reading my letters. Funnily enough as soon as I did, people started telling me all sorts of things about her. Apparently two years ago she was trying to get to England, we wouldn't give her a visa because she was an orphan and since then she's been trying to get off with any foreigner who comes around. That was why she took up with me in the first place—'

'This is Derek Loasby, Adam Karpinski.'

Derek's eyes reached conclusions, his face candidly summed it all up, he even half-nodded. He offered cigarettes, and lolled back in his chair, and ten minutes later he was still with them. Rose simmered with irritation. The thought of the English was slightly repulsive to her now, half-raw and embryonic as they were; this particular specimen, roaming at large with his self-complacency in the area of pain, gave special reason for feeling ashamed. If there was such a thing as commonness of soul, it was his.

Derek looked from Adam back to Rose. To him she wore

a completely English look, with her clear skin and petulant mouth. He believed you could not interest her except by shock.

Abruptly he said: 'I'm leaving.'

'Good night, Derek.'

'No, no.' His hands tortured a cigarette pack. 'Really leaving. I could stay on but somehow I've lost interest here. Everything's got so messy, I can't concentrate any longer. You know how there's a time in a foreign country when you simply can't stand anything, any aspect of the place any more?'

Adam asked him a few civil questions about the work he was doing and the people he knew, but it was no use. Derek twisted about, exaggerated and lied. His sensibilities were scorched by the blaze of too much experience; not the experience of action, but of intention, the heavy pressure of future and past in this marginal place.

Finally he stood up and shook hands with Adam and then Rose. Rose said: 'I understand what you were talking about. But shouldn't you learn to forgive people and trust them?'

'How can I trust them?' the young man asked plaintively. He disappeared into the crowd of dancers.

## Chapter Twenty-nine

'So there we are,' said Rose.

Mark Tatham, who was walking beside her in the public garden, paced more slowly.

'What do you think?' she asked.

'Since you've got the father's permission to take the boy to England, isn't it all right?'

'I hope so.'

By now they were at the statue of the poet Kochanowski, in front of the University. They could have been seen by Witek from his office window, but at this moment his head was bowed into the intricacies of his broken tape recorder: when he looked up it was only to worry out the technical terms from the German brochure. He loved machinery and would have spent his life with it, had it not been for the greater prestige involved in academic life.

Alexandra was visiting an aged princess, an aunt of Krysia Kazimierska, who was holed up in a tiny room somewhere on the outskirts of the city.

The sun shone on the budding trees, on the sellers of strings of pretzels, sprinkled with rock-salt, which people munched to stave off hunger. Old men basked in rows on the park benches. The inhabitants of Biala Gora looked especially unprosperous in their weekday clothes. The English people seemed extraordinarily out of place, and every now and then an incredulous stare came towards them from one of the bleak old faces on the benches. A bunch of workmen gave Rose surprised smiles, not just of sexual appreciation but of pleasure, at whatever had happened to bring so exotic a figure to this town.

'There won't be any difficulty about the visa?'

'I don't see why there should be. As long as you send him back.'

'Of course.' Now her footsteps went a little faster, pecking the asphalt among the courting pigeons; she saw, in spite of everything, some happiness ahead. 'Thank you, Mark.'

'Nothing to do with me at all. But you must be sensible, you know, Rose.'

Rose was being belittled by this. 'Why?'

'He is certain to find out about the money quite soon.'

'Oh no. We've told nobody. I don't see how he could find out. No, what we must do is wait.'

He smiled. 'What for, Rose?'

'For – for Tadeusz to grow up. For the Cold War to – well, you know.' Her voice trailed off, because he was still smiling and such hopes always appeared feeble, even on the sunniest mornings here.

A cluster of students went by them on their way to lectures in the main building of the University. The pony-tailed girls, the awkward and intense young men were all talking at once; caught up in the swirling air of ideas and feelings, they sounded like a rookery in full cry. The smile faded from Mark's face and he looked appalled. He really is pompous, Rose thought.

'And this student?' he asked.

'Which student?'

'Loasby. He came to see me this morning. The whole business seems rather a muddle. Does he really want to marry this girl?'

Rose squeaked. 'No. Of course not.'

'That's what he said.'

'He must be stark staring. Only last night he was saying the most frightful things about her.'

'Evidently there was a grand reconciliation.' The distaste stiffened his face. 'Have you seen her?'

'Yes. I don't know what she's like though. She doesn't speak English. A bit cross-looking I thought, but that may indicate banked-down fires.'

Evidently Mark did not need this information. He did not ask for opinions or give them.

She wondered how much Derek had told him. Derek might be involved in promises and complications which he was ashamed of and which, for various social reasons, he could never confess to anybody like Mark. He was desperate to interest people, had probably only come to Biala Gora in the first place to make himself more interesting, but it would be no use with Mark. Derek was a raw clumsy person but one did not like to think of him as irretrievably in a jam.

Mark looked at his watch. 'Let's go in and have a drink. We've brought down some whisky.'

'All right.'

'Only be careful what you say at the hotel. Our room's probably wired up like a telephone exchange.'

'All right.'

A warning like this brought a mixture of feelings now, no longer just the discomfort of living in a world of suspicion. It was like a comment on the physical deformity of someone dearly loved. Those she did love, Adam, Tadeusz and even Witek, could have made this comment as easily as Mark did. But then they were sufferers; since Mark was immune, he ought not to blame.

## Chapter Thirty

The hotel was not far away. Just as they reached it a taxi drew up, and Alexandra was in it, with Adam seated beside her. It was a slight surprise to Rose because he had not mentioned he would be with Alexandra.

In Alexandra's presence, though, any such speculations were quickly forgotten. Her bell-voice rang out to greet Rose, whom she kissed. Adam hustled them briskly into the hotel and informed them that, since the restaurant service was so slow, there would be no time for a drink upstairs. Adam was quite altered when Alexandra was there and so was Mark. It was like having a wireless turned up: everyone had to talk a little louder, push a little harder. Or else, as Rose did now, keep silence.

Adam proved correct, and in spite of his efforts, and perhaps because of the Western air of assurance the four of them exuded among all those drab trade delegates, their lunch was interminably delayed. For long periods their table-cloth was adorned only with clogged ash-trays, and vodka and mineral-water glasses; the carafe of crystalline spirit waited in a frost-bloomed bucket beside it. The tables were small, though so widely separated in the huge room that you were out of earshot of your neighbours. They had to sit very close together; feet and knees, not immediately recognizable, bumped under the table; above it, Alexandra was the brightest and biggest. The vodka made her eyes sparkle but in any case her tongue was already loosened. She was in fine fig and blossoming with her pregnancy. Perhaps it was the complete lack of compassion in her voice which gave what she said the feeling of wit; her sense of timing was superb and the indiscretions she let out were fairly venial ones: the boring behaviour of United States Embassy wives, the antics of a South American minister in pursuit of the younger members of the League of Socialist Youth. Mark managed to sit through this with only a slight expression of constraint and the occasional interpolation of a mild 'Darling!' Meanwhile Adam was echo and chorus and stimulus to everything she said. Like Krysia Kazimierska and her friends, he found any proof that people continued with their ludicrous behaviour was an assertion of life.

Not, however, if they were Poles. When Alexandra turned on any of his compatriots, she always was wrong. 'He may seem like that to you,' he would tell her, 'but he's a brilliant fellow,' and Alexandra always replied: 'Of course, Adam, I'm sure he's marvellous.' For himself Adam permitted quite different judgements: the political set-up was composed of conspirators and swine. But even then his attack never coincided with Alexandra's. He was out to dispraise when she praised, to commend where she chose to denigrate. It was like a game of catch in which they turned and twisted in pursuit of each other and neither managed to hold the other. Even on this minor occasion, the tension and the impassable barrier had to be there.

Mark drank more than the rest of them, nourishing his boredom. It tugged at his sleepy eyelids and bleared his long face like the onset of a sneeze. He shifted in his chair, long-legged and uncomfortable, clutching his knees. He watched the others as though they were part of something he had been staring at for a long time, part of the *longueurs* of his ambition. Across him, Adam's gaze held Alexandra's, while she talked on and on. Alexandra dominated. She had not had much education and all the confidence of the upper class was needed for such set-to's with men on their own level. Of course, Adam said he adored her. Rose disliked her, felt herself diminished by her.

Mark murmured 'Darling!' once again at something of Alexandra's. His gaze flickered away to Rose. Their eyes met.

Rose was scared, and blushed. The boredom had gone from Mark's face and instead there was a glitter of malice there. He was beckoning to her to enter a conspiracy against the other two. Because of Adam she did not want any part of it, but suddenly she began to feel a good deal more cheerful about Alexandra.

They had finished the cups of beetroot soup. Adam grew serious. He had embarked on his usual discourse, his effort to draw his country's boundaries in the empyrean above the shifting lines history had always provided. Even Alexandra could not pursue him as far as this region. Later, when he was portentously comparing the nation to his favourite, Sir Gawain, summoned to a mysterious destiny by a headless figure out of myth, she only muttered: 'Bully for Sir Gawain!' Adam smiled awkwardly and Rose was anguished because he might not know what Alexandra meant. He might be made fun of and she could not help him, though she ached to touch him and touch him again.

She shot her hand over her glass as the waiter tried to refill it. Adam's glass was refilled: he upended it and went on talking. Ah, couldn't he see how boring he had become? 'People will not want to listen when Gomulka is saying that the blanket is not big enough to cover us all. They want to see the blanket flying up there, like the flag.'

Mark emitted a sort of plopping sound. A single word, unvoiced: 'Balls.'

Rose, the only one of them to hear it, felt his knee press against hers.

His eye followed a line down Rose's cheek and neck until he could spy out the warm corner above the collar bone, the little pit that fell between the breasts. Everything else retreated into a dim and echoing haze of alcohol, the clang of metal trays in the kitchen, the waiters' feet padding on the red drugget, the squeal of a door opening on to sunlight brilliant enough to make you sneeze.

When Mark emerged from this contemplation, Alexandra was watching him, fierce and nasty.

'Our car will be waiting for us,' Adam said at last.

And Mark: 'Rose, what a pity you can't come along with us.'

And Alexandra: 'Let's go upstairs and pee, shall we, Rose?'

Released at last from the necessary constraints of the hotel dining-room, Rose began to chatter unwisely.

She walked round the Tathams' suite, examining, with more attention than they deserved, the prints of old Biala Gora on the walls, fingering the ungainly pottery statuettes and squares of folk-weave which are the official decoration of such places. 'It's not too bad, really, is it?' She peered through the net curtains at the cobbled street below, then turned back and began to wander round the room again. 'I must admit I'm fascinated by the micr – you know. Where do you think they hide them?'

Alexandra did not answer.

Rose was crushed: she had made a tactless remark, perhaps one which would be recorded, if They were listening. Less assured, she crossed over to the brass bedstead. 'These mattresses are pretty hard, aren't they? Why do they always make them in three bits, so you always get the gap just underneath you? And this sort of eiderdown thing, either too hot or too cold.'

These remarks, too, were left to die out.

Alexandra, who was seated in front of a mirror, knew how to treat another person's effort at conversation as though it were an inevitable mechanical noise. She bent down and straightened a stocking.

Awkward and unwelcome, Rose hung on. It had been

ridiculous to expect good will of any sort from Alexandra, and rather careless to have let herself into this position at all. But somehow a worse thing was that Adam and the Tathams were now going away and leaving her forsaken and stranded in Biala Gora. It was not flattering to the Rudowskis to think this, but it seemed to be true.

Alexandra stood up and looked out of the window.

'Adam is waiting for Mark and me,' she said. It was the only thing she said in that room, but when they were out in the corridor and she had locked the door, she went on in her usual chiming voice: 'I'm so glad you like Adam. Mark and I are quite fond of him. It's so nice to be spied on by somebody who's so *like* one, don't you know.'

Downstairs Rose, who was now quite white, refused their offer of a lift.

'No, I'll take the tram. I would rather, really.'

Mark was pompously affectionate in his farewell. 'Rose, you simply must come and stay when you return Warsaw-wards. Alexandra and I insist.'

Adam was giving instructions to the driver of the hired car.

## Chapter Thirty-one

At the stop outside the School of Engineering, Janet Rudowski pulled herself wearily on to the tram. While she stood among the crowd of people returning from work and waited to pay her fare, she noticed that Rose was sitting up in front. Rose's shoulders were hunched as though she huddled away from cold; she looked unprotected. Janet watched her with apprehension.

Apprehension – so often the feelings Janet had for her own family amounted only to this. Apprehension during the war, whenever she returned home on her leaves from the hospital. Apprehension growing as you approached Barnham up the asphalt drive and the school-building gave off a dull tone like a bell that someone has jarred against, a thrumming noise which was a mixture of banged radiators, shouting in corridors, wireless sets shrilling the Forces programme, and all the semi-articulate hums and moanings that are emitted by a mass of schoolboys. All that life beyond the green baize doors which had made her desperately shy as a child. Home-comings were always anguish. The greatest anguish had been when Nico was killed and there was nobody to protect her any more, but it was always there: every time she approached the green door of School House, her heart burst with being sorry for Daddy and hating Mummy.

Now when she saw Rose in front of her in the tram, she experienced that identical jab of hate. Their mother, aesthete and convert and flower-arranger, had always let it be known that she had the finer perceptions; she had looked on Janet, by then a staff nurse, as a plain member of an unprivileged race, trying her best to be useful. And Rose was the same, since her return from Krakow. Rose was special: whatever happened to people, it happened to her differently. Rose went off to meet her grand friends, and never said where she was going.

Janet paid her fare and went and sat next to Rose. Rose clutched her arm and gave her a half-blind look. 'I don't want to talk.'

Once inside the flat, however, Rose talked and talked.

At the end she said: 'You won't tell Witek, will you? Please.'

'No.'

The spoilt child was stopped in her tracks: their mother, through Rose, had got her deserts at last. You could have worked this all out from the beginning, at Barnham. But because they were in Biala Gora, at the extreme edge of the known world, everything was different. Family apprehensions could not exist in the presence of true fear.

Janet had known this fear since her arrival. She had spoken the language badly and everyone took her for a German. Only Witek could protect her then. The disasters that followed, the confiscation of their savings, the police terror, lack of food and the loss of their second child, were a progression that was pointing in only one direction, towards their final destruction. The apprehensions of the English middle class were a mockery compared to this, and yet they had done their work. The Poles grew stockier, squarer and uglier in those years, as though they were holding up the low sky with the brute strength of spines and shoulders. Janet endured with her husband and with friends like Krysia, but sometimes she felt that they had an idea of what happiness was, and she had not.

Even now, Rose was still demanding action.

'I'll keep him in England. I don't care what I promised Witek. I want to keep Tadeusz there for ever, away from this appalling place. I'll do anything you ask. He simply must not grow up here.'

'Let's not talk about it now, I want my tea.'

'I'll get it.' This was the first time Rose had offered to help with anything so simple.

Janet lay back on the divan, her eyes closed. Because with Rose you paid the full emotional cost of family life, she was more tired than ever.

Rose went into the kitchen. Tadeusz was standing by the table. There was no other door; he must have been there the whole time.

'Hullo,' he said.

Was he trembling at what he had overheard, or from the gaucheness, the minor stresses of adolescence? From now on she would never be able to tell what he was feeling. There were secrets everywhere and anybody could deceive Rose. Once you had heard of the existence of a world of lies, you felt their presence everywhere. Perhaps, under the influence of some drug or other, one might see a chair or a table as totally evil; it was a quality of perception like this.

Tadeusz slithered past her. He went into the sitting-room and began talking to his mother.

Beyond the door their voices rose and fell in the monotonous uncoloured English of exiles.

'Mrs Kazimierska has telephoned. She wants to see Rose before she is leaving. She has a package for her to bring to England.'

'All right.'

'And about May Day Parade. I will be marching with my class but I can show Rose where to see best.'

His voice was raised, strained. Perhaps he was talking so that Rose would be able to overhear in the kitchen.

'Of course, darling,' Janet said. 'Why did you come back so early today?'

'It is because we must go back this evening for the meeting that is discussing our excursion.'

'Oh, I see.'

'I must go now, to fetch my colleagues.'

'Give me a kiss.'

When Tadeusz had left, Rose came in with two glasses of tea.

'Do you think he heard what we were saying?'

'What you were saying, Rose. I wasn't saying anything.'

Rose put down the tea. 'One tries to help, one does everything and—' she began to howl. 'Oh God, it's too awful here, awful. I want to go home.'

## Chapter Thirty-Two

On the morning of the First of May Tadeusz led her into the middle of the town until they reached a spot on the pavement opposite the Party Headquarters. Exactly there, he left her. He had to join the contingent from his school, the Tenth Gymnasium, who were waiting in a side street nearly a mile away on the other side of the town.

Tadeusz ran through the streets against the crowd. Everything was closed for the holiday, but not many people were about, for the spring feast of the workers was a dying rite. No procession was taking place in the capital this year, and hardly anything even in Red Square, Moscow. Biala Gora kept the privilege because there had recently been disturbances in the factories and a pro-religious riot in a local industrial settlement. The procession here was a show of force.

When he arrived among his school-fellows, he took up his place without speaking to any of them. The sense of responsibility, which affected him very much at this time, made him feel dumb and rude. Even when he forgot Rose, he had the usual resentment at taking part in politically organized activity. He didn't want it to be either a success or a failure, yet he was annoyed when other people in his class made a joke of it. There was no point in being like them; you ended up half-sickened with boredom and frustration. He desperately wanted to do things properly, as his mother and Rose had told him they were done in England, but there seemed to be no chance.

After some preliminary shuffling and marking time, the contingent of the Tenth Gymnasium moved off. Now Tadeusz began to be irritated by Basia Wengorzewska, the girl marching in front of him. Couldn't she march straight, without wobbling and swaying around like that? A mass of hair, light brown but blonde-streaked as though it had been tumbled in fresh pollen, kept on escaping from underneath her cap. From time to time she glanced around her, and he tried to catch her eye to frown at her. But she was not watching, only seeing whether she was being watched. His agony grew. He longed to stop her and pull her together: she was so soft, so inadequate compared with the stolid girls marching on either side. He stared and stared at her until he felt dazed.

Meanwhile Rose felt she had been waiting for hours in front of the Party Headquarters. The local leaders were beginning to appear on the first floor balcony and above them the huge images of Marx, Gomulka and Lenin, bellying and shrinking in the fresh breeze, seemed alternately to smirk or to pull long faces at the crowd lining the street below. Rain earlier had wettened the party flags so that they had lost their brightness and were now the colour of an old nose-bleed. The wind had also twisted up the long streamers across the street. As a result they seldom showed more than one word at a time: Long Live...Peace...War...Capitalism...Reconstruction. Twigs were being blown off the trees and Rose felt one of them falling past her face. She picked it up. The plane tree blossoms were just unfolding on it, yellow-green, with the flower stalks still as fragile as stamens. She held it up and yawned, and let the unborn flowers flick against her cheek.

Now, from the inner recesses of the plane trees, loudspeakers crackled into full voice. The march past began, stopped for a speech, for applause and for ritual shouting, and began again. How small the factory-workers were, particularly the older ones! They wore berets or cloth caps, raincoats or blue-grey jerseys with zip-fronts. Their faces were grey and expressionless. Because of the recent disturbances participation was compulsory and their sections took an age to go past. With the exception of a few medalled veterans on Armistice Days, Rose had never seen civilians march like this and it felt wrong. This should have been a march of protest. They should be protesting now, because they were so poor, so ill-dressed, so ugly with their swinging work-distorted heads. Yet as they passed the balcony and the huge floating faces (Lenin, blown to one side now, was showing his back to the other two) each man stiffened, straightened his arms and turned eyes right.

After half an hour, the sheer weight of numbers began to make its effect. Every public demonstration, if it is massive enough, creates this willing doubt. It becomes the reality itself. Individual protest is eccentricity; private reservations are merely reflex twitches like those a dog makes when it is dreaming. The tramp of boots on the cobbles, the applauding spectators, the desperately cheerful music blot out everything. Long live the First of May!

Long live the First of May! The slogan is meaningless, but what does anybody's protest mean? If you are Adam, nothing at all. For him all arguments end in nihilism. He is still in the Labour Camps, less free than any of these workers. He is out of date but not far enough. To protest now you need to remember far back to a time, infinitely long ago to Rose, when she was a small child. Then you can remember what it was to be free. And who can remember, except for the old has-beens, people like Krystyna Kazimierska? At least you would never find her taking part in this drilled stampede past Party Headquarters.

By now Rose was completely involved, her throat sore and her eyes smarting with tears. She couldn't decide what she thought about the onset of the school children, who seemed to bring a lightening of the atmosphere, a flicker of smiles along the stolid length of spectators on the opposite side of the street. Brought up at a school, she was used to smiling at the seriousness children bring to a rigmarole of no real importance; it was hard to do that here with old Karl Marx flapping away like a luffing mainsail against the building over there. All she could do was feel a pang of sympathy for the plain faces of the little girls above the nineteenth-century uniforms with sailor collars, and feel pleased, too, that nobody had wasted time on teaching them to march properly. And a moment later all this was forgotten in the tenseness of knowing that Tadeusz was approaching, of feeling his presence like a wave washing along between these two banks of onlookers.

His class was the best turned out, except for Basia Wengorzewska, pink-faced with exertion now, pouting with boredom and always out of step: an infant Bardot whose sulks made everyone's seriousness seem doltish. But Rose did not notice her at all. Her eyes were on Tadeusz.

## Chapter Thirty-three

He, however, had completely forgotten about her. Once, at an intersection of streets near the Main Post Office, he failed to see that the line in front was marking time; he stumbled straight into Basia, collided on to the soft shock of her warmth and retreated, slightly overwhelmed. Trying to think of something different, he looked at the clock on the Post Office. It was after eleven, past the time when he usually had his 'second breakfast' but he didn't feel hungry. The line stopped there for about ten minutes and then they moved off again. Basia kept tripping over the cobbles where they had risen up under the winter's frosts.

At about ten yards from the balcony, he glanced up. Rose wasn't waving or anything else, just staring at him, and for the first time for several days they looked each other in the face.

Then he blushed, until his face grew quite shiny. He laughed; the laugh fluttered and trembled all over his face. The moment was a long one and in its confusion he forgot to turn to the balcony, to the row of dark suits, and the steel-rimmed spectacles which were just beginning to glint in the first sunshine of that day.

Then he was gone.

Rose was ridiculously gratified. At first she could not tell why, except that Tadeusz had not looked at the row of Party bigwigs but at her instead. Then she knew it was because she had got through to him at last.

The sun was really shining now and all around people were smiling and nudging each other into attention.

From a window one floor above the balcony and invisible to its load of occupants, a small man had set out to grapple with the recalcitrant image of Lenin. There was a rope around his waist and the heavy brown façade of the nineteenth-century German building afforded him plenty of holds. Above him the great banner, free of its guy ropes, swooped backwards and forwards on the wind. His hand flew out, like a white star on the dark brickwork, seized one of the flying ropes and hauled it in. Mouths were open in the crowd and nobody spoke. The march past of children continued but now only the most devoted parents were watching it. With the finicky attentiveness of an ant selecting and trundling a fragment of twig, the man tied the rope tightly down on to the front of the building. At length he looked down, expecting some silent evidence of praise from the face upturned beneath him. Above, the banner hung motionless. From where he was, he could not see that it was the wrong way out: beside Marx and Gomulka hung a blank sheet, where Vladimir Ilyich had finally turned his face to the wall.

The crowd enjoyed this very quietly. But, as the last contingents of children gave way to the first deputations from the University, militiamen began signalling to the little man on the window-sill. The officials on the balcony, disquieted by all the attention they had seemed to be receiving, began squinnying upwards into the sunlight. Even the professors and students broke step to watch what was going on. One of their number, however, was determined to pretend that nothing odd was happening. At exactly the correct moment Witek's head turned rigidly towards the building and then forward again. Witek did not see Rose at all.

A minute later, in the contingent from the Faculty of History, Rose saw the tall striding figure of Krysia Kazimierska, and this seemed the final evidence of fear, of the naked power still generated by the drab group on the balcony.

As soon as the parade was finished, the onlookers flooded out over the streets and began hurrying home. Tadeusz made his way back against the crowd to fetch Rose but, when he reached the place where she had stood all morning, he found her gone.

Rose walked to the tram stop and then took fright at the rush of shoving, short-tempered people. She remembered that Tadeusz had promised to come back for her but now it was too late to look for him. Frustrated, she decided to wait until the trams were emptier, and to sit down for a while and think.

But as people do who intend to go away and think, she soon gave herself up to exorbitant fantasy. From this morning she had already made up her mind that, while other people including Adam were venal time-servers, Witek actually enjoyed the world he inhabited. That it was ultimately terrifying she knew from seeing Mrs Kazimierska marching by. And above all she believed that Tadeusz's blushes meant that now he was properly humiliated by it, and must be rescued, which was what she was going to do. These thoughts took perhaps the minute or two in which she was looking for a seat on one of the park benches. Once she sat down she was off dreaming about having Tadeusz in London with her. Having Tadeusz was a compensation for the loss of Adam.

An hour later she arrived home. She let herself quietly into the hallway, because there was nearly always work in progress somewhere in the flat. Now, though, there was the sound of violent quarrelling, breathing silence, then sobbing. She stood for a moment wondering what to do.

Then she decided to go in. It would give Witek and Janet a rest: they usually desisted in her presence. She opened the door.

Janet had her back turned. Witek was sitting on one of the divans: it was he who was weeping.

He saw Rose first, and rushed at her. 'There she is!'

*Chapter Thirty-four*

A t first everything was confusion and shouting.
Rose sat down. 'Please, please tell me what has happened.' Witek was in full cry and could not easily be brought back to the beginning. 'She says, Tell me what's happened!' He stood over her. '*You* tell *me* nothing at all. Why did you come here? I think you came here to Poland because of love. I forget that you English do not love your families at all. Yes, I can tell that the minute I meet your family at Barnham. It is all cold and unhappy. You do not love each other at all.'

For a time the sisters were too scorched by this to speak.

'You English go away to find – to found colonies because you do not love each other at all.'

Rose was frightened now. As soon as there was no possibility of thinking him ridiculous, all her English resources would be gone. 'Please, please, what has happened?'

'The money. Why didn't you tell about the money?'

'Oh. That.'

'Yes. Speak, please.'

"We – we thought it might make things difficult for you.' Rose was determined not to be alone in this. 'Janet knew, too.'

'She is always against me now,' said Witek quietly. 'But you, Rose, can you tell the truth?'

'That is true. And because of your beliefs.'

'My beliefs! *Boze,* you think I am a child?'

'I wanted to be helpful, really I did.'

'So you did not tell me about this money. Because you wanted to be helpful. Because of my beliefs. Yet why are you telling everyone else?'

'That's not true. And I won't be shouted at. I never told a soul, did I, Janet?'

'I don't know, Rose. Didn't you?'

'Oh, blast you, you might at least help. Can I have a cigarette?'

Witek pushed the box towards her. 'You told this Dr Karpinski who you know wants my job.'

'No, that's not true, Witek.'

'It is true, you went off to Zakopane with him?' The place name for him had a sexual weight: something like Brighton or Atlantic City. 'It is true?'

Rose was silent. She twitched her shoulders and said: 'Very well. Yes.'

'Then you told him. You knew who he was and what he was trying to do to me, to my career. You and he ...' His voice ran into a dry patch. He seemed ready to weep again. 'You told him.'

'I didn't. It may sound silly when I explain it. But here in Poland there is something competitive about misfortune. When we come from the West we don't want to say how well off we are. You make us feel ashamed, as though we had cheated to get what we have. So I didn't tell Adam. In fact, if you want to know another silly thing, I told him Daddy had been a master at a grammar school, not a public school.'

Witek was not much interested in these subtleties. 'Whether you tell him or not, he knew. Perhaps he was reading your letters.'

'I didn't have anything written down. I was advised not to—' She broke off. When she remembered who had given her this advice, everything was quite clear.

'It makes no difference, Rose. Whatever happened, he informs the Party and they accuse me that I have large reserves of foreign currency which I have not declared. Not only my future job is in danger but also my present one. In fact, we are all in danger.'

'Oh, Witek darling, how awful.'

'Darling, now. And you still deny it?'

'Yes, I do. You must stop bullying me. I know I was wrong about Adam Karpinski but so was everybody else. I didn't believe anybody could be like that. I happen not to be used to lies.'

He pounced on this last phrase.

'Not used to lies! She says, not used to lies! Rose, you have been lying since you first set your foot through that door.'

At this point she broke into tears.

He watched her closely. He was extremely conscious of the erotic aspects of distress. When she bowed her head, with the fine hair scented by the fragrant shampoos she brought from England and her face damp and agonized, she was at least half-raped in his mind. He ached with unused violence because he could not hit a woman he had never slept with. Trembling, he recovered himself.

Janet patted him on the shoulder. 'Better leave her, old boy.' There was more understanding in her voice than was quite decent. The thing resembled those moments of extreme intimacy when all behaviour is imperiously dictated.

The sisters were alone.

'Here's some tea.'

'I don't want any, thank you.'

'Cheer up. Things like this have happened before and we have always managed to pick up the pieces.'

'You sound like the w.v.s.,' Rose said.

'What?'

'Nothing.' Rose blew her nose and wiped her eyes. 'Actually, I know now exactly what happened. It was that frightful bitch who told Adam. She probably thought it was fearfully amusing.'

'Who?'

'Alexandra Tatham. You see, old Mark has always been a bit of a *coureur* and when she saw that I—'

'Oh God. Here we go again.'

'What?'

'Nothing. Nothing, Rose.'

Rose kept an offended silence while Janet drank her tea.

'Witek and I'll get over this, never you fear. In the old days it was dangerous to admit you had relatives abroad. You remember those desperately cheerful letters I used to write?

Now, it'll be all right. It isn't as if we had ever seen any of the money. Witek will be able to explain it all away, he is very good at that sort of thing and he has the right friends.'

Rose was doubtful. She was the only one who knew Adam personally. Whatever they might think of him, he had twice the brains and force of Witek, and he would not be easy to choke off. To Rose the path was still wide open to disaster.

'Witek doesn't know about our plans for Tadeusz?'

'No. But that's done with now, isn't it?'

'I suppose so, ' Rose said. 'What's going to happen to you?'

'You might have asked that a bit sooner, I must say. All I want is some peace. It will be better when you have gone.'

'Yes,' said Rose. 'It will.'

When Tadeusz came in, Rose questioned him about the May Day Parade. It was her last chance to make him feel close to her. 'You didn't seem to be enjoying it very much, if I may say so.'

Tadeusz blushed. 'I was.'

'Were you? Sorry.'

'I was enjoying it very much,' he said sullenly. 'I was proud to be with my school-mates.'

Rose sighed with disappointment. Even that compensation was to be taken away. But perhaps Tadeusz's social activities were a phase parallel to that of the boys at Barnham, who would lose all charm and grow sourly humourless just before Confirmation. It was the sore, creaking stage in the evolution of the dragonfly.

## Chapter Thirty-five

A few days later he departed at three in the morning on his excursion to the mountains. Breathing like a pack animal under his apparatus of canvas and rubber, he clumped through the room in which Rose was lying awake, and went out into the asphalt silence before sunrise, when pigeons and motor-cycles were still locked away, and a taxi was depositing the last drunks outside the doors of the apartment buildings:

Rose spent most of the day typing out translations for the Rudowskis. There were times when she imagined she would go to Warsaw to look for Adam. But she knew she would not because, like Janet, she was tired. She was glad to have a firm booking on the LOT plane to London, leaving in five days' time.

In the late afternoon she went into town to visit Mrs Kazimierska.

'Come in, Rose. My husband is at a hospital conference, so you will not meet him after all. In any case he is not very interesting.'

The flat, which Rose was visiting for the first time, was half-dark, crammed with furniture and heavy with the smell of furniture polish and cabbage.

'These things were all mother's. You see, our own house was in Warsaw. When we returned after the Rising – look, I will show you what we found.' She rummaged in a drawer and brought out half a blue and gold china plate. 'I found that in what used to be our garden. Our son and daughter were both killed, you know, so this is all we have from before the war.'

Rose looked stiff and slightly offended.

Mrs Kazimierska laughed suddenly. She put back the plate and slammed the drawer. 'And how has it been, dear Rose?'

'Terrible.'

'That I can easily believe. Mr Rudowski is a difficult proposition.'

'It is my fault, too. It seems none of us can say anything we mean. When I was a child we had a nanny like that. She was so easily shocked that in the end everybody told her lies.'

Mrs Kazimierska looked at her with some detachment.

'*We* had an English nanny,' she said, 'and everybody confessed everything to her, even my dear brothers. The water is now boiling. Nescafé?'

She mixed in the sharp-smelling powder and poured out two cups.

'It is because Rudowski is so stupid,' she said. 'Intelligent people can always converse, whatever their politics.'

'I'm afraid it isn't just him. When I first saw Janet again and realized properly all she had suffered, I thought I couldn't do enough for her. But in fact it made me hate her. Not just because we are sisters, I mean – she was always quite nice to me when I was small. It's because of everything here.'

'I think I understand. When relatives sometimes send me a parcel, I can hardly bring myself to thank them for it.'

'Has this happened to everyone?'

'When our friends come from abroad it is often like that. It is so impossible to explain things, we give up trying. When I told you just now about the Warsaw Rising, you were very, very bored.'

'Oh, I am sorry, I didn't mean—'

'Young people here are the same. It is sad but it is true. All the same, I am sure you are glad you have been here.'

'No. I'm afraid I wish I'd never come, if it meant finding them both so miserable.'

'You must know enough about the Rudowskis now, but perhaps they are not so miserable as you think. One thing perhaps I can tell you: she will never leave him.'

'I know she won't,' Rose said. 'Isn't it awful?'

On her way home, carrying the parcel for Mrs Kazimierska's niece, she went into the Self-Service, looking for something to take back with her. Beyond the bare necessities the only things on sale were greyish packets of soup-mix and the glass jars of Bulgarian apricots which, when you attempted to open them, left your hands covered with blood. Instead she bought a bottle of Georgian wine.

Janet was still out. Rose opened the bottle of wine, sweetish, tasting slightly of prunes. She searched in Janet's shelves for something to read. She pulled out an anthology of modern verse and leafed right through it, finding nothing to attract her attention beyond the first few lines, until she got to Yeats:

That girls at puberty should find
Original Adam in their thought –

She banged the book shut, put it quickly back in the shelf even adjusting the other books so that no one could see it had been taken out. Then she heard the clink of the bicycles in the passage and knew Witek was coming through the flat towards her.

## Chapter Thirty-six

He stood in the doorway, visibly making up his mind whether or not he was about to step into the middle of a baited trap. When he saw her lying on the divan, quick and tricky as she was, the project became worthwhile.

'Witek, have some wine,' she said sharply.

The effort at welcome in her voice did not work out as she meant it to, but he was too intent to notice. Chuckling at something – perhaps it was the fact that she had been out, had actually bought the wine and then opened it all by herself – he sat down at the table. He picked up the bottle and examined the label closely.

'Please translate what it says.'

'"Sweet Table Wine". Is that correct?'

'Damn, I thought it must be. Anyway, have some. I'll get a glass.'

He looked appreciatively at the glass and laughed again. Then formality descended on him: he had already decided on no account to be put off. Pulling a small memorandum out of his pocket, he proceeded to install his own special type of social unease.

'I—' they both said at once.

'No, please.'

'No, you go on, Witek. I had nothing important to say,' she shrugged. 'How could I?'

'Very well, I have one or two points that I wish to discuss.'

She put her feet up again, getting more comfortable. 'Go ahead.'

He gave her legs a haggard look.

'I was wondering if before you leave us you will be willing to record your voice for our department? It would be most helpful to us in our work. Janet has not the time, also it seems to me her voice acquired some Polish intonations which cause it to be less good for us.'

'All right. Tell me when.'

'Monday morning, then? Now to my second point.'

He was silent for a while and she watched him labouring at it.

'With regard to this second point we must be very careful. It is about this money.'

Another silence.

'I think, I think' – he coiled a little with embarrassment – 'that you were discreet, and that Dr Karpinski found out through other sources.'

'Well, thank you!'

He laughed miserably. 'In fact you were so discreet that I was not informed! However, you have appreciated that the situation is difficult for me to understand. You see, here the salaries are – well, in higher education they are – well, most people have no money at all. Also it seems to me, if this money comes to Tadeusz, it must by law be transferred into our currency.'

'I know that, Witek.'

'You have observed our position. It is not easy. With a car, for instance, you see—'

'But it all belongs to Tadeusz.'

'A car.' He sipped some wine. 'That would make all the difference.'

He was much out of his depth about the money and could be fuddled by an appeal to English legality, which is universally considered respectable.

'We have laws, too, Witek. I don't even know if the money can leave England. In any case you keep saying it will damage your position with your job.'

'That is my third point.' He gently hiccuped. 'Today I have a long and very valuable talk with Dr Zwiersz. I think you don't know him, he is the chief representative of our Party at the University. Naturally I was explaining to him how this rumour about the money is false. And he in return told me that it is very uncertain that Karpinski comes here. He is unwilling to give up all his jobs in Warsaw. Dr Zwiersz insists he must, for the students' sake. Dr Zwiersz is very good to the students.'

'So, after all this bloodiness, there is no danger for you at all?'

'There is always danger when nothing is certain. I have many problems still. There is Janet, she is very unsettled,

And Tadeusz. You wanted him to visit England, he is impressionable and not sure of himself. That is the fourth point I had for discussion.'

'I thought as much. I have no rights now, have I?'

'After all this trouble of course he must stay here. With this money of his you might keep him in England.'

'What a beastly thing to say!'

He shook his head. 'Rose, you have shown you do not understand some problems here.'

She ran her hands through her hair. 'Oh, what's the use? You meet nobody, you and Janet. The other Poles aren't like you: they – they have free souls.'

He looked nasty at this. 'I think you did not know those people so well. You could be disappointed.'

'All right. All right.'

Witek sat back and finished his wine.

He had won. At every moment his score was going up. His future expanded and soared like a balloon hard with gas. In a short time he would have a permanent place in the academic world, and earn a respect that he would never have known as a language teacher. He would be able to tap that reservoir of deference that still existed years after the death of an aristocratic society; he would be called 'Professor' by concierges and sellers of cabbage. His promotion would help Tadeusz as well, for university examiners were benevolent to the children of academic colleagues.

And in addition there now might be the bonus of a car, perhaps even a summer cottage in the mountains.

At the same time he knew that when Rose left he was going to be as miserable and unsettled as Janet was. On all counts Rose had bequeathed nothing but disquiet. Witek had always thought he agreed with arguments against the West; in his wartime memories, England had looked very like Biala Gora today. But he was the child of Silesian farmers, and materialism was a terrible temptation to him. He hated to be ascetic: let others play chess and listen to Szymanowski! He wanted to feel things solid in his hands, the good finish, the safe shininess that would not wear away. He thought of Rose's stockings, the neatness of her pants and suspender belt lying round the flat. He would have pretty students from time to time but he would never again get in range of anyone like this girl who was sitting in front of him, her complexion dulled a little by tiredness, but her hair bright and her body small and firm.

'Rose,' he said very quietly.

'Yes?'

'Rose, please let us part as good friends. It is important to me.'

'You've won, Witek. Isn't that enough?'

'No, it is not.'

'Please, Witek. No!'

She stood up and pushed the round table at him, so that the edge caught him in the stomach. Then they were both quiet, hearing Janet come in.

## Chapter Thirty-seven

The telephone rang while they were at supper on Sunday evening.

Janet spoke briefly and handed the receiver to Witek.

'*Tu Rudowski.*'

With his tongue exploring his teeth for a fragment of sausage skin he listened.

'*Tak.*'

His mouth was still, and his face gradually set rigid.

'*Tak.*'

From across the room the women could hear an urgent voice rising and falling on a flood of narrative. Witek did not move.

'*Tak, tak.*'

Rose looked inquiringly at her sister. So far Witek had said nothing more than 'Yes', but Janet's head was bowed towards the table and her fists were clenching and unclenching.

'Janet!' Witek called to her and she stared fixedly at him. Now he began to speak, with his face still grim and his eyes held by hers. The words buzzed, repeated and insisted until, after about four minutes, he put the telephone down and there was silence. Witek was gazing straight at Rose and she put on an inquiring expression to attract his attention, but he was not seeing her at all. Still in silence he dialled a number, then spoke again.

Janet gave Rose a small indifferent smile.

'Is it something about Tadeusz?'

'Yes.'

'Serious?'

'We don't know yet. He's had a fall. He's got concussion and they've taken him to hospital. Witek's putting a call through to the hospital now.'

Rose made lines with a fork on the tablecloth. Would they accuse her of communicating a disease of clumsiness which causes people to fall off mountains?

When Witek at length came back to the supper table, his normal manner, of heavy politeness, had quite gone. He looked solid and blunt and might never have had an ambition in his life. Still, out of civility to Rose, he spoke in English.

'I have a colleague who has a motor-cycle. I think he will drive me there tonight.'

'Is it very bad?' Rose asked.

The Rudowskis turned to her as though this curiosity from a bystander occasioned them some surprise. Rose felt herself slipping out of their lives at last.

'It's concussion and his leg is perhaps broken. Nothing else.'

'Thank God.' But they made Rose feel it was not her business to say this.

While Witek telephoned his colleague, Rose began putting the supper things together. Obviously they were not going to be eating any more. She was herself afflicted by nervous pangs of hunger and, once through the kitchen door, she quickly devoured some slices of sausage and licked her fingers. Tadeusz's bed, flat and empty with the blankets folded up, accused her of callousness but she was unconvinced. Did she feel so detached because she was seldom quite sure what was going on? Or because Tadeusz falling off a mountain came too late in a long progression of shocks and portents and disequilibria?

Outside in the twilight they found Witek's colleague: another small and solid man.

After handshakes and farewells, the motor-cycle roared and spluttered off towards the main road. There was a hint of wartime in this bleak departure, and in the image of the two men on the little machine pitting themselves against all that distance. It was also a very Polish image: only human beings, loved or hated, could give meaning to the bare landscape and the looming approach of night.

Janet took Rose's arm. 'I do hope he'll be all right.'

'I'm sure the hospital is looking after him.'

'No, I mean Witek.'

'What could go wrong with him?'

'Oh, it's dark, and a long way, and at night it's dangerous, there are drunk peasants lurching all over the roads.' They walked slowly back to the door of the building. 'If only we had a car! God, why is life so hard? Why?'

Rose, who for the first time wanted to cry, squeezed her arm. 'Let's do some work. I'm sure it's the only thing.'

Janet dictated translations of two articles on plant disease and her sister took them down in shorthand. They spent a good deal of time leafing through a technical dictionary whose accuracy they did not trust, and checking it with the Shorter Oxford. When Rose had typed out the articles there were so many further corrections to be made that she had to do them again. They were working to fill in time and yet, despite a nagging anxiety, felt comfortable and easy together in a way they had not experienced till now. It was nearly midnight when they finished. Both were exhausted. The telephone rang while Rose was in the kitchen making tea. When Janet had replaced the receiver she came through to the kitchen.

'Tadeusz is all right. He's quite conscious and talking. Poor old Witek sounds in a terrible state though. He's starting back now as he has early classes tomorrow. I suppose he'll get here some time in the small hours.'

Rose, who was sitting up in bed with her face still swelled with sleep, was trying to discover what was going on. It was half past five in the morning. Witek was shouting. It was a noise that had been going on for some time, but she had woken into the middle of it.

Perhaps this time he had become insane.

For Rose's sake, he tried to curse in English, but contact with Janet had provided him with no word much stronger than 'beastly'. He went back to Polish. There too words failed him; he knew no distinction between sincerity and violence. When you really meant anything, you broke things. He now destroyed two folk art vases and tore up a square of peasant weave. They did not much matter, but Rose was shocked and frightened; she had the wincing, English respect for property.

In retreat, she put her head under the pillow and stayed there, glad that Witek had no sense of the ridiculous and hoping that, when she returned to the light, everything would somehow have changed.

Janet had disappeared, Witek sat at the table, weeping. He was still in his plastic raincoat, and the dust of the country roads shadowed his eye-sockets and ran down in dark trickles with his tears. He stared out on to a prospect of misery, a man endlessly betrayed by his women.

Rose emerged from under her pillow, dishevelled, with hair all over a hot face, and asked: 'What am I supposed to have done now?'

'You tried to steal my son from me, that is all. He heard you tell Janet about it. All the time you plan to deceive me, from the very beginning. You make him fond of you so that he is frightened to tell me. He tried to kill himself in the mountains because he could not think of any way to get away from you. He walked and walked and hoped he would die. But they were finding him in time.'

'No.'

'This is true and all the other things too.'

It was no use telling him that the plans had been Janet's;

after all, she had not told Janet of Witek's blundering passes at her. Peace must come now, with the causes of war undecided, with everything important unsaid. Meanwhile she listened to Witek's wild cry, the cry of a man always excluded from the possibilities of life.

'Why did you work against me, Rose? Why am I always so disgusting and dismissed and dishonourable? I am doing the best for my son. Rose, this is a terrible world we are in here, and you come – you come from Kensington and you try to ruin everything.' He stopped. In a silence he said: 'You ruin my poor life.'

And so she had it at last, if she wanted it: the stiletto thrust of her victory – his admission that he hated his life. It was what she had shamelessly worked for, and it was now quite useless to her. The end was here, now. She did not speak.

Janet came out of the kitchen. Rose watched her with a sudden imploring sympathy.

'Don't worry about me,' Janet said briskly. 'I shall be all right. Just leave here as soon as possible. That's all I want now.'

## Chapter Thirty-eight

To and fro the train rattled on ill-found sleepers. Alternately Rose felt the upholstered right haunch of the woman on her left, the upholstered left haunch of the man on her right. First they had gazed at her luggage with suspicion, then settled down into fat silence, members of a potato-eating race well adapted to the unending discomfort of train journeys.

The train was slowly proceeding through a marshy landscape near the remains of a prehistoric lake village. From time to time its whistle gave out a ringing, lacustrine cry, the sort of cry that wild fauna might have emitted across these Tennysonian meres on every rainy afternoon since the Ice Age. Rain spat again and again on the windows. Today was one of the chill weeping days in the early part of May, the days of the Ice Saints, St Pancras, St Servace and St Boniface, whose arrival affords a reminder that all is by no means well with the year. If you had confidence in the spring, your trust was misplaced: it will let you down. And if you are a pessimist you can give the satisfied snort of those whose worst fears are justified, and continue toting the burden of existence a little farther on.

For Rose, who looked forward to nothing at all, the day remained abysmally sad. She was returning to London. God must come and blast the inhabitants of Beauchamp Place, and frizzle up those on the pavements outside Harrods. Only then, surely, could He bring about a balance of the world's pain.

The carriage was darkened by someone standing in the doorway.

'Please, you remember me?'

At the first words of a foreign language the faces of the other passengers stiffened: they were no longer present. To Rose the question sounded oddly humble. Here was someone who knew her yet did not know how far down the bill she had actually gone. He was a tall young man wearing a beret, and a black sweater which was hidden under another of those smelly plastic raincoats.

'Of course I remember you!' But the puzzle in her voice told him clearly that she had forgotten his name.

'Miroslaw Sypniewski.'

'Mirek, of course.'

She surprised him by getting to her feet at once. Half-stumbling across her neighbour's plump legs, she arrived beside Mirek in the corridor, like a swimmer grabbing the boat's edge.

'You remember the evening at the Students' Club?'

'Of course I remember. You were very sad.'

He laughed. 'Where are you travelling now?'

'To Warsaw.'

'You are staying with friends?'

'No, I'm going home.'

And so he looked sad again. 'I think you are pleased,' he said though her voice had given him no cause to think this.

'No, I'm not. Everything has gone wrong, you see, and I had hoped for so much.'

'In this country we must be very careful with hope.'

'I know.'

A station drew up outside the window. Loud-speakers were playing elderly cheerful music but inside the train it was quiet.

'What happened to Derek?' Rose asked suddenly.

'He has left. But his girl has not yet got the English visa. She is waiting in Biala Gora. I think there is some difficulty.'

'There might easily be. What's she like really?'

He shrugged. 'She is the first Polish girl Derek is getting to know. For him perhaps it is different. But it is a pity, I think.'

She liked him for his sympathy. He was a really kind man. Of course Loasby had distrusted him, but even now, after everything else that had happened to her, she was certain that Loasby was wrong. She watched Mirek's tall body swaying to and fro in front of her and felt a curious sensation of peace. He had been appointed to lead her out of this wilderness and into the sane world.

'I can understand about Derek. One feels, if one had started with different people, everything would have turned out differently. One might have discovered something.'

Mirek looked at her ruminatively. 'I'm afraid you don't have a very good impression.'

'I do, really.'

'Not really, I'm afraid.' He laughed. 'When is your aeroplane?'

'This afternoon. At four o'clock. The LOT plane.'

'I may take you to the airport?'

'Oh, please do.'

The train started again. As they approached the Warsaw area, the sandy earth along the track began breaking out with the spiked vegetation of the seashore. Though Poland is in the heart of Europe, much of it looks as though it were near the edge of the sea. Rose and Mirek stood talking in the corridor; in his presence there was never any sense of strain. He bought her a scorching glass of tea. When the ticket collector came round, he was obliged to pay extra.

'Why do they make you do that? I thought you were a student and paid half fare anyway.'

'It is nothing. It is not important.' He seemed embarrassed.

Later she saw that he had been given a new ticket. She realized then that he had intended getting off at the last station. Now, for her sake, he was coming on to Warsaw, even though, after today, he would not be seeing her again. Because he had been in prison, he could never leave Poland. His kindness was like a small bunch of roses at the end of an arduous journey.

Two hours later they were in the airport shed.

Around them stood the strangely clad members of an excursion of American Poles, escorted by their own priest. All of them had the shiny coarseness given by a generation or two in the Middle West, but under this they kept a look of their forebears, of people like Witek, for instance, or of the passengers in the train. None of them looked at all like Mirek. He and Rose stood apart, without talking. A whole cloud of possible emotions made them distrust speech.

The tourists spoke a mixture of Polish and American. Now and then while they talked, they slapped at their chests and sides as though stabbed by pain. There the hand felt the limp oblong and was reassured. Then a doubt; might it after all be only a forgotten wallet or a neglected letter? And so they fished out the olive-green passport and stared at it for a moment, as intently as in a mirror; it was their reality. Their faces lost anxiety and they looked as though they had just been kissed.

The sight of these people, the strident result of so much that is both desired and detested, had finally driven Rose and Mirek speechless; there was so little to say and so much to explain. At last a stewardess shepherded the excursion through into the customs. Rose kissed Mirek quickly, and followed.

By the gate on to the airfield there was almost a stampede: elbows thrusting, feet stamping, silence and laboured breath, as the visitors fought once more to escape from the soil of their ancestors.

Again Rose stayed till last.

Looking back, she saw Mirek standing in his pale raincoat behind a wire fence, and beyond him a whole landscape waiting for explanation.

## About the author

John Francis Tuohy (1925–1999) was a novelist and short story writer. After studying Moral Sciences and English Literature at King's College, Cambridge, he worked for the British Council in a number of academic posts abroad including Finland, Brazil, Argentina and Portugal. It was his posting in Kraków, Poland, that provided the inspiration for *The Ice Saints*, his third novel, which won the Geoffrey Faber Memorial Prize and the James Tait Black Memorial Prize. Winning plaudits from C.P. Snow and Muriel Spark, Tuohy's work was favourably compared with Chekhov and acclaimed for its exploration of Englishness.

## About the introducer

Neal Ascherson is a Scottish journalist and writer. He read history at King's College, Cambridge, where he was taught by Eric Hobsbawn who later described Ascherson as 'perhaps the most brilliant student I ever had. I didn't really teach him much, I just let him get on with it'. For his National Service he was posted to Malaya with the Royal Marines. He graduated with a triple-starred first but declined offers to pursue an academic career. Instead he chose a career in journalism, reporting from Asia, Africa and Central Europe for the *Guardian*, the *Scotsman*, the *Observer* and the *Independent on Sunday*. He has written and lectured widely on Polish and Eastern Europe affairs and contributes regularly to the *New York Review of Books* and the *London Review of Books*. He is Visiting Professor at the Institute of Archaeology at UCL and is editor of the journal *Public Archaeology*. His books include *Black Sea*, *Games with Shadows* and *The Polish August*. His first novel, *The Death of the Fronsac*, will be published later this year.